The Great American Political Trivia Challenge

Political Trivia on Steroids

Are You Up for the Challenge?

**2,175 Trivia Questions
From American Politics, Past and Present**

By Rich Rubino

Library of Congress Control Number: 2021920884

ISBN 978-0-578-98385-1

Dedication

I dedicate this book to C-SPAN, a most unorthodox dedication choice, I imagine. I started watching C-SPAN during school snow-cancellation days decades ago while in middle school. Before I knew it, I was desperately hooked, a C-SPAN addict. Perhaps I should have entered a 12-step program, if only such a program had existed back then. Before I knew it, I couldn't get enough of the U.S. Congress live proceedings. I became transfixed by the U.S. House Special Orders. I often wondered if there were others out there suffering in silence from the same addiction, unable to get the treatment that they so desperately needed. Unable to get the proper therapy, my C-SPAN addiction worsened and began to spread into my weekends. My passion for political history was gratified by watching *Booknotes* with Brian Lamb every Sunday evening.

I am proud to say that after years of C-SPAN addiction therapy, I am in recovery. I have redirected my political interests into more positive channels, writing humorous political books. Thank you C-SPAN, I could not have written this book without you.

Table of Contents

Introduction

Are you ready to take The Great American Political Trivia Challenge? This is my humble attempt to end the great political divide. The best part is that this book is non-ideological and non-partisan. Accordingly, it might help to break the acrimonious political divide! If the book doesn't solve that lofty goal, it should at least be challenging, fun, and possibly exasperating. Most importantly, I will put a few coins in my coffers. Politics has become a contact blood-sport. You'll find no bloodshed here. This book exhibits the peculiar, bizarre, captivating, and unusual side of American politics.

I have been a political junkie for most of my life. This is my fifth political book. Three of the four books dealt with political facts, quotations, and political stories or the ridiculous side of American politics. My fourth book was about the Electoral College, not exactly a page-turner. If you are engrossed with the esoteric and intricate workings of the Electoral College system, this book could be for you.

During my previous book tours, many television and radio hosts would attempt to stump me with obscure political trivia questions. That gave me the impetus to write this book. This book is political trivia on steroids.

Politicians are just like the rest of us, except they live under a microscope. It's the magnification that often gets them in trouble. If we make a mistake, people groan, laugh, and then forget about it. If a politician makes a mistake, it goes down in the annals of history, and eventually is unearthed by political junkies such as myself, to live on in infamy in political trivia books.

You can read the book from cover-to-cover, or flip through the pages for fun, or you can take the challenge seriously and keep score. It's up to you.

Whenever possible, I have provided context and as much of a back story as possible so readers will learn as well as test their political prowess. I have included page numbers where the answers can be found if you have a proclivity to cheat, or let's say peruse the answers in advance. Don't worry, no one is watching you. This is NOT an academic task. So take a journey on the wild, bizarre, and humorous side of American politics. Buckle-up and get ready for a bumpy, humorous ride.

Below are some examples of interesting stories contained in this book.

1) The President who gave the Pope a five-inch bust of himself. (Pages 1-2)

2) The President who sold the Federal Government's tool supply so they could not be used for public works projects during an economic depression. (Pages 1-2)

3) The President who is a national hero in Paraguay but largely forgotten in the U.S. (Pages 3-4)

4) The only President not mourned after his death in Washington, D.C. (Pages 37-38)

22) The U.S Congressman who when asked if he would support Ted Cruz should he win his party's Presidential nomination, responded: "I'll jump off that bridge when I come to it." (Pages 221-222)

23) The Presidential candidate who told a coterie of dairy farmers: "None of you have made the sacrifices for the dairy industry that I have. I got indicted because of it." (Pages 225-226)

24) The Vice President who took a nine-month leave of absence from his job to open up a tavern and spa. (Pages 259-260)

25) The former Vice President who died in the middle of delivering an address. (Pages 275-276)

26) The former U.S. Secretary of State who admonished that "Congress is too damn representative. It's just as stupid as the people are." (Pages 290-291)

27) The Republican National Committee Chairman who excoriated "the moral lasciviousness" of the administration of Democratic President John F Kennedy after guests were spotted performing "The twist" at a White House dinner. (Pages 305-306)

28) The U.S. Representative who branded a colleague as "a Howdy Doody looking nimrod" on the House Floor. (Pages 307-308)

29) The U.S House member who maintains that the only difference between a cactus and a caucus is that "on a cactus, the pricks are on the outside." (Pages 315-316)

30) The U.S. Representative who upbraided Vice President Spiro Agnew for contemplating being tried in the U.S. House of Representative rather than in Court for charges of accepting bribes and falsifying tax returns, averring: "He's trying to take the decision out of the hands of twelve honest men, and give it to 435 Congressmen." (Pages 317-318)

31) The U.S. Representative who deadpanned: "Mississippi gets more than their fair share back in federal money, but who the hell wants to live in Mississippi?" (Pages 319-320)

32) The U.S. House Candidate who berated an opponent for being a Unitarian, averring: "A Unitarian is a person who believes that our Lord and Savior is a funny little man with a beard who runs around in his underclothes." (Pages 324-325)

33) The Democratic U.S. House Speaker, who, when asked to campaign in the Congressional District of the Republican Minority Leader, refused, maintaining: "Hell, if I lived up there, I'd vote for him" (meaning he would give his vote to his Republican counterpart). (Pages 333-334)

34) The U.S. Representative who attacked a U.S. Senator with a cane. (Pages 338-339)

35) The U.S. Senator who responded to a charge of being "the dumbest Congressman" by holding a press conference to deny the charges. (Pages 347-348)

36) The Governor and U.S. Senate candidate who claimed that his opponent's campaign tried to poison him. (Pages 367-368)

37) The U.S. Senate Majority Leader who appeared in a magazine advertisement for Lucky Strike Cigarettes. (Pages 371-372)

38) The U.S. Senator, who, when asked what she would do if she woke up in the White House, responded: "I would go to the President's wife and apologize, then leave at once." (Pages 371-372)

39) The U.S. Senator from a tobacco state who deadpanned: "I was with some Vietnamese recently, and some of them were smoking two cigarettes at one time. That's the kind of customers we need." (Pages 381-382)

40) The Governor who danced like a monkey before the State Board of Education, exhibiting his vociferous opposition to text books which teach evolution (Pages 407-408)

41) The Governor who had his press secretary hand out press passes with the words: "official jackal" printed on them. (Pages 409-410)

42) The future Republican who saved the life of Bill Clinton, and who was pardoned by Clinton. (Pages 415-416)

43) The Illinois Gubernational nominee who called the hometown Chicago Cubs: "a bunch of losers." (Pages 437-428)

44) The time Hillary Clinton interrupted a press conference of a political opponent of her husband's to talk about his past praise of Bill Clinton later in his life. (Pages 433-435)

45) The former President who labeled Richard M. Nixon a "squirrel head." (Pages 465-466)

46) The Connecticut Governor who labeled Donald Trump "a dirt bag." (Pages 467-468)

47) The Governor who was asked by a political opponent why he speaks out of both sides of his mouth, responded this way: "So people like you with only a half a brain can understand me." (Pages 471-472)

48) The time Joe Biden said to a political opponent: "The thing I like best about you is your wife." (Pages 477-478)

49) The Democratic Presidential candidate who was not invited to participate in a debate, who then showed up as a member of the assembled audience, and who heckled the moderator. (Pages 479-480)

50) The Presidential candidate who told a crowd in Concord, NH, that "You're in the state where the shot was heard around the world at Lexington and Concord, and you put a marker in the ground and paid with the blood of your ancestors." (Pages 485-486)

51) The dirty trickster who arranged for his opponent to speak to a room with seating reserved for 2,000 people, but did not advertise the event. Only 23 people showed up, and the trickster delivered a long introduction, then told the paltry crowd that the candidate would speak about the International Monetary System. (Pages 491-492)

52) The adult film star who supports Republican candidates because when you are rich, you want a Republican in office. (Pages 497-498)

Chapter I

The Presidents

The Presidents

Q1: After Pope Paul VI gave this President a painting of the nativity scene, which President reciprocated by giving the Pope a five-inch bust of himself, the President?

Q2: Harry S. Truman brandished a sign on his desk that read: "The Buck Stops Here." The sign was a gift to Mr. Truman from a prison warden. What did the back of the sign read?

Q3: Which President wrote his own edition of the Bible, which he titled *The Life and Times of Jesus of Nazareth*?

Q4: Which President answered his own telephone at the White House?

Q5: Which President was offered contracts from the Detroit Lions and the Green Bay Packers?

Q6: In 1974, when Bill Clinton was contemplating challenging U.S. Representative John Paul Hammersmith (R-AR), he met with which Governor for campaign advice, who was also the Chairman of the Democratic Governor's Campaign Committee?

Q7: Which President did not register to vote until age 62?

Q8: Which President had twenty-three pets while President, including a garter snake, a pony, and a one-legged rooster?

Q9: Thomas Jefferson's grave stone at Monticello in Charlottesville, VA reads: "Here was Buried Thomas Jefferson Author of the Declaration of American Independence of the Statute of Virginia for Religious Freedom and Father of the University of Virginia." What major office that Jefferson held was left off of the grave stone?

Q10: Which Democratic President was steadfastly opposed to using the government as a means of employing workers on public works projects? In fact, during an economic depression he literally sold the federal government's tool supply so that the government could not use the tools for public works projects.

The Presidents

A1: Lyndon B. Johnson. Johnson had 200 of these busts manufactured and often handed these statuettes out as gifts to heads of state. They came in many different colors.

A2: "I'm from Missouri"

A3: Thomas Jefferson wrote his own Bible, crossing out any reference to the supernatural.

A4: Grover Cleveland

A5: Gerald R. Ford. He was the Center for the University of Michigan Wolverines. He turned down the contracts to attend Yale Law School.

A6: Jimmy Carter of Georgia. Carter later recalled at the dedication of the William J. Clinton Presidential Library and Museum in Little Rock, AR: "I came to meet an unknown Congressional candidate in Little Rock, in a Little Rock hotel. It may be a surprise to some of you to learn that he was late for the appointment. Finally, what I thought was a young messenger arrived, and I said, where the devil is -- and I looked down at my notes to see who I was talking about, and the young man said, "I'm William Clinton."

A7: Zachary Taylor cast his first vote at age 62. He had been a soldier and traveled so much that he never had the required permanent address needed to register to vote.

A8: Theodore Roosevelt

A9: The Presidency

A10: Martin Van Buren

The Presidents

Q11: Which President is a national hero in Paraguay?

Q12: Which President had no formal education (his wife Martha taught him reading, writing, and arithmetic)?

Q13: Which future President, while working part-time as a model in 1942, was featured on the cover of *Cosmopolitan Magazine* with his girlfriend?

Q14: Which President paid a substitute $300 to serve for him in the Civil War?

Q15: What name did Barack Obama go by while growing up in Indonesia?

Q16: The Boston Massacre took place in 1770. British soldiers killed five Bostonians. This was an important event leading up to the American Revolution. Which future President was the defense counsel for the British soldiers?

Q17: Which future President designed the Virginia State Capitol Building in Richmond?

Q18: The renowned painting, *Washington Crossing the Delaware* by German painter Emanual Leutze in 1851 includes which two future Presidents?

Q19: Who was the only President to be awarded a Purple Heart (A military decoration awarded for being wounded or killed in military action)?

A11: Rutherford B. Hayes. He is a national hero in Paraguay for his role in arbitrating a land dispute between Paraguay and Argentina with the help of U.S. Secretary of State William Everts. Hayes allowed Paraguay to keep a large swath of the cattle-farming Chaco territory, which comprises about 60% of its land. November 12th is a national holiday in Paraguay to honor him. There is an industrial city in the nation named Villa Hayes, Spanish for "Hayesville." It is the capital of the state of Presidente Hayes. In addition, there is a postage stamp and a soccer team in Paraguay named for Hayes. A reality television show aired in Paraguay offered the winner a free trip to Freemont, OH to visit the Rutherford B. Hayes Presidential Library and Museum. There is even a Rutherford B. Hayes Scholarship in Paraguay, where winning students can matriculate into Ohio Wesleyan University in Delaware, OH, the municipality where Hayes was born. Hayes birthplace is largely ignored by Americans. It is a plaque emplaced in front of a BP gas station. His home was torn down in 1926.

A12: Andrew Johnson

A13: Gerald R. Ford

A14: Grover Cleveland. This practice was legal at the time.

A15: Barry Soetoro

A16: John Adams. He got most of the British soldiers off by arguing self-defense to the jury.

A17: Thomas Jefferson

A18: George Washington and James Monroe. Monroe was an advisor to George Washington. However, there is no historical record indicating that he was on the same boat with Washington. Washington is seen standing in the middle of the boat, while Monroe is behind him carrying an American flag.

A19: John F. Kennedy. He was a Navy Lieutenant in During WWII. After the Japanese sank his Patrol Boat (PT-109), Kennedy suffered a back injury. In the process Kennedy saved three of his crew members.

The Presidents

Q20: Which eight Presidents were born British subjects?

Q21: When a President resigns, who does he submit his resignation letter to?

Q22: In 1965, Lyndon B. Johnson signed legislation establishing the Medicare system. Which former first couple received the first Medicare registration cards?

Q23: When John F. Kennedy assumed the Presidency in 1961, there were 600 military advisors in Vietnam. How many advisors were in Vietnam at the time JFK was assassinated in 1963?

Q24: Who was the last President to serve without a Chief of Staff?

Q25: Who painted the official portrait of President James Monroe?

Q26: Which President founded what today is the State University of Buffalo?

Q27: Which future President, while serving as Governor of Ohio from 1868-1872, helped to found Ohio State University?

Q28: Which President's Farewell Address was never delivered orally, but instead was published in *The Daily American Advertiser* and other U.S. newspapers?

Q29: Which President made it a custom for U.S. Presidents to salute the Marine standing outside of "Marine 1" (The current President's helicopter) when boarding or egressing the helicopter?

The Presidents

A20: George Washington, John Adams, Thomas Jefferson, James Madison, James Monroe, John Quincy Adams, Andrew Jackson, and William Henry Harrison. Martin Van Buren was the first U.S. President to be born as an American citizen.

A21: The U.S. Secretary of State

A22: Harry and Bess Truman

A23: 16,000

A24: Lyndon B. Johnson

A25: Samuel Morse. The inventor of Morse Code and the Single-Wire Telegraph.

A26: Millard Fillmore in 1846, just four years before he became President.

A27: Rutherford B. Hayes. After leaving the Presidency, he served as a member of the University's Board of Trustees.

A28: George Washington. The written address was published in 1796.

A29: Ronald Reagan

Q30: Instead of playing the traditional Hail To the Chief, which President often ordered the U.S. Navy band to play the University of Michigan victory song titled: *The Victors*?

Q31: Which President spent a three-month summer vacation at a mansion known as "White Court" in Swampscott, Massachusetts?

Q32: What was Ronald Reagan's Secret Service code-name?

Q33: Which four Presidents were members of the Whig Party?

Q34: Which President is buried wrapped in an American flag with a copy of the U.S. Constitution underneath his head?

Q35: What does the acronym "POTUS" stand for?

Q36: Which President was in so much debt in his later years that he was forced to sell his property and move in with his daughter in New York City?

Q37: Who are the only two Presidents who founded a University?

Q38: Which two Presidents had stints working at North Pownal Academy in Pownal, VT?

Q39: Which President loved Brooks Brothers suits, and ordered his dress uniform for the Spanish-American War from there?

The Presidents

A30: Gerald R. Ford

A31: Calvin Coolidge: The mansion was later owned by Marion Court College.

A32: Rawhide

A33: William Henry Harrison, John Tyler, Zackary Taylor, and Millard Fillmore.

A34: Andrew Johnson: He died in 1876.

A35: President of the United States

A36: James Monroe

A37: Millard Fillmore founded the University of Buffalo. Thomas Jefferson founded the University of Virginia.

A38: Chester A. Arthur and James Garfield. Arthur served as the school's principal. Garfield taught penmanship.

A39: Theodore Roosevelt

The Presidents

Q40: Which President fathered 15 children?

Q41: As a young man, which Church parishioner sent a donation of coins that he had saved to the reverend Billy Graham?

Q42: Which President wore gloves to cover up an unsightly skin condition?

Q43: What does the "S." stand for in Harry S. Truman?

Q44: Who was the only President known to have killed a man?

Q45: Which President's father, two sisters, and brother all died from pancreatic cancer?

Q46: Who was the first known person to threaten the life of John F. Kennedy?

Q47: Which President was named after the doctor who delivered him?

Q48: Which President smoked about 20 cigars per day?

Q49: Which two Presidents did not issue any pardons while in office?

A40: John Tyler

A41: Bill Clinton

A42: Benjamin Harrison. His critics, not cognizant of his medical condition, gave him the moniker: "Kid Gloves Harrison."

A43: Harry S. Truman's two grandfathers, Anderson Shipp Truman and Solomon Young, could not agree on a middle name for Harry, so they decided to use the letter "S" because one of each of their names begins with the letter "S."

A44: Andrew Jackson killed attorney Charles Dickenson in a duel. He did so in response to Dickinson insulting his wife Rachel.

A45: Jimmy Carter

A46: Richard Pavlick: On December 11, 1960, President Kennedy's life was threatened in Florida by a postal worker who had loaded his car with dynamite and who was planning to crash his car into Kennedy's car. However, moments before the planned assassination, 73-year-old Richard Pavlick backed off when he saw Kennedy saying goodbye to his wife and daughter. He could no longer go through with his plan. Pavlick was arrested just three days later when, after a traffic stop, it was discovered that his car was filled with dynamite. Pavlick was sent to prison for six years.

A47: Chester A. Arthur was named after Dr. Chester Abell, the doctor who delivered him as a baby.

A48: Ulysses S. Grant. This likely contributed to his death from throat cancer in 1885.

A49: William Henry Harrison and James Garfield. Both Presidents died in their first year in office.

Q50: Which two future Presidents had offices directly across from each other when in the U.S. House of Representatives?

Q51: When this future President was serving in the Massachusetts General Court (State Legislature) as Lieutenant Governor, and then as Governor of Massachusetts, he rented an apartment in the state's capital, Boston. His wife Grace and their children stayed at the family home in North Hampton, Massachusetts, 56 miles west of Boston. Who is this President?

Q52: Which President signed legislation posthumously restoring the U.S. citizenship of Confederate President Jefferson Davis?

Q53: Which President, a former Governor traveled back to his home state of New Jersey to excoriate members of the State Assembly who had opposed his plan for taking the power away from county sheriffs to decide who gets to sit on grand juries? The proposal by then Governor Wilson would vest that power instead in a commission appointed by the Governor.

Q54: Which President was mocked as "His Rotundity" behind his back?

Q55: Who was the first President to have a full-time bodyguard?

Q56: Which President had little use for the U.S. Congressmen, labeling them: "pygmy minds?"

Q57: Which President walked a pet raccoon around the White House grounds?

Q58: Which President owned a pet parrot named "Poll" that had to be removed from a funeral service because it was using profane language?

Q59: Which President earned the unfortunate nickname "Ten Cent Jimmy" because he said publicly that the average American could live on just ten cents a day?

A50: Gerald R. Ford and John F. Kennedy

A51: Calvin Coolidge

A52: Jimmy Carter

A53: Woodrow Wilson. The same day that Wilson resigned his incumbency to get ready to assume the Presidency, the Legislature voted resoundingly against bringing the proposed statute for a second reading, effectively killing it. Wilson was inflamed that his fellow Democrats in the Assembly had not supported him on this measure. As President, Wilson took an expedition to Elizabeth, NJ to excoriate the recalcitrant legislators. After the event, the esteemed photographer Isidore Fieldman shot a photograph of Wilson and his coterie. This is one of the first photographs where flash photography was used.

A54: John Adams. This was because he was short and overweight. In addition, he enjoyed formal titles.   In fact, he thought the President should be labeled: ""His Highness, the President of the United States of America, and Protector of the Rights of the Same" or more simply: "His Majesty, the President."

A55: Franklin Pierce, in 1853

A56: Woodrow Wilson

A57: Calvin Coolidge. The racoon was named Rebecca.

A58: Andrew Jackson. In fact, it was Andrew Jackson's 1845 funeral that the parrot had to leave because of his profane language.

A59: James Buchanan

The Presidents

Q60: What were the names of Lyndon B. Johnson's two beagles?

Q61: Which Indiana University has awarded 10 U.S. Presidents an honorary degree?

Q62: While this President was fishing, a rabid swamp rabbit swam toward his small boat. Which President swatted at the rabbit with his canoe paddle, scaring it away?

Q63: Which President would not travel on the 13th day of the month because he was superstitious about the number 13?

Q64: Which President, a crossword puzzles enthusiast, was featured in the 2006 documentary *Wordplay*? In 2017, he teamed up with his long-time friend, District Judge Victor Fleming in constructing the *New York Times* crossword puzzle.

Q65: Which President once owned a bar in Springfield, IL?

Q66: Abraham Lincoln delivered the famed *Gettysburg Address*, which lasted only about two minutes. He gave his speech after this former U.S. Secretary of State delivered a campaign speech that lasted more than two and a half hours. Who was this former U.S. Secretary of State?

Q67: Who was the only President born in Delaware?

Q68: During which President's term did federal spending eclipse $1 Billion for the first time?

Q69: At the beginning of a baseball game between the Washington Senators and the Philadelphia Athletics on April 14, 1910 at Griffith Stadium in Washington, D.C., Umpire Billy Evans handed a baseball to this President. He then asked him to throw it over home plate. The President did, and since then, it has become a tradition for Presidents to throw out the first pitch on Opening Day. Who was the first President to throw out the ball?

A60: Him and Her

A61: The University of Notre Dame in South Bend, IN.

A62: Jimmy Carter

A63: Franklin D. Roosevelt

A64: Bill Clinton. Fleming is a District Judge in Little Rock, AR, who first met Clinton in 1984 when their daughters took swimming lessons from the same teacher.

A65: Abraham Lincoln

A66: Edward Everett

A67: Rutherford B. Hayes. He was born in Delaware, OH on October 4, 1822.

A68: Benjamin Harrison (1889-1893)

A69: William Howard Taft

Q70: Which President was the only President to have been an Eagle Scout?

Q71: In 1817, which President became the first President to be inaugurated outdoors?

Q72: In 1923, this President became the first President to light the official White House Christmas Tree. Who was this President?

Q73: Who was the first President to work from the Oval Office?

Q74: Who was the first President to preside over all 50 states?

Q75: In January of 1835, Richard Lawrence, who was mentally ill and who believed he was King Richard III of England, attempted to assassinate this President at a funeral. Mr. Lawrence believed he was keeping money from him and had killed his father. His shot misfired. This is the first known attempt to assassinate a U.S. President. Who was this President?

Q76: Who was the first President born West of the Mississippi River?

Q77: Who was the first President to have his voice transmitted by radio?

Q78: Who was the first President to visit a nation not recognized by the U.S?

Q79: Who was the only member of the U.S. House of Representatives to advance directly to the Presidency?

The Presidents

A70: Gerald R. Ford. He was a proud member of Troop 15 in Grand Rapids, MI. In 1970, while serving as U.S. House Minority Leader, Ford was awarded the Distinguished Eagle Scout Award. Four Hundred Eagle Scouts, ages 15-18 lined the road to the Gerald Ford Presidential Museum in Grand Rapids, MI, as Ford was driven to his final resting place. Ford once said: "One of the proudest moments of my life came in the court of honor when I was awarded the Eagle Scout badge. I still have that badge. It is a treasured possession."

A71: James Monroe

A72: Calvin Coolidge

A73: William Howard Taft in 1909. The Oval Office burned down in a 1929 fire. Herbert Hoover ordered the Oval Office re-built in 1930.

A74: Dwight D. Eisenhower. Hawaii and Alaska were admitted to the Union during his Presidency, making him the first President to preside over all 50 states.

A75: Andrew Jackson

A76: Herbert Hoover. He was born in West Branch, IA on August 10, 1874.

A77: Warren G. Harding. He was addressing a crowd at the dedication of the "Orpheus" memorial site in Baltimore, honoring Francis Scott Key, the composer of *The Star-Spangled Banner.* In addition, Harding had a radio installed at the White House.

A78: Richard M. Nixon. He visited Romania in 1972.

A79: James Garfield, in 1880

The Presidents

Q80: Who was the first incumbent President to be photographed?

Q81: Who was the first President to hold a Hanukah Party in the White House?

Q82: Who was the first President to be born a U.S. citizen?

Q83: Who was the only President to see combat during WW1?

Q84: Who was the first President to publicly acknowledge the celebration of Hanukah? He lit the National Menorah.

Q85: Who was the first President to admit to wearing contact lenses?

Q86: Who was the first President to have a telephone installed in the White House?

Q87: Who was the only President to serve in both WW1 and WW11?

Q88: Which President held the first live television news conference?

Q89: Who was the first President to have served in the U.S. Congress?

The Presidents

A80: James K. Polk. The photograph was taken in 1848 by the famous early photographer Mathew Brady.

A81: George W. Bush, in 2001

A82: Martin Van Buren. He assumed office in 1837.

A83: Harry S. Truman saw combat as an artillery officer.

A84: Jimmy Carter, in 1979

A85: Ronald Reagan

A86: Rutherford B. Hayes. The telephone was installed by its, inventor, Alexander Graham Bell, offered the 4-1-1 on how to operate the device safely.

A87: Dwight D. Eisenhower

A88: John F. Kennedy on January 25, 1961, just five days after being inaugurated as President.

A89: James Madison. He was elected President in 1812. He was a member of the U.S. House of Representatives from Virginia from 1789-1797.

The Presidents

Q90: Who was the nation's first left-handed President?

Q91: Prior to becoming President, which future President was 99th in seniority in the U.S. Senate?

Q92: During his senior year at Phillips Academy in Andover Massachusetts, this future President was "Head Cheerleader." Who was this future President?

Q93: Who was the first African-American invited to the White House?

Q94: Who was the first President to have electricity installed in the White House?

Q95: Who was the First President to be born after the death of George Washington?

Q96: The Washington Nationals baseball team have had seven Presidential look-a-like mascots which chase each other around the field in the middle of the fourth inning. This event is referred to as The Presidential Race. Which seven Presidents have been featured in this race?

Q97: Who was the first President to visit all fifty states while in office?

Q98: Who was the first President to open the Olympic Games?

Q99: Who was the first President to visit Albania?

The Presidents

A90: James A. Garfield. He could also write legibly with his right hand.

A91: Barack Obama

A92: George W. Bush

A93: Booker T. Washington, the author of *Up From Slavery*, accepted the invitation from Theodore Roosevelt in 1901.

A94: Benjamin Harrison was the first President to have electricity installed in the White House. But fearing his own electrocution, he was unwilling to touch any of the White House light switches.

A95: Millard Fillmore was born on January 7, 1800. George Washington died on December 14, 1799.

A96: George Washington, Abraham Lincoln, Thomas Jefferson, Theodore Roosevelt, William Howard Taft, Calvin Coolidge, and Herbert Hoover

A97: Richard M. Nixon

A98: Ronald Reagan opened up the Olympic Games in Los Angeles in 1984.

A99: George W. Bush, in 2007. There is a 9.3-foot-tall statue of Bush in the municipality of Fushe Kruje to commemorate the occasion.

Q100: Who was the first sitting President to attend a College Basketball game?

Q101: Which President survived smallpox, malaria, and tuberculosis but finally died of a streptococcal throat infection which resulted from a medical practice called bleeding?

Q102: Who was the only member of the U.S. House of Representatives to advance directly to the Presidency?

Q103: Which four Presidents had alliterative initials?

Q104: Which two Presidents were sworn into office by a former President?

Q105: Who was the first President to visit Malaysia while in office?

Q106: As a college student, which President was asked by his philosophy professor to consider becoming a Jesuit?

Q107: Who was the only President sworn into office by a woman?

Q108: Who was the only Person to be elected twice as Vice President and President?

Q109: Who was the only President to earn an MBA degree?

The Presidents

A100: Bill Clinton. He attended a game between the University of Arkansas Razorbacks and the Texas Southern Tigers in Fayetteville, Arkansas.

A101: George Washington. Unfortunately, this procedure resulted in losing so much blood that he blead to death.

A102: James Garfield

A103: Calvin Coolidge, Herbert Hoover, Ronald Reagan, and Woodrow Wilson

A104: Calvin Coolidge in 1925 and Herbert Hoover in 1929. Former President (and at the time Chief Justice of the United States) William Howard Taft swore in both men.

A105: Lyndon B. Johnson, in 1967

A106: Bill Clinton. He told Georgetown University professor Otto Hentz that he was a Southern Baptist. The professor responded: "I don't believe you. I've been reading your papers. You couldn't write this stuff if you weren't a Catholic. "

A107: Judge Sarah T. Hughes swore-in Lyndon B. Johnson after the assassination of President John F. Kennedy in Dallas, Texas. Hughes, a Johnson ally, was a Federal District Judge for Texas. Johnson requested her to perform the Oath of Office. Interestingly, Johnson was not sworn in on a Bible, but on a missel, which is a Roman Catholic book containing Mass prayers. It was unearthed wrapped in cellophane, in a cardboard box. Someone on board the aircraft thought it was the Holy Bible and gave it to Hughes to swear in Johnson. The Oath was purely ceremonial, as the Vice President becomes President upon the death of an incumbent President automatically under the U.S. Constitution.

A108: Richard M. Nixon. He was elected Vice President under Dwight D. Eisenhower in 1952 and 1956, and President in 1968 and 1972.

A109: George W. Bush earned an MBA degree from The Harvard Business School in 1975.

Q110: Which two future Presidents signed the U.S. Constitution?

Q111: Who was the only President to affirm, rather than swear, at his Inauguration?

Q112: Who was the only President to be outlived by a grandparent?

Q113: Who was the only Republican President to serve between the years 1933 and 1969 (a 36-year span)?

Q114: Who are the only two Presidents buried at Arlington National Cemetery?

Q115: Who was the only former President to serve on the U.S. Supreme Court?

Q116: Which two Presidents were Quakers?

Q117: Who is the only former President to be awarded the Nobel Peace Prize?

Q118: Who was the only former President to visit China his last year in office?

Q119: On his last day in office in 1913, President William Howard Taft signed legislation creating a new federal Cabinet department, which today employs over 17,000 people. Which new Cabinet was this?

A110: George Washington and James Madison

A111: Franklin Pierce. He did this because he believed God had punished him when his only son Benjamin was killed in a train collision just two months before his inauguration. Because of this incident, he began to question his Christianity, and accordingly, he decided not to swear on the Holy Bible.

A112: John F. Kennedy was outlived by his grandmother, Mary Josephine "Josie" Hannon. She died in 1964, less than a year after Kennedy was assassinated.

A113: Dwight D. Eisenhower. He served from 1953-1961.

A114: William Howard Taft and John F. Kennedy

A115: William Howard Taft. President Warren G. Harding nominated Taft and the U.S. Senate confirmed him in 1921 to the position of Chief Justice of the United States. He served until his death in 1930.

A116: Herbert Hoover and Richard M. Nixon

A117: Jimmy Carter won the award "for his decades of untiring effort to find peaceful solutions to international conflicts, to advance democracy and human rights, and to promote economic and social development."

A118: Barack Obama, in 2016

A119: The U.S. Department of Labor

The Presidents

Q120: Which President has the dubious distinction of having his veto overridden the most?

Q121: Which President held the most press conferences?

Q122: Which President delivered the shortest Inaugural Address in history?

Q123: In 1862, Abraham Lincoln signed legislation establishing which new Federal Cabinet Department?

Q124: What was the only state George W. Bush did not visit as President?

Q125: Bill Clinton visited all 50 states while President. What was the last state he visited?

Q126: Who was the youngest President?

Q127: Which President nominated the most U.S. Supreme Court Justices?

Q128: Which President served the shortest term?

Q129: Which President garnered the lowest recorded job approval rating in history?

A120: Andrew Johnson had his veto overridden 15 times in four years. Jackson was a Democrat who contended with a Republican U.S. Congress.

A121: Franklin D. Roosevelt held a record 998 press conferences during his 998 days in office.

A122: George Washington's 1793 Address was contained just 135 words.

A123: The U.S. Department of Agriculture

A124: Vermont

A125: Nebraska

A126: Theodore Roosevelt ascended to the Presidency upon the death of William McKinley in 1901. He was just 41 years old.

A127: George Washington nominated ten justices during his eight years in office.

A128: William Henry Harrison served for just 32 days before contracting and dying from pneumonia.

A129: Harry S. Truman left the Presidency in 1953 with a job approval rating of 22%, mostly because of his prosecution of the Korean War.

Q130: Which President owned a Chesapeake Bay retriever named "Sailor Boy"?

Q131: Who was the only President to visit Mongolia while in office?

Q132: Which five future Presidents served as U.S. Ambassadors to the Court of Saint James (England)?

Q133: Jeremiah Wright, the former pastor of the Trinity Church of Christ in Chicago to which Barack Obama belonged while a resident of Chicago, served as a Navy Hospital Corpsman and assisted with the medical care of which President?

Q134: Which President's first inauguration was the warmest day in history, while his second was the coldest in history?

Q135: Which President married his wife before her divorce was finalized?

Q136: Which President had the shortest ex-presidency?

Q137: Lyndon B. Johnson died on January 22nd, 1973. Which landmark decision was handed down by the U.S. Supreme Court on this same day?

Q138: When informed that a second plane hit the World Trade Center, George W. Bush was reading to elementary school pupils at Emma E. Booker Elementary School in Sarasota County, Florida. What book was he reading?

Q139: Which President earned the nickname: "Mr. Veto"?

A130: Theodore Roosevelt. The dog was a descendent of one of General Armstrong Custer's dogs, which had followed Custer into battle.

A131: George W. Bush, in 2005

A132: John Adams, James Buchanan, James Monroe, John Quincy Adams, and Martin Van Buren

A133: Lyndon B. Johnson

A134: Ronald Reagan was sworn into office on January 20, 1981. The temperature in Washington, DC reached a warm 56 degrees that day. The coldest day was four years later in 1985 during his second Inauguration, when the temperature in the District of Columbia reached just 9 degrees. Reagan's' Inauguration was taken inside to the Capitol Rotunda because of the extreme cold.

A135: Andrew Jackson married Rachel before she was divorced from her husband, making her a bigamist. The couple's political opponents exploited this issue.

A136: James K. Polk. He died of Cholera in 1849 at the age of 53, just 103 days after egressing from office. Contrariwise, his wife, Sarah Polk, lived until 1891, dying at the age of 87.

A137: *Roe v. Wade*. This ruling allows a woman the right to terminate her pregnancy until the fetus is viable.

A138: *A Pet Goat* by Siegfried Engelmann and Elaine C. Brune

A139: Gerald R. Ford. A Republican, he vetoed 66 pieces of legislation given to him by the Democratic Congress in his 895 days in office. Fifty-four of those vetoes were sustained, while the U.S. Congress overrode twelve of the vetoes.

Q140: Both Whig Party nominees who were elected President died while in office. Who were they?

Q141: In 1845, who was the President who achieved the dubious distinction of becoming the first President to have a veto overridden by the U.S. Congress?

Q142: Who were the only two Republicans who defeated Bill Clinton for office?

Q143: Which President vetoed twelve pieces of legislation during his eight years in office? His seven predecessors had vetoed only nine bills combined.

Q144: Which President signed legislation raising the top income tax rate from 25% to 63%?

Q145: What play was Abraham Lincoln watching when he was assassinated in 1865?

Q146: Which five Presidents earned their undergraduate degrees from Harvard University?

Q147: In Jimmy Carter's 1979 speech known as *The Malaise Speech*, what key word was never used?

Q148: Who was the last President to sport a beard while in office?

Q149: Which President worked as a janitor at his college, to help pay his tuition bill?

The Presidents

A140: William Henry Harrison and Zackary Taylor

A141: John Tyler. The bill eliminated the Presidents' plenary executive power to purchase revenue-cutter ships.

A142: John Paul Hammerschmidt and Frank White. Hammerschmidt, a U.S. Representative, defeated Clinton in Clinton's bid to unseat him in 1974. White defeated Clinton in his re-election bid as Governor of Arkansas in 1980 (Clinton came back and defeated White in 1982).

A143: *My American Cousin*

A144: Andrew Jackson

A145: Herbert Hoover

A146: John Adams, John Quincy Adams, Theodore Roosevelt, Franklin D. Roosevelt, and John F. Kennedy

A147: Malaise. The media propagated the term. The actual name of the speech was *The Crises of Confidence Speech*.

A148: Benjamin Harrison

A149: Lyndon B. Johnson. He was a student at Texas State Teacher's College in San Marcos, TX.

Q150: How old was Thomas Jefferson when he wrote "The Declaration of Independence?"

Q151: Lyndon B. Johnson served as President for 1884 days. He spent 490 days of it where?

Q152. How many names were on Richard M. Nixon's Enemies List?

Q153: After a meeting at the White House the Reverend Billy Graham posed for a photograph praying with three of his colleagues on the White House Lawn. Which President, viewing this as political grandstanding, banned him from the premises?

Q154: Which President had the original White House tennis courts installed?

Q155: The Presidential retreat, named Camp David, in Frederick County, MD, was named after the son of which President?

Q156: What was Bill Clinton's birth name?

Q157: Which future President coined the term: "Founding Fathers?"

Q158: Where was the first presidential library built and for which President?

Q159: Which President singed the Military Peace Establishment Act, which funded the United States Military Academy in West Point, NY?

A150: 33-years-old

A151: On his Texas ranch. It was nicknamed: "The Texas White House"

A152: 47,000

A153: Harry S, Truman. After Truman left office, Graham apologized to him for having the photograph taken, telling Truman it was an "embarrassing experience." Truman accepted his apology.

A154: Theodore Roosevelt

A155: Dwight D. Eisenhower

A156: William Jefferson Blyth. Blyth was the surname of his birth father that died before Clinton was born. At age 15, Bill took the surname of his stepfather, Roger Clinton Sr.

A157: U.S. Senator Warren G. Harding (R-OH). He used the term "Founding Fathers" during his keynote address at the 1916 Republican Convention, which nominated Charles Evans Hughes for President.

A158: The Rutherford B. Hayes Presidential Center in Freemont, OH In 1922

A159: Thomas Jefferson, in 1802

Q160: What is Bill Clinton's favorite gospel song?

Q161: Which five Presidents have four-letter last names?

Q162: Which President claims to have saved 77 lives?

Q163: Which President had never amassed more than 131,461 votes prior to running for a full Presidential term?

Q164: Although Bill Clinton is known as "The man from Hope," he actually spent only his first seven years as a resident of this municipality before moving to which Arkansas city?

Q165: James Garfield was shot at the Baltimore and Potomac Rail Station. He was getting ready to board a train for a class reunion at the college he graduated from. What is the name of this college?

Q166: Which President vetoed 414 pieces of legislation? That number of vetoes is more than all of his predecessors combined.

Q167: Which President signed legislation declaring Florida the twenty-seventh state on his last day in office?

Q168: Ulysses S. Grant, Bill Clinton, and Barack Obama all vacationed on what Massachusetts Island during their presidencies?

Q169: Which President alleged to have read a book a day, even while President?

A160: *If anyone asks you where I'm going, I'm going up yonder* (By Walter Hawkins)

A161: James K. Polk, William Howard Taft, Gerald R. Ford, and George W. Bush

A162: Ronald Reagan makes this claim. He served a stint as a lifeguard at Rock River in Lowell Park in Dixon, IL.

A163: Gerald R. Ford as a member of the U.S. House of Representatives

A164: Hot Springs

A165: Williams College in Williamstown, Massachusetts

A166: Grover Cleveland

A167: John Tyler, in 1845

A168: Martha's Vineyard

A169: Theodore Roosevelt

Q170: Which President was a Yale University fullback for the Club Rugby team?

Q171: Who was the first President to visit American Samoa while President?

Q172: Which President imbibed a pint of whiskey in a day?

Q173: Which two Presidents died the day after Christmas?

Q174: What two books did Barack Obama write prior to becoming President?

Q175: Which President was a member of the first graduating class of Stanford University in Stanford, CA in 1895?

Q176: In 1975, President Gerald R. Ford offered the position of U.S. Secretary of Commerce, U.S. Secretary of Transpiration, and U.S. Ambassador to the United Kingdom (Court of Saint James) to which recently departed Governor?

Q177: In 1853, which president delivered his Inaugural Address without any notes?

Q178: When Franklin D. Roosevelt signed the Social Security Act in 1935, what was the average life expectancy for Americans?

Q179: Which President coined the term: "lobbyist?"

A170: George W. Bush

A171: Lyndon B. Johnson. He visited American Samoa in 1966 to see the progress effectuated by Governor H. Rex Lee. Two years later, the Lyndon B. Johnson Tropical Medical Center (LBJ) was dedicated. It is the only hospital in the U.S. Territory. The first admitted patient was a mother who delivered a baby that she named Lyndon in the President's honor.

A172: James Madison. Gouverneur Morris, a fellow founding father tattooed Madison as "a fool and a drunkard."

A173: Harry S. Truman in 1972 and Gerald R. Ford in 2006

A174: Dreams *from My Father* was his first book. *The Audacity of Hope* was his second book.

A175: Herbert Hoover

A176: Ronald Reagan. Instead of accepting one of the three nominations, the former California Governor unsuccessfully challenged Ford for the Republican Presidential nomination in 1976.

A177: Franklin Pierce

A178: Sixty-one

A179: Ulysses S. Grant. He called those individuals "lobbyists" who represented special interest groups and who bothered him while he attempted to rest in the "lobby" of the Willard Hotel in Washington, DC.

Q180: Which two world capitals are named after Presidents?

Q181: Which President, with the help of private donations, had a one-lane bowling alley built in the White House?

Q182: What is the only day that the William J. Clinton Presidential Library and Museum in Little Rock, AR offers free admission?

Q183: Who was the only deceased President not mourned in Washington, DC?

Q184: Which former Republican President did Democratic President Harry S. Truman appoint to lead a commission to reconstruct the U.S. Government?

Q185: Who is the only President to write a book about a predecessor?

Q186: Which two Presidents served as U.S. Secretary of State, Vice President, and President?

Q187: Who was the only President to be outlived by both parents?

Q188: In 1872, which former President lost a race to serve as a U.S. Representative from his home state of Tennessee?

Q189: In 1883, six years after egressing from the White House, which former President became the President of the National Rifle Association (NRA)?

A180: Washington, D.C. is named after President George Washington, and Monrovia, Liberia is named after President James Monroe. As President, Monroe supported the repatriation of freed slaves in America to colonize Liberia.

A181: Richard M. Nixon

A182: August 19, Bill Clinton's birthday

A183: John Tyler. He was a steadfast Confederate supporter, was elected to the House of Representatives of the Confederate Congress during the Civil War, but died before he could assume the office. Because of his fidelity to the Confederacy, he was the only President not mourned in Washington, D.C.

A184: Herbert Hoover

A185: Herbert Hoover authored *The Ordeal of Woodrow Wilson.*

A186: Thomas Jefferson and Martin Van Buren

A187: John F. Kennedy

A188: Andrew Johnson

A189: Ulysses S. Grant

The Presidents

Q190: Who was the only former President to win a seat in the U.S. House of Representatives?

Q191: Who was the only former President to serve in the U.S. Senate?

Q192: Which five Presidents share a last name with another President?

Q193: Which future President was elected as Speaker of the New Hampshire House of Representatives at age 26?

Q194: In 1975, President Gerald R. Ford signed *Executive Order 11905*, barring what practice?

Q195: In 1902 in Pittsfield, Massachusetts, a trolley car rammed into a horse-carriage carrying which President and Massachusetts Governor Winthrop Crane?

Q197: After graduating from High School, which future President, along with five friends, moved from Texas to California where they performed odd jobs. He worked as an auto mechanic before hitchhiking back to Texas where he attended Texas State Teachers College?

Q198: Which future Republican President was a Democrat until the 1960's, at which point he changed his partisan allegiances to the Republican Party?

Q198: Which four Presidents went by their middle name?

Q199: Which future President was captain of the Yale University baseball team?

The Presidents

A190: John Quincy Adams. He served the Twelfth Congressional District of Massachusetts from 1831-1848. Unfortunately, Adams suffered a cerebral hemorrhage on the House Floor during a debate honoring veterans of the Mexican-American War. He died two days later.

A191: Andrew Johnson. He represented his native state of Tennessee in 1875. He died less than five months into his term.

A192: President Adams (President John Adams and President John Quincy Adams), President Harrison (President William Henry Harrison and President Benjamin Harrison), President Johnson (President Andrew Johnson and President Lyndon B. Johnson), and President Bush (President George Herbert Walker Bush and President George Walker Bush).

A193: Franklin Pierce

A194: The assassination of foreign leaders

A195: Theodore Roosevelt: Secret Service agent William Craig died from his injuries. Craig was the first Secret Service Agent to die in the line of duty.

A196: Theodore Roosevelt

A197: Lyndon B. Johnson

A198: Ronald Reagan

A198: Hiram Ulysses S. Grant, Steven Grover Cleveland, Thomas Woodrow Wilson, and John Calvin Coolidge.

A199: George H.W. Bush. As captain of the Yale University baseball team, he officially accepted a donation from Baseball Hall of Famer Babe Ruth. Ruth donated the manuscript of his autobiography, *The Babe Ruth Story*, to the Yale University Library.

The Presidents

Q200: Which President met with Liberty University founder Jerry Falwell more than any other President?

Q201: During the energy crisis, which President ordered 32 solar heating panels to be installed on the White House roof?

Q202: Who was both the eighth Vice President and the eighth President?

Q203: In 1965, which former President became the first former President to address the U.S. Senate?

Q204: Who were the only Presidents named Thomas?

Q205: Who coined the nickname "Teflon President" for Ronald Reagan?

Q206: In 1989, George H.W. Bush was inaugurated on the same Holy Bible used to swear in which other President?

Q207: In 1964. Lyndon B. Johnson signed a proclamation declaring a day for which Scandinavian explorer?

Q208: Which future President was nicknamed "The Kansas Cyclone"?

Q209: Which President met with Singer Elvis Presley and gave him a "Bureau of Narcotics and Dangerous Drugs" badge, making Presley a "Federal-Agent-At-Large?"

The Presidents

A200: Ronald Reagan

A201: Jimmy Carter. His successor, Ronald Reagan, ordered the panels removed when maintenance was being performed. They were never put back up on the White House roof. Most of these original solar panels are now owned by Unity College in Unity, Maine.

A202: Martin Van Buren

A203: Harry S. Truman. He did this on his eightieth birthday.

A204: Thomas Jefferson and Thomas Woodrow Wilson. Wilson liked his middle name better, and went with it as an adult.

A205: U.S. Representative Patricia Schroeder (D-CO). She averred: "He has been perfecting the Teflon-coated presidency. He sees to it that nothing sticks to him." Schroder later said in *USA Today* that she came up with the moniker "while fixing eggs for my kids. He had a Teflon coat like the pan."

A206: George Washington in 1789

A207: Leif Erikson. He is believed to be the first European to reach the North American continent.

A208: Dwight D. Eisenhower. He was a running-back for the football team at the United States Military Academy at West Point.

A209: Richard M. Nixon

The Presidents

Q210: The birthday of which President is a state holiday in Texas?

Q211: What was Gerald R. Ford's birth name?

Q212: Which President officially launched the White House Website in 1994?

Q213: Who was the only President who had four names?

Q214: Which President was enamored with the movie *High Noon* so much so that he ordered it played 17 times in the White House Movie Theater?

Q215: The term "New Deal" (which was used to refer to Franklin D. Roosevelt's domestic policy) was originally coined by which author?

Q216: Which two Presidents did not issue any pardons as President?

Q217: Which President was enshrined in the Wrestling Hall of Fame in Stillwater, OK in 1992?

Q218: Al Bundy, portrayed by Actor Ed O'Neill on the television series *Married with Children,* often relived the time he scored four touchdowns in one game while a student at a High School named after which former President?

Q219: Which Ohio Governor and future President went bankrupt during the Panic of 1893 (a financial depression)? He had naively co-signed a $100,000 loan for a friend whose factory went under.

A210: Lyndon B. Johnson. August 27, his birthday, is an optional workday for Texas state workers.

A211: Leslie Lynch King Jr. He was named after his paternal father, Leslie Lynch King Sr.). The senior Ford divorced Ford's mother Dorothy before Gerald was a year old. Dorothy Gardner eventually married Gerald Rudolf Ford Sr. Gerald took his stepfather's name.

A212: Bill Clinton, in 1994

A213: George Herbert Walker Bush

A214: Bill Clinton

A215: Samuel Clemens, a.k.a., Mark Twain, in the 1889 novel: *A Connecticut Yankee at the Court of King Arthur*. In the book, Twain asserted: "It seemed to me that what the nine hundred and ninety-four dupes needed was a new deal."

A216: William Henry Harrison and James Garfield. Both men died during their first year in office.

A217: Abraham Lincoln. At about 6"4 and 185 pounds, Lincoln fought over 300 matches over a 12-year period, losing just one. He won the Sangamon County's wrestling championship. He once challenged an entire crowd, averring: "I'm the big buck of this lick. If any of you want to try it, come on and whet your horns." No one took Lincoln up on his offer. The only person to defeat Lincoln was Hank Thompson, who defeated him for the regimental championship while both men were serving as part of the Illinois Volunteers during the Black Hawk War in 1832.

A218: James K. Polk

A219: William McKinley

Q220: Who was the first President to welcome a sports team to the White House?

Q221: Which President pranked the Secret Service by hiding behind the drapes?

Q222: Which President risked his life battling a fire that engulfed the Library of Congress?

Q223: Which future President completed the Houston Marathon in 3 hours, 44 minutes, and 52 seconds?

Q224: Which President enjoyed drinking Fresca so much that he actually had a Fresca-only soda-fountain installed in the Oval Office?

Q225: Who was the first former two-term President to seek a third term?

Q226: Which President earned the nickname "Blue Whisky Van"?

Q227: After graduating from West Point Military Academy, which President coached the Peacock Military Academy football team?

Q228: Who were the first two Presidents to be filmed together?

Q229: Which President began smoking a pipe at eight years of age?

The Presidents

A221: Calvin Coolidge.   His goal was to make the Secret Service believe that he had been kidnapped. His prank proved to be a failure as his feet were sticking out from the bottom of the curtain.

A222: Millard Fillmore. He subsequently signed legislation to appropriate money to supplant all the books that had vanished in the fire. He was an avid reader.

A223: George W. Bush

A224: Lyndon B. Johnson

A225: Ulysses S. Grant. Though he never declared himself a candidate, he pushed his surrogates to advance his name as a candidate in 1880 for the Republican Presidential nomination. He lost the nomination to U.S. Representative James Garfield (R-OH).

A226: Martin Van Buren. His diet was comprised of rich fatty foods washed down with glasses of whiskey. His unhealthy diet resulted in the President suffering from heart problems and gout in later life.

A227: Dwight D. Eisenhower. He made $150 for the job. A year later, he coached the St. Louis University Football team. (The school is now called St. Mary's.)

A228: Outgoing President Grover Cleveland and incoming President William McKinley were the first Presidents to be filmed. They were filmed at McKinley's inauguration in 1897.

A229: John Quincy Adams. Due to smoking pipes, his teeth denigrated to a horrible condition and he eventually lost all of his teeth. Unwilling to wear dentures, he instead preferred to speak with a lisp.

Q230: In 1972, Darrell K. Royal, the Head coach of the University of Texas Longhorns Football team, asked which former President to help him recruit High School football player Joe Washington to play for the school?

Q231: Before entering elective politics, which future President was accepted for a position with the Federal Bureau of Investigation?

Q232: Which future President first visited the White House at a gala held for the Apollo 8 spaceflight team?

Q233: Who was the only President to be baptized while in office?

Q234: Who was Richard M. Nixon named after?

Q235: Who was the only President to serve two non-consecutive terms?

Q236: In the 1930's, which future President delivered play-by-play action for Chicago Cubs baseball games on radio station WHO, the Des Moines, Iowa *NBC* affiliates?

Q237: Who was the first blogger to ask a question of a President at a news conference?

Q238: Who were the only two Presidents who suffered from urethral stones while in office?

Q239: Which President was arrested and accused of running over a woman with his horse?

A230: Lyndon B. Johnson. Royal was a friend of Johnson, and their families would vacation together in Acapulco, Mexico. Johnson invited Washington and his family to the LBJ ranch. However, Washington turned down the overtures. He had already made up his mind to attend the University of Oklahoma and said "I didn't think that would be kosher, as much as I would have loved to have done that. To go ahead and take the trip knowing I was going to the University of Oklahoma." Washington became a star at the University of Oklahoma, coming in third in the Heisman Trophy balloting in 1971 and went on to spend 10 years as an NFL player.

A231: Richard M. Nixon. However, federal budget cuts eliminated what would have been his position.

A232: George W. Bush. He was on a blind date with First Daughter Tricia Nixon. The future President explained: "I fired up a cigarette, prompting a polite suggestion from Tricia that I not smoke." After the dinner, Tricia told Bush to drive her back to the White House. No further dates followed.

A233: Dwight D. Eisenhower. He always called himself a Christian, but had never been baptized. In 1953, just 11 days after assuming office, Eisenhower was baptized at the National Presbyterian Church in Washington, D.C.

A234: Richard the Lionheart, the King of England from 1189 to 1199. Three of his four brothers were also named after English Kings.

A235: Grover Cleveland. He served from 1885-1889. He lost re-election to Benjamin Harrison in 1888, then came back and defeated Harrison in 1892. His second term lasted from 1893-1897.

A236: Ronald Reagan. He did this from the radio studio through a telegraph machine. Although he never saw the games that he would broadcast, his description of the plays was flawless.

A237: Sam Stein of *The Huffington Post* asked a question of Barack Obama in 2009.

A238: Andrew Johnson and Lyndon B. Johnson (James K. Polk had a urinary stone dislodged when he was 17 years old.)

A239: Franklin Pierce. Luckily for him, the charges were dropped because of the lack of evidence and witnesses to the incident.

Q240: Which President was sworn into office by his father?

Q241: Who was the only U.S. Senate President Pro Tempore to later become President?

Q242: Which four state capitals are named after a U.S. President?

Q243: In 1989, George W. Bush paid $800,000 to be part owner of the Texas Rangers Major League Baseball franchise. Nine years later, while serving as Governor of Texas, Bush sold his shares for how much money?

Q244: This President ordered the Federal government to hold his salary and pay him in a lump sum at the end of his term?

Q245: What was the salary for George Washington when he assumed the Presidency in 1789?

Q246: Richard M. Nixon had a close personal relationship which lead actor of the hit television program *Honeymooners*?

Q247: During halftime at the University of Michigan v. Michigan State University football game, which President had his jersey retired?

Q248: Which future President was wounded during the Revolutionary War at the "Battle of Trenton?"

Q249: Before serving as President, which U.S. House Minority Leader requested an investigation into the existence of UFO's?

A240: Calvin Coolidge. Vice President Calvin Coolidge received word that President Warren G. Harding had died. The Vice President's father, John Calvin Coolidge Sr., who was a Notary Public, swore him in as President. Later that day, Coolidge went back to Washington and was sworn in again by Federal Judge Adolph A. Holing Jr. The U.S. Attorney General, Harry M. Daugherty, feared that the legitimacy of the first oath could be questioned because Coolidge's father was not a federal official.

A241: John Tyler

A242: Jackson, Mississippi (Andrew Jackson), Jefferson City, Missouri (Thomas Jefferson), Lincoln, Nebraska (Abraham Lincoln) and Madison, Wisconsin (James Madison).

A243: $15 million

A244: Martin Van Buren

A245: $25,000

A246: Jackie Gleason. Gleason was a UFO aficionado, and was denizen of a home shaped like a UFO. Gleason's second wife, Beverly, alleges that Gleason told her that the President brought Gleason along for a visit to Homestead Air Force Base. While there, Gleason told her that Nixon showed him embalmed bodies of four two feet long aliens and "the wreckage for a flying saucer." Gleason's former wife averred that Gleason told her they had "larger-than-normal heads and dark eyes which were terribly mangled."

A247: Gerald R. Ford. He played football for the University of Michigan in the 1930's.

A248: James Monroe. He was struck by a musket ball in his shoulder. It proved non-fatal.

A249: Gerald R. Ford. Ford was getting letters and calls from his constituents alleging to see UFO's. Ford demanded an explanation. When Dr. J. Allen Hynek, a consultant to Project Blue Book, the Air Force department which investigates UFOs theorized that the sightings have been an optical allusion, perhaps involving swamp gas, Ford became inflamed, intimating that Hynek was insulting the intelligence of his constituents. He called the swamp gas supposition "flippant." Accordingly, Ford lobbied unsuccessfully for a House inquiry into the matter." However, Ford did get a report from Project Blue Book. The report averred that between 1947 and 1969, there were 12,618 reports of UFOs. Most had explanations, like weather balloons and classified flights. However, 701 did not have a logical explanation.

The Presidents

Q250: Who were the only two Presidents to live in the White House with and without electricity?

Q251: Which future President ran a forced labor camp in Missouri called White Haven prior to fighting for the union and serving as President?

Q252: In 1974, which three Republican leaders came to the White House to tell President Richard M. Nixon that he did not have enough votes to survive impeachment and conviction for his role in the Watergate imbroglio?

Q253: Which future President proposed to his future wife on their first date?

Q254: President Gerald R. Ford was ridiculed by conservative Republicans for signing what agreement, (which was also signed by the Soviet Union and 33 other nations) which stated that each country would agree to respect the autonomy of every nation-state in Europe and not encroach upon their territory?

Q255: Which President, so annoyed by the rodent infestation in The White House, would hunt rats with his family in the White House under the guise of embarking on a safari.

Q256: Which wealthy landowner was forced to sell his 600-acre tract of land so that the Executive Mansion (Now known as The White House) could be built?

Q257: Which President was a music aficionado, who would often play the violin to unwind? Some White House employees allege that he continues to give free concerts for everyone who would like to hear him in the Yellow Oval Room (located on the South side of the second floor of the White House).

Q258: In 1990, Indonesian President Suharto gave President George H.W. Bush which type of a pet, which grew to 9 feet and weighed over 300 pounds?

Q259: Which former President became the chancellor of the University of Buffalo?

A250: Grover Cleveland and Benjamin Harrison. Cleveland lost re-election to Harrison in 1888, then came back to the White House in 1893 after defeating Harrison in Harrison's bid for re-election. Electricity was installed when Harrison was in the White House. Cleveland then beat Harrison, and came back to the White House with electricity.

A251: Ulysses S. Grant

A252: U. S. House Minority Leader John Rhodes (R-AZ), U.S. Senate Minority Leader Hugh Scott (R-PA) and U.S. Senator Barry Goldwater (R-AZ). Goldwater had been the Republican Presidential nominee in 1964. Goldwater told Nixon: "You have six votes [against conviction] and I'm not one of them." The next day, Nixon resigned from office.

A253: Lyndon B. Johnson

A254: The Helsinki Accords. Ford withstood a redoubtable challenge in the Republican Presidential primaries from former California Governor Ronald Reagan, who said the Helsinki Accords: "Put a stamp of approval on Russia's enslavement of captive nations."

A255: Theodore Roosevelt

A256: David Burns. One day, a White House Security Guard during the Presidency of Harry S. Truman heard a ghostly voice repeating the line: "I am David Burns." Burns evidently never let go of his grievances even after his death about being forced to sell his land to the Federal Government.

A257: Thomas Jefferson

A258: A Komodo Dragon. Bush did not keep him in the White House. Instead, he donated him to the Cincinnati Zoo. The Komodo dragon is a fierce predator that can bring prey down twice its size, including animals as big as a water buffalo.

A259: Millard Fillmore

Q260: Who was the only living former President between 1933 and 1953?

Q261: After leaving office, which President had surgery for phlebitis?

Q262: Which President wore the largest hat?

Q263: Preferring to work to advance legislation written by others, during his 25-years in the U.S. House of Representatives, which future President was never the chief sponsor of a piece of legislation signed into law?

Q264: Which President was nicknamed: "The sly fox from Kinderhook"?

Q265: After the British burned down the Capitol in the War of 1812, including the 3000-volume library of books, which former President sold his personal book collection to the U.S. Congress for $23,950?

Q266: Francis Ballemy wrote the *Pledge of Allegiance* on the 400th anniversary of the discovery by Christopher Columbus of the land that was to become the United States of America. In that year, which President signed a proclamation declaring that pledge the official pledge of the United States?

Q267: The First formal White House Easter Egg Role was held on the White House lawn. Which President welcomed children to the White House lawn after the annual Easter Egg Role was banned from the Capitol Grounds?

Q268: Which President invented the swivel chair?

Q269: Which President was the special guest at a ceremony inaugurating Springfield College in Springfield, MA, in 1913?

A260: Herbert Hoover

A261: Richard M. Nixon

A262: James Garfield. His hat size was 7 3/4.

A263: Gerald R. Ford

A264: Martin Van Buren. He was known for his political dexterity and was a native of
Kinderhook, NY.

A265: Thomas Jefferson

A266: Benjamin Harrison, in 1892

A267: Rutherford B. Hayes, in 1878

A268: Thomas Jefferson

A269: William Howard Taft

Q270: Which future President made his first appearance in court arguing to the U.S. Supreme Court?

Q271: Which two Presidents died before reaching the age of fifty?

Q272: In 1909, which President asked Vice President James Sherman to be his conduit to U.S. House Speaker Joe Cannon (R-IL.)?

Q273: Which President, who was shot, was sent to the New Jersey beach community of Elberton to recover? His doctors hoped the sea air would revive him. The effort failed, and the President died just twelve days after arriving in the community.

Q274: Which President took the U.S. off the Gold Standard?

Q275: Who was the first President to hold a press conference?

Q276: Which President delivered a speech to the United Nations General Assembly called "Atoms for Peace?"

Q277: Which future President was the sole creator and author of the Constitution of Massachusetts?

Q278: Political opponents mocked which President as: "That little man from Missouri."

Q279: Which President signed legislation creating the first National Park in the U.S.?

A270: James Garfield. He argued the case of *Ex parte Milligan*.

A271: James Garfield and John F. Kennedy. Garfield died at age 49. Kennedy died at age 46. Both men were assassinated while in office.

A272: William Howard Taft. Taft did not like Cannon. He viewed him as too conservative and autocratic, and wanted Sherman to meet with him so he would not have to. Sherman had a cordial relationship with Cannon when the two men served in the House. Taft told Sherman: "I am going to rely on you Jim to take care of Cannon for me. Whatever I have to do there will be done through you." Sherman would have none of it. He retorted: "You will have to act on your own account. I am to be Vice President and acting as a messenger boy is not part of the duties as Vice President." Accordingly, the President met with Cannon himself.

A273: James Garfield

A274: Franklin D. Roosevelt, in 1933

A275: Woodrow Wilson, in 1913

A276: Dwight D. Eisenhower. This was a program for the peaceful distribution of nuclear technology around the world.

A277: John Adams

A278: Harry S. Truman

A279: Ulysses S. Grant, in 1872

The Presidents

Q280: After leaving the White House, which former President returned to his home in North Hampton, Massachusetts, where he enjoyed sitting on his front porch in the evening, but due to the hordes of onlookers who wanted to see him, he was forced to move to a more secluded house in the municipality?

Q281: Who was the only grandfather-grandson duo to serve as President?

Q282: Which President was the Great Grandson of a signer of the Declaration of Independence?

Q283: Which President served during the Bicentennial of the inauguration of George Washington? During his Presidency, he reenacted the Washington inauguration in New York.

Q284: Who was the first President born in a hospital?

Q285: Which four Presidents won the Noble Peace Prize?

Q286: Why is there a pen at the Pro Football Hall of Fame in Canton, Ohio from legislation signed by President Lyndon B. Johnson?

Q287: Which President, a former General, lashed out at Southerners who threatened to secede from the Union? He promised to personally lead an army to quash the rebellion?

Q288: Which President signed the most Executive Orders?

Q289: As a U.S. Senator, which future President sponsored a resolution to create a monument to the esteemed African-American inventor George Washington Carver?

The Presidents

A280: Calvin Coolidge

A281: William Henry Harrison (1841) and Benjamin Harrison (1889-1893)

A282: Benjamin Harrison. His Great Grandfather was Benjamin Harrison V, who was a delegate to the Continental Congress.

A283: George H.W. Bush, in 1989

A284: Jimmy Carter. He was born on October 1, 1924 at the Wise Clinic in Plains, GA.

A285: Theodore Roosevelt, Woodrow Wilson, and Barack Obama. Jimmy Carter received the award in 2002, as a former President.

A286: Because he signed legislation in 1966 allowing for a merger of the American Football League and the National Football League.

A287: Zachary Taylor

A288: Franklin D. Roosevelt. In his over 12 years in office, he signed 3,522 Executive Orders.

A289: Harry S. Truman. He was from Missouri where Carver hailed from. President Franklin D. Roosevelt signed the resolution in 1945. The monument was the first in the U.S. dedicated to an African-American and the first of a non-U.S. President.

The Presidents

Q290: Warren and Florence Harding are buried in The Harding tomb in which Ohio city?

Q291: How long does the U.S. Secret Service protect a President?

Q292: Which President earned the moniker: "Old Rough and Ready" for his willingness to get his boots dirty leading his troops into battle when he was a General in the Mexican-American War?

Q293: As torrential downpours enveloped Washington D.C., which President suffered the ignominious task of holding an umbrella over the head of the man who had defeated him in the Presidential election while he assumed the Oath of Office?

Q294: On the day President John F. Kennedy was shot and killed, Secret Service Agent Gerald Blaine was on duty guarding the new President Lyndon B. Johnson's Washington D.C. home. Blaine heard footsteps and fired his submachine gun in the air to ward off any potential intruders. However, the person continued to walk toward Blaine. Blaine then put his finger on the trigger ready to shoot what he thought was an intruder. Fortunately, Blaine then recognized the man walking toward him. It was President Johnson. Had Blaine pulled off the shot, who would have assumed the Presidency?

Q295: In 1842, U.S. Secretary of State Daniel Webster persuaded President John Tyler to nominate this author, who wrote the book *Rip Van Winkle,* as U.S. Minister to Spain?

Q296: Which President appeared in the 1951 movie Bedtime *for Bonzo* as Professor Peter Boyd?

Q297: In 1964, Bill Moyers, the Press Secretary for President Lyndon B. Johnson, leaked to which Newsweek reporter that the President was set to fire FBI Director J. Edgar Hoover? This would have been an elephantine story, in that Hoover had been head of the FBI since 1924. He was feared in the nation's capital.

Q298: In 1985, the Presidents of the American and National Baseball Leagues chose which former President to arbitrate a dispute between Major League Baseball and the Major League Baseball Umpires Union?

Q299: Which Arkansan served for the longest time as a Legislator while Bill Clinton was an executive?

A290: Marion, OH. This was their hometown.

A291: Their entire lifetime

A292: Zachary Taylor

A293: Grover Cleveland. He held the umbrella over the head of Benjamin Harrison. Cleveland came back to defeat Harrison in 1892.

A294: U.S. House Speaker John McCormack (D-MA), 72-years-old, who appeared to have no ambitions beyond the House, would have assumed the Presidency.

A295: Washington Irving

A296: Ronald Reagan

A297: Ben Bradley. He reported the story, shocking much of the nation. Johnson then announced an impromptu press conference, and announced that he was appointing Hoover as FBI leader "for life" embarrassing Bradley. After the press conference, Johnson turned to Moyers and averred: "You can tell Bradley to go f--- himself."

A298: Richard M. Nixon. After listening to both sides of the dispute, Nixon ruled that: "The arbitrator's decision is that because the championship series have been expanded by a factor of 40%, the working umpires are entitled to receive a 40% increase in compensation, which amounts to an increase of $4,000 per umpire, or a total of $48,000 per year for the 12 working umpires for the years 1985 and 1986."

A299: Tim Hutchinson. He was elected in 1985 to the Arkansas State Legislature while Bill Clinton was Arkansas Governor, and served until 1993. He served in the U.S. House from 1993-1997, and in the U.S. Senate from 1997-2003. Bill Clinton was President from 1993-2001.

The Presidents

Q300: When Lyndon B. Johnson was leaving Washington at Andrews Air Force Base to go back to Texas after his term expired, an assemblage of mostly Democrats was there to wish him well. Despite this assemblage of Democrats, one future Republican President was also there to wish President Johnson well. Who was this Republican?

Q301: In 1905, this future President suffered the only loss of his political career when he ran for a seat on the local School Committee in his adopted hometown of North Hampton, MA. Who was this future President?

Q302: Who was the only President to fly aboard a public commercially scheduled flight while in office?

Q303: Which President was accepted to Harvard University but did not attend because he had to care for his parents' grocery store while his mother took care of his brother Harold?

Q304: Which former President personally lobbied for passage of the 1993 ban on semi-automatic weapons, and may have made the difference in its passage?

Q305: Who was the first President to ride in an airplane?

Q306: Which President left law school at George Washington University in Washington D.C., to become the Texas state director of the National Youth Administration?

Q307: Which future President was a British Prisoner of War during the American Revolution?

Q308: Which future President personally performed two executions, earning him the moniker: "The Buffalo Hangman?"

Q309: In 1844, which President was aboard the *USS Princeton* on a pleasure cruise with top government dignitaries when a Peacemaker canon accidently exploded, killing the U.S. Secretary of State, the Secretary of the Navy, and four others?

A300: U.S. Representative George H.W. Bush (R-TX)

A301: Calvin Coolidge

A302: Richard M. Nixon. In 1973, he boarded *United Airlines Flight 55* from Washington Dulles International Airport to Los Angeles International Airport. This event was secret, and even the pilot did not find out about it until about an hour prior to the flight. Nixon spent much of the flight talking with his fellow passengers. The point of the flight was to exhibit confidence in the commercial airline industry during the energy crisis.

A303: Richard M. Nixon. Accordingly, he attended Whitter College in Whittier, CA instead.

A304: Ronald Reagan. He worked with President Bill Clinton to pass a ban on semi-automatic weapons. In fact, he may have been the person who got the legislation over the finish line. The bill passed in the U.S. House 216-214. Reagan wrote a personal letter to U.S. Representative Scott Klug (R-WI,) beseeching him to vote for the legislation. Klug mentioned the letter in a statement announcing his support of the legislation. In addition, Reagan directly lobbied U.S. Representative Dick Swett (D-NH) to vote for the legislation. Swett came from a gun-friendly Congressional District. Swett, who had been opposed to the legislation said it was the lobbying by Reagan that persuaded him to change his position and support the legislation. Swett landed up losing his Congressional seat, in part for his support of the legislation, and was forced to wear a bullet-proof vest after threats were made on his life.

A305: Theodore Roosevelt. He did this as a former President. In 1910. The aircraft was piloted by esteemed aviator Arch Hoxsey, and flew for 4 minutes at Kinlock Field in St. Louis, MO. The aircraft was constructed by the Wright Brothers.

A306: Lyndon B. Johnson

A307: Andrew Jackson. After Jackson refused to clean the boots of a British Officer, he was slashed with a sword, leaving him with permeant scars.

A308: Grover Cleveland. He did this when he served as the Sheriff of Erie County, NY.

A309: John Tyler. He survived the event. Former First Lady Dolly Madison was also aboard and survived. In no other day have this many top government officials died.

The Presidents

Q310: Which 6-year-old future President watched the funeral procession of President Abraham Lincoln from his grandfather's mansion in 1865?

Q311: What did the first act passed by the first U.S. Congress and signed by President George Washington provide for?

Q312: Which Washington DC church was regularly attended by President Rutherford B. Hayes and President Bill Clinton?

Q313: Which President carried a carnation around for good luck? As fate would have it, he gave the carnation to a young girl standing in line just before he was shot and killed?

Q314: Eliza Hendricks, the wife of Vice President Thomas Hendricks, who served under Grover Cleveland, was born in the small village of North Bend, OH. What President was also born in North Bend, OH?

Q315: Who is the only President to hold a patent?

Q316: Who was the first incumbent President to attend a Major League Baseball game?

Q317: Who was the first President to be awarded The Order of Muhammad, a.k.a., the Order of Sovereignty, the highest state decoration of the Kingdom of Morocco?

Q318: Which Presidential home boasts the fact that 90% of the furnishings and artifacts presently in the home were in the home when a President lived there?

Q319: The first Presidential library was built in 1870 in what city?

The Presidents

A310: Theodore Roosevelt

A311: A protective tariff. U.S. Representative James Madison of Virginia proposed the legislation.

A312: Foundry Methodist Church

A313: William McKinley

A314: Benjamin Harrison

A315: Abraham Lincoln. It was for a device which lifts boats over shoals. It accrued a patent in 1849. It was never manufactured.

A316: Benjamin Harrison. The game was played in 1892 in Boundary Field, just two miles away from the White House (Known at the time as the Executive Mansion). The game was played between the hometown Washington Senators and the Cincinnati Reds. Harrison was a native of North Bend, OH, part of the Greater Cincinnati area. Harrison arrived in a horse-drawn carriage and sat in the press box. Harrison egressed from the game early.

A317: Donald Trump. He won this award for his work in negotiating a deal normalizing relations between Israel and Morocco.

A318: The Hermitage, in Nashville, TN. This was the home of President Andrew Jackson.

A319: Quincy, MA. It was built by Charles Francis Adams Sr. to honor his father, John Quincy Adams.

The Presidents

Q320: Which former U.S. Senator presided over the funeral of Ronald Reagan at the National Cathedral in Washington, DC?

Q321: Who is the only President to be survived by a grandparent?

Q322: Who were the only three Presidents to have two parents living when they were inaugurated?

Q323: Who was the first President to be portrayed on *Saturday Night Live*?

Q324: Which future President's mother and first wife died on the same day, on Valentine's Day, February 14, 1884?

Q325: Which four men, who had been Governors of New York, became President?

Q326: Which President could not serve in the Revolutionary War due to epileptic seizers?

Q327: What is Joe Biden's middle name?

Q328: Which President first assembled the National Governors together?

Q329: Who was the first President to fly in a helicopter?

The Presidents

A320: John Danforth (R-MO). He is an ordained priest.

A321: John F. Kennedy

A322: Ulysses S. Grant, Franklin D. Roosevelt, and John F. Kennedy

A323: Gerald R. Ford. Actor Chevy Chase played him. The two men met for the first time in 1976 at the 32nd Annual Radio and Television Correspondents Dinner. Ford said to Chase: "Mr. Chevy Chase, you're a very, very funny suburb" (referring to Chevy Chase, MD).

A324: Theodore Roosevelt

A325: Martin Van Buren, Grover Cleveland, Theodore Roosevelt, and Franklin D. Roosevelt

A326: James Madison

A327: Robinette

A328: Theodore Roosevelt. He did this in 1908 to drum up support for his conservation measures. Since then, Governors have continued the practice of assembling, and have established The National Governors Association.

A329: Dwight D. Eisenhower. He requested that the U.S. Secret Service allow him to be flown on short trips. He thought it would be safer than the Presidential motorcade. The practice continues to this day, as Presidents are flown on the official Presidential helicopter called *Marine One*.

Q330: Which President is hailed by Princeton University, then called Kings College, as their first graduate student?

Q331: Why did the leader of The Church of Latter-day Saints, Brigham Young, name the first territorial capital of Utah "Fillmore" and the county around it "Millard?"

Q332: What renowned explorer did Millard Fillmore send to Japan to open up the nation to the rest of the world?

Q333: Which President presided over the annexation of Hawaii?

Q334: Before being elected to the U.S. Senate, what was the only other elected position Joe Biden ever held?

Q335: Before transferring to the Wharton Business School of the University of Pennsylvania, in Philadelphia, PA, what college did Donald Trump attend?

Q336: Which future President taught a course called *Selected Topics in Constitutional Law* while a member of the U.S. Senate?

Q337: Which future President's first public office was Surveyor of Culpeper County, Virginia?

Q338: Who was the first President to send an email while in office?

Q339: Which President had a buzzer installed in the Oval Office so that the Secret Service could warn him when his wife was on the way?

A330: James Madison. After graduation, he stayed on campus for a year to study Hebrew with college President John Witherspoon.

A331: He did this to thank President Millard Fillmore for declaring him the first Governor of the Utah Territory.

A332: Commodore Matthew C. Perry. His voyage led to the singing of the Kanagawa Treaty between the U.S. and Japan, which opened the ports of Hakdote and Shimoda to American vessels.

A333: William McKinley. He signed the treaty for the annexation of the Republic of Hawaii in 1897. The Republic was annexed in 1898.

A334: He was a member of the New Castle County Council for about one year.

A335: Fordham University, in New York City

A336: Joe Biden. He was an adjunct professor at Widener University Delaware Law School from 1991 until 2008. The class met just once a week on Saturdays. He taught the class by himself until 2003, when he team-taught the course with Professor Robert Hayman Jr., because he no longer had the time to teach it solo. He taught the course in 2007, even while running for the Democratic Presidential nomination. He was the third highest paid member of the U.S. Congress who taught a course. He earned $20,500 annually for teaching he course.

A337: George Washington. He served in this position from 1849-1850.

A338: Bill Clinton. It was a test email sent in 1993.

A339: Lyndon B. Johnson. He had a reputation as a serial philanderer.

The Presidents

Q340: Which President inaugurated the Presidential press briefing?

Q341: Who was the first President to tour the Forbidden City in China, a coterie of palaces which housed Chinese emperors for almost 50 years?

Q342: Who is the only President to be awarded the Presidential Medal of Freedom prior to assuming office?

Q343: While serving in the State Senate, Barack Obama also taught Constitutional Law at which esteemed Illinois University?

Q344: Which President's first name was Steven?

Q345: Which President ushered in the annual tradition of celebrating Diwali in the White House?

Q346: Which President was notorious for having advisors and news reporters follow him and continue to speak with him while he was in the bathroom with the door open?

Q347: Who was the first President to send military personnel to South Vietnam?

Q348: Less than five years before ascending to the Presidency, which political figure was re-elected in the Democratic primary to the U.S. Senate with just 40.91% of the vote, and re-elected in the General Election with just 51.17% of the vote?

Q349: Which President coined the phrase: "Like nailing jelly to a wall?"

Q350: In 1939, Jerry Parr watched the movie *Code of the Secret Service* starring actor Ronald Reagan. It inspired him to become a Secret Service agent as an adult. In that capacity, he was instrumental in saving the life of what famous political figure?

A340: Theodore Roosevelt. He gave the assembled press, which was camped out on the White House Lawn, a room in the White House. This effectively began the Presidential Press Briefing.

A341: Donald Trump. He did this in 2017.

A342: Joe Biden. He was awarded the honor by President Barack Obama in 2009.

A343: The University of Chicago. Obama taught as a lecturer from 1992-1996, then as a senior Lecturer from 1996-2004.

A344: Grover Cleveland. He went by his middle name of Grover.

A345: George W. Bush. He did this in 2003. Diwali is a holiday also known as the Festival of Lights. It celebrates the triumph of light over darkness. It is celebrated by Jains, Sikhs, and Hindus.

A346: Lyndon B. Johnson

A:347: Dwight D. Eisenhower. He sent 700 military advisors to aid the government of South Vietnam.

A348: Harry S. Truman. He beat back a formidable challenge by Missouri Governor Lloyd Stark and U.S. Attorney Maurice M. Milligan in the primary, and then defeated Missouri State Senator Manvel H. Davis in the General Election in 1940. In 1944, he was selected as the Running-mate for President Franklin D. Roosevelt, and then assumed the Presidency in 1945, upon Roosevelt's death.

A349: Theodore Roosevelt. In a letter written to William Roscoe Thayer (in April of 1912), the former President discussed his failure to secure an agreement with Columbia during the chasm between Columbia and Panama over granting the U.S. acquisition rights to the Panama Canal Zone. Roosevelt averred: "Somebody asked me why I did not get an agreement with Colombia. They might just as well ask me why I do not nail cranberry jelly to the wall. It would not be my fault or the fault of the nail, it would be the fault of the jelly."

A350: Ronald Reagan. Parr helped to save him from an assassination attempt in 1981. Interestingly, Reagan had said that the movie was "the worst picture I ever made."

Chapter II

Presidential Quotations

Presidential Quotations

Q1: When this taciturn President died, satirist Dorothy Parker deadpanned: "How do they know"?

Q2: Which President said: "Every man has a right to a Saturday night bath"?

Q3: Which President described two predecessors this way: "I tend to pair up Benjamin Harrison and Dwight Eisenhower because they're the two presidents I can think of who most preferred laziness to labor.... There's not much else you can say about Harrison except that he was President of the United States"?

Q4: Which former President's last words before he dropped dead were: "The nourishment is palatable" as he ate soup in 1874?

Q5: Commenting on the failed attempts by John F. Kennedy to assassinate leaders inhospitable to the U.S., which President said Kennedy: "had been operating a damned Murder Inc. in the Caribbean"?

Q6: Upon learning of this President's death in 1923, Poet Edward Estillin Cummings made the following comment about this President: "The only man, woman, or child who ever wrote a simple declarative sentence with seven grammatical errors is dead." Which President was Cummings referring to?

Q7: A dinner party guest told which President that she made a bet with her friend that she could get the President to say at least three words? The President deadpanned: "You lose."

Q8: Which President, an inveterate politician, commented: "I seldom think of politics more than eighteen hours a day"?

Q9: Which President advised: "Tell the truth, work hard, and come to dinner on time"?

Presidential Quotations

A1: Calvin Coolidge

A2: Lyndon B. Johnson

A3: Harry S. Truman

A4: Millard Fillmore

A5: Lyndon B. Johnson

A6: Warren G. Harding

A7: Calvin Coolidge

A8: Lyndon B. Johnson

A9: Gerald R. Ford

Presidential Quotations

Q10: In a 1930 Newspaper column, which former President stated: "The final solution for unemployment is work"?

Q11: Which President gave the following advice for giving a good speech: "Be sincere--be brief--be seated"?

Q12: In explaining his decision to appoint future President James Buchanan to the post of U.S. Minister to Russia, the President quipped: "It was as far as I could send him to get him out of my sight, and where he could do the least harm. I would have sent him to the North Pole if we kept a Minister there." Which President made this statement about James Buchanan?

Q13: Which President averred: "I pity the man who wants coats so cheap that the man or woman who produces the cloth will starve in the process?"

Q14: Which President humbly declined receiving an honorary degree from Oxford University, humbly declaring: "I have neither literary nor scientific achievement?"

Q15: Which President is credited with the expression: "If you can't stand the heat, get out of the kitchen?"

Q16: Which President told sportscaster Frank Gifford: "I have often thought that if I had my life to live over again and did not go into politics, I would like to have your job, you know, be a sportscaster or writer"?

Q17: Which President, who was known as an inveterate reader, mused: "Not all readers are leaders, but all leaders are reader"?

Q18: Which President publicly stated: "Moslems, Hindus, Buddhists, as well as Christians, pause from their labors on the 25th day of December to celebrate the birthday of the "Prince of Peace"?

Q19: Which President averred: "I know two songs. One of them is *Yankee Doodle* and the other one isn't"?

A10:   Calvin Coolidge

A11:   Franklin D. Roosevelt

A12:   Andrew Jackson

A13:   Benjamin Harrison

A14:   Millard Fillmore

A15:   While Harry S. Truman is credited with originating the line, Truman was actually quoting his military aide and confidant Harry H. Vaughan.

A16:   Richard M. Nixon

A17:   Harry S. Truman

A18:   John F. Kennedy. in 1962. Kennedy also called Christmas "Universal."

A19:   Ulysses S. Grant

Q20: Which President stated: "I have nothing but contempt for any man who can spell a word only one way"?

Q21: Which president often mused: "If one morning I walked on top of the water across the Potomac River, the headline that afternoon would read 'President Can't Swim'"?

Q22: When U.S. Senator Albert Fall (R-MT) visited this sickly Democratic President who recovering from a stroke, Fall informed the President: "We have been praying for you Mr. President," The President, in a momentary surge of mental dexterity, retorted: "Which way Senator?" Which President made this interesting response?

Q23: Which President, who had many quarrels with the U.S. Congress, bemoaned: "In my many years I have come to a conclusion that one useless man is a shame, two is a law firm, and three or more is a Congress"?

Q24: Which President wrote: "Nothing can now be believed which is seen in a newspaper. Truth itself becomes suspicious by being put into that polluted vehicle"?

Q25: When this President found out that his granddaughter was born, he said: "Thank God she doesn't have to be confirmed by the [U.S.] Senate." Which President said this?

Q26: Which President told the American people he would: "work until the last hour of the last day in office"?

Q27: John Quincy Adams refused to attend an awards ceremony at his alma mater, Harvard University, for this President who received an Honorary Degree from Harvard but who had no formal education. Adams described this current President as "A barbarian who could not write a sentence of grammar and hardly could spell his own name." Which President was John Quincy Adams referring to?

Q28: Lyndon B. Johnson said of which FBI Director: "I would rather have him inside the tent pissing out than outside the tent pissing in"?

Q29: When this President was told in a cable from General George Dewey that the U.S. had captured Manila, the Capital of the Philippines, he lamented: "I could not have told where those dammed islands were within 2,000 miles." Who was this President?

Presidential Quotations

A20: Thomas Jefferson

A21: Lyndon B. Johnson

A22: Woodrow Wilson

A23: John Adams

A24: Thomas Jefferson

A25: Herbert Hoover

A26: Bill Clinton. He made this statement after being impeached by the U.S. House of Representatives in 1998. During his last Presidential radio address, on January 20, 2001, Clinton averred: "I pledged that I would work until the last hour of the last day. Well, here we are. So, this morning, we're building on our commitment to make our streets safer by awarding more than $100 million to fund 1,400 more police officers in communities throughout our land."

A27: Andrew Jackson

A28: J. Edgar Hoover

A29: William McKinley

Q30: Theodore Roosevelt called this Presidential successor: "Dumber than a guinea pig, a fathead." Which President was he referring to?

Q31: Which Democratic President had no use for the Republican-controlled U.S. Senate, and stated that they "have no use for their heads except to serve as a knot to keep their bodies from unraveling"?

Q32: Which President once said of President William McKinley: "McKinley has no more backbone than a chocolate éclair"?

Q33: When this President learned that his wife was visiting a penitentiary, he quipped: "She's in prison. I'm not surprised, but what for?" Which President uttered these words?

Q34: This President quipped: "My choice early in life was either to be a piano-player in a whorehouse or a politician. And to tell the truth, there's hardly any difference." Which President made this peculiar comment?

Q35: At a 2012 memorial dedication for Vice President Hubert Humphrey, a flag fell behind this former President as he was speaking. The President responded: "I once saw a State Senator of mine get hit by the American Flag and he said you know I risked my life in WWII, and I don't think I should get killed by it." Which President made this remark?

Q36: This former President told Journalist David Frost: "Well, when the President does it, that means it is not illegal." Which President made this interesting comment?

Q37: Which President said: "You teach a child to read, and he or her will be able to pass a literacy test"?

Q38: This future President wrote: "You have to be confident as you face the world each day, but you can't be cocky. Anyone who thinks he's going to win them all is going to wind up a huge loser?" Which President made this comment?

Q39: At the end of a Presidential press conference, a reporter asked this President: "Is there anything we have overlooked Mr. President?" The President responded: "I don't believe there is. If I could think of any, why would I give it to you?" Which President uttered these words?

Presidential Quotations

A30: William Howard Taft

A31: Woodrow Wilson

A32: Theodore Roosevelt. He said this before McKinley selected him as his Vice Presidential running-mate in 1900.

A33: Franklin D. Roosevelt

A34: Harry S. Truman

A35: Bill Clinton

A36: Richard M. Nixon

A37: George W. Bush

A38: Donald Trump: He wrote those words in his 2004 book: *Trump: Think like a Billionaire: Everything You need to Know About Success, Real Estate, and Life – yet another New York Times Bestseller*

A39: Harry S. Truman

Presidential Quotations

Q40: Which President described an intellectual as "a man who takes more words than necessary to tell more than he knows"?

Q41: Lyndon B. Johnson said of this future President: "He's a nice guy, but he played too much football with his helmet off." Which future President was he referring to?

Q42: Which President described Washington, D.C. as: "twelve square miles bordered by reality"?

Q43: *BBC* News Reporter Gordon Hodgson asked the following question of an incumbent President: "Mr. President, as you look back on your years in this office, what do you think has been your greatest achievement?" This President answered: "Sometimes, I think just staying alive." Who was this President?

Q44: Which President quipped about Warren G. Harding: "Harding is incapable of thought, because he has nothing to think with"?

Q45: Which Democratic President said of the Republican Party: "They simply don't know how to manage the economy. They're so busy operating the trickle-down theory, giving the richest corporations the biggest break, that the whole thing goes to hell in a handbasket."

Q46: This President, after a failed fishing excursion, was asked how many trout were in the river? His response was: "About forty-five thousand. I haven't caught them all yet, but I've intimidated them." Who was this President?

Q47: This President described his job as "like running a cemetery: You've got a lot of people under you and nobody's listening." Which President made this humorous comment?

Q48: Which President called a conservative: "A man with two perfectly good legs who, however, has never learned to walk forward"?

Q49: U.S. Representative John Sherman (R-OH) quipped about this Democratic President: "The Constitution provides for every contingency in the executive, except a vacancy in the mind of the President." Which President was the target of this remark?

A40: Dwight D. Eisenhower

A41: Gerald R. Ford. Ford was U.S. House Minority Leader. Ford had been the Center on the University of Michigan Football team.

A42: Andrew Johnson

A43: Ronald Reagan. He survived an assassination attempt in 1981.

A44: Woodrow Wilson

A45: Lyndon B. Johnson

A46: Calvin Coolidge

A47: Bill Clinton

A48: Franklin D. Roosevelt

A49: James Buchanan

Q50: When German Chancellor Ludwig Erhard visited this President, he asked if he was born in a log cabin. The President answered: "No, Mr. Chancellor, I was born in a manger." Which President made the comment about being born in a manger?

Q51: Which former President told the Nebraska Republican Convention: "Blessed are the young, for they will inherit the national debt"?

Q52: In 1915, which former President admonished that :"the professional pacifists, the peace-at-any-price, non-resistance, universal arbitration people are now seeking to Chinafy this country. The moral fiber of the Chinese people has been closely eaten into by the doctrines of the professional pacificists, so that she has shown herself incapable during the last thirty years of preparing herself against war and for self-defense. No nation ever amounted to anything if its population was composed of pacifists and poltroons"?

Q53: This President had to make many political appointments. An advisor objected to one of his proposed appointments saying that the man was a "son of a bitch." This President answered: "Don't they deserve to be represented too?" Which President made this comment?

Q54: Which President said: "if you're interested in avoiding World War III, it seems like you ought to be interested in preventing them [Iran] from having the knowledge necessary to make a nuclear weapon?"

Q55: Which President refused to use a telephone, explaining that: "If you don't say anything, you won't be called on to repeat it."

Q56: This President said: "We're not just going to be waiting for legislation in order to make sure that we're providing Americans the kind of help they need. I've got a pen and I've got a phone"? Which President made this comment?

Q57: Which President had two cats, Dixie and Tabby? He fed them under the table and joked: "Dixie is smarter than my whole cabinet! And furthermore, she doesn't talk back."

Q58: In 1991, which former New York City Mayor commented: "I wouldn't believe Donald Trump if he had his tongue notarized"?

Q59: Which President said: "The great pandemic certainly was a terrible thing where they lost anywhere from 50 to 100 million people." The president also noted that the 1918 flu pandemic: "Probably ended the Second World War, all the soldiers were sick. That was a terrible situation"?

A50: Lyndon B. Johnson

A51: Herbert Hoover

A52: Theodore Roosevelt

A53: Calvin Coolidge

A54: George W. Bush

A55: Calvin Coolidge

A56: Barack Obama

A57: Abraham Lincoln

A58: Ed Koch

A59: Donald Trump. In actuality, the pandemic occurred in 1918, whereas WWII ended in 1945.

Presidential Quotations

Q60: Which President made the following statement: "I'm proud that I'm a politician. A politician is a man who understands government, and it takes a politician to run a government. A statesman is a politician who's been dead 10 or 15 years"?

Q61: This President (a former Brigadier General in the U.S. Army) sent a letter home to his family in which he said that cannabis is "about the only good thing" in the war. Who was this President?

Q62: Which President popularized the term "bloviating?" He defined it as: "The art of speaking for as long as the occasion warrants without saying anything."

Q63: When Richard M. Nixon averred: "I am not a crook" where was he?

Q64: This President jocularly deadpanned: "I want to make a policy statement. I am unabashedly in favor of women." Who made this policy statement?

Q65: Which President said of his daughter: "I can be president of the United States — or — I can attend to Alice. I cannot possibly do both"?

Q66: At a ceremony interring this President in a Cleveland Mausoleum, President Benjamin Harrison said that his legacy continues "to be instructive and inspiring incidents in American history." Who was this deceased President?

Q67: Which President, a lawyer by trade, coined the axiom: "A man who acts as his own attorney has a fool for a client"?

Q68: When presented with a memorandum from economic advisor Leon Henderson, this President admitted: "Are you laboring under the impression that I read these memoranda of yours? I can't even lift them." Who was this President?

Q69: This future Governor and President deadpanned five years before becoming Governor: "You know, I could run for governor and all this but I'm basically a media creation. I've never really done anything. I've worked for my dad. I worked in the oil industry. But that's not the kind of profile you have to have to get elected to public office." Which future President made this statement about himself?

A60: Harry S. Truman

A61: Franklin Pierce. He served in the Mexican-American War.

A62: Warren G. Harding

A63: He was at Disney World's Contemporary Resort in Orlando, FL.   He was there to address the Associated Press Managing Editors Annual Conference. Nixon's statement was made during a question-and-answer session. He was asked about the proliferating Watergate imbroglio.

A64: Lyndon B. Johnson

A65: Theodore Roosevelt

A66: James Garfield. He died in 1881. The mausoleum was dedicated to Garfield in 1890.

A67: Abraham Lincoln

A68: Franklin D. Roosevelt

A69: George W. Bush

Q70: Which President died in office on his way back to Washington D.C. from Alaska? His wife was reading him the newspaper. The Presidents last words were: "Could you please read that again?"

Q71: Which President stated: "We're enjoying sluggish times, and not enjoying them very much"?

Q72: Which President reveled in telling the story of an old man who was arrested and taken before the judge for being drunk and setting a bed on fire? The old man said to the judge, "Judge, I plead guilty to being drunk, but the bed was on fire when I got in it."

Q73: Which President called members of the U.S. Congress who opposed the ratification of the Treaty of Versailles "Pygmy minds"?

Q74: In 1930, this New York Yankees Right Fielder was asked what it was like to make more money than President Herbert Hoover. His response was: "What the hell has Hoover got to do with it? Besides, I had a better year than he did." Who was the baseball player who made this comment?

Q75: Which President drank a gallon of coffee per day? His son joked that the President's Coffee mug was "more in the nature of a bathtub."

Q76: In 1967, this President was presented with his official portrait painted by artist Peter Hurd. The President said it was "the ugliest thing I ever saw." Hurd was not offended and mentioned that he only had a half-hour to draw the painting and that the President kept falling asleep. The rejected portrait garnered a record number of visitors at the Diamond Museum in Snyder, Texas. Which President was the subject of this portrait?

Q77: Which former President stated: "Every reform has a lunatic fringe"?

Q78: Which President declared in his inaugural address: "We are all Democrats; we are all Republicans"?

Q79: When asked by reporter Leslie Stahl on the *CBS News* program *60 Minutes*: "Are you going to be tweeting?" which President answered: "I'm going to be very restrained, if I use it at all."

A70: Warren G. Harding: He was at the Palace Hotel in San Francisco when he died.

A71: George H.W. Bush

A72: Jimmy Carter

A73: Woodrow Wilson. The treaty would have allowed the U.S. to join the League of Nations.

A74: Babe Ruth

A75: Theodore Roosevelt

A76: Lyndon B. Johnson

A77: Theodore Roosevelt. He wrote this in his 1913 autobiography.

A78: Thomas Jefferson, in 1801

A79: Donald Trump

Q80: At a 1974 farewell party for Herbert Stein (the Chairman of the Council of Economic Advisers), which President quipped: "I think an economist has been described as a person who tells you there will definitely not be a hurricane and then shortly thereafter helps you repair and rebuild the roof"?

Q81: Before an interview with Journalist David Frost, this President bizarrely asked: "Well, did you do any fornicating this weekend?" Which President asked this question?

Q82: After attending a Sermon one Sunday, a reporter asked this President what the preacher had talked about. A man of few words, he replied: "Sin." The reporter asked what he said about it. The President deadpanned: "He was against it." Who made this funny comment?

Q83: Which President repeated the following story about a constituent? "I went to a reception elsewhere in town. A sweet old lady came up to me, put her gloved hand in mine, and said, 'You spoke here tonight' 'Oh, it was nothing' I replied modestly. 'Yes', the little old lady nodded, 'that's what I heard.'"

Q84: After leaving office, which President said: "As to the Presidency, the two happiest days of my life were those of my entrance upon the office and my surrender of it"?

Q85: This President lashed out about the media, alleging that they do not report what he had accomplished, telling *Rolling Stone Magazine*: "That's the press' fault too, damn it! I have fought more battles here for more things than any President has in 20 years, with the possible exception of [Ronald] Reagan's first budget, and not gotten one damn bit of credit from the knee-jerk liberal press, and I am sick and tired of it, and you can put that in your damn article!" Which President said this?

Q86: When this Boston Red Sox Outfielder did not show up for a White House reception honoring the 2007 Boston Red Sox, President George W. Bush joked: "I guess his grandmother died again. Just kidding. Tell him I didn't mean it." Who was this Red Sox baseball player?

Q87: Which President said of Dwight D. Eisenhower: "The General doesn't know any more about politics than a pig knows about Sunday"?

Q88: In a State of the Union Address, this President declared: "I urge the Congress to join me in mounting a major new effort to replace the discredited 'president.'" He meant to say "replace the 'discredited' present system." Which President made this error?

Q89: Which President said: "Trees cause more pollution than automobiles do"? His Press Secretary then warned news reporters to: "Watch out for the killer trees."

Presidential Quotations

A80: Gerald R. Ford

A81: Richard M. Nixon

A82: Calvin Coolidge

A83: Gerald R. Ford

A84: Martin Van Buren

A85: Bill Clinton

A86: Manny Ramirez

A87: Harry S. Truman

A88: Richard M. Nixon

A89: Ronald Reagan. His Press Secretary was James Brady.

Presidential Quotations

Q90: Which President's wife, when asked about her husband's numerous affairs, quipped: "You have to understand, my husband loved people. All people. And half the people in the world are women"?

Q91: The family of this President's wife had the surname "Todd." The Todd's were patrician and had the reputation for being snobby. When the family officially took off one of the 'd's' in Todd (to become "Tod"), this President joked: "One "d" was good enough for God but not for the Todd's." Which President made this joke about his wife's family?

Q92: Which President quipped: "Government does not solve problems, it subsidizes them"?

Q93: This future President wrote notes for a law lecture before becoming President. He offered this insightful advice: "If in your own judgment you cannot be an honest lawyer, resolve to be honest without being a lawyer." Which future President uttered these words?

Q94: This President, an amateur piano player, told an assembled crowd of musicians: "I don't want you to say this out loud. It might hurt the Metropolitan Opera. There is usually one aria or one song in nearly every great opera that is worth listening to – most opera music is boring." Which President made this statement?

Q95: Which President said: "I remember the old man who said he had a great many troubles in his life, but the worst of them never happened"?

Q96: Which former President said of James Madison: "He acquired more glory, and established more Union, than all his three predecessors, [George] Washington, [John] Adams, and [Thomas] Jefferson put together"?

Q97: This President delivered an address in Fredericksburg, Virginia on the nation's economy. However, before the oration, he stopped into Fredericksburg Hardware Store. He stated at the beginning on his speech: "She [his wife] told me I'd better come back with the tools to fix Millie's doghouse or else I'd be in one myself." Which President stopped at the hardware store on his way to delivering an economic speech?

Q98: Which President declared: "The Lord prefers common-looking people. That is the reason he makes so many of them"?

Q99: Which President, when attempting to quote the African Proverb: "Fool me once, shame on you; fool me twice, shame on me": said instead: "There's an old saying in Tennessee - I know it's in Texas, probably in Tennessee - that says, fool me once, shame on - shame on you. Fool me - you can't get fooled again"?

A90: Lady Bird Johnson. She was the husband of Lyndon B. Johnson

A91: Abraham Lincoln

A92: Ronald Reagan

A93: Abraham Lincoln

A94: Harry S. Truman

A95: James Garfield

A96: John Adams

A97: George H.W. Bush. Millie was the Bush's dog.

A98: Abraham Lincoln

A99: George W. Bush. This awkward attempt to quote the African Proverb was done during an appearance in Nashville, Tennessee in 2002.

Presidential Quotations

Q100: What President told British Prime Minister Harold Macmillan: "If I don't have a woman for three days, I get terrible headaches"?

Q101: Which President openly stated that he hated politics, averring: "Politics when I am in it makes me sick"?

Q102: Commenting on a recent trip to the Washington National Geographic Society, where he viewed the preserved Incan mummy Princess of Ampato, which President explained: "I don't know if you've seen that mummy. But you know, if I were a single man, I might ask that mummy out. That's a good-looking mummy. That mummy looks better than I do on my worst days"?

Q103: Former Georgia Governor Joseph Brown belittled which President, stating: "The people are tired of a man who has not an idea above a horse or a cigar"?

Q104: U.S. Representative Barney Frank (D-MA) quipped that this President is "proof that you can be totally impervious to the effects of Harvard and Yale education." Which President was Barney Frank referring to?

Q105: This President was adamant that the General Public understands his speeches. He would often modify the speeches written for him. On one occasion, the White House Speechwriter quoted Greek Philosopher Aristotle. The President thought his audience would not know who Aristotle was, so he crossed out Aristotle and wrote: "As my dear old daddy used to say." Which President modified his speeches in this way?

Q106: After he learned that the Library of Congress had purchased an original Gutenberg Bible, which President deadpanned: "I should think that an ordinary copy of the King James Version would have been good enough for those Congressmen"?

Q107: When actor Clint Eastwood announced he would run for Mayor of Carmel-by-the-Sea, CA in 1986, which President opined: "What makes him think a middle-aged or who's played with a chimp could think he has a future in politics?"

Q108: In a news conference, *CBS* White House Correspondent Dan Rather said: "Thank you Mr. President, Dan Rather of *CBS* News." The crowd reacted with a mix of cheers and boos. The President joked: "Are you running for something?" Rather retorted: "No sir, are you?" Who was Dan Rather of *CBS* News referring to?

Q109: This President ran for office as a reformer. He refused to appoint corrupt politicos to administration posts. He said facetiously to one corrupt office seeker: "Do you want me to appoint another horse thief for you?" Which President said this?

A100: John F. Kennedy

A101: William Howard Taft

A102: Bill Clinton

A103: Ulysses S. Grant

A104: George W. Bush

A105: Lyndon B. Johnson

A106: Calvin Coolidge

A107: Ronald Reagan. Eastwood won the election and served one, two-year term as Mayor. He did not seek re-election.

A108: Richard M. Nixon

A109: Chester A. Arthur

Presidential Quotations

Q110: Which President lashed out at the negative media coverage for allegedly halting air transportation at Los Angeles International Airport so that he could get his haircut on the runway aboard Air Force One. He called into *Morning Meeting* on *KMOX* radio in St. Louis, MO, and exclaimed: "Did you know there were press people on the aircraft carrier? Did you know that the carrier had been fully reimbursed out of the private pocket of a White House staff member who was so upset about it? No. Why didn't you know about that? Because the press reporting it didn't say so."

Q111: This President was an avid baseball fan. However, he once explained in error how he watches the games. He said: "I watch a lot of baseball on radio." Which president made this blunder?

Q112: This President's daughter sang at Constitution Hall in Washington, D.C. *Washington Post* Music critic Paul Hume wrote that she "cannot sing very well and is flat a good deal of the time." The President retorted: "Someday I hope to meet you. When that happens, you'll need a new nose, a lot of beefsteak for black eyes, and perhaps a supporter below!" Which President made this threatening statement?

Q113: When Richard M. Nixon was preparing to resign from office, this former Nixon ally quipped: "I suppose we shall sing Bail to the Chief." Which former ally said this?

Q114: In self-deprecating wit, this President deadpanned: "I know I am getting better at golf because I am hitting fewer spectators." Which President made this funny statement?

Q115: At the funeral for French President Charles de Gaulle, this President inexplicably called the event: "A great day for France." Who made this statement?

Q116: When Air Force One landed, a young Air Force officer said to the President: "Sir, your helicopter is over here." The President replied: "Son, they're all my helicopters." Which President said this?

Q117: This President was critical of Special Assistant on Foreign Affairs Nelson Rockefeller: He said of Rockefeller: "He is too used to borrowing brains instead of using his own." Which President made this statement?

Q118: This President made the following observation: "Once upon a time my political opponents honored me as possessing the fabulous intellectual and economic power by which I created a world-wide depression all by myself." Which President said this?

Q119: In 1968, President Lyndon B. Johnson labelled this California House Speaker: "Probably one of the most selfish men I have met in politics." Who was Johnson referring to?

A110: Bill Clinton

A111: Gerald R. Ford

A112: Harry S. Truman

A113: U.S. Senator Howard Baker (R-TN)

A114: Gerald R. Ford

A115: Richard M. Nixon

A116: Lyndon B. Johnson

A117: Dwight D. Eisenhower

A118: Herbert Hoover

A119: Jesse Unruh. Unruh came to the White House to meet with Johnson. He told the President that he wanted to run for the U.S. Senate Seat occupied by Thomas Kuchel (R-CA). However, he would only do it with the support of Johnson. Johnson informed Unruh that he would support his candidacy. Johnson then asked Unruh if he would support his re-election bid as President. Unruh would not commit to this. In fact, Unruh urged U.S. Senator Robert F. Kennedy (D-NY) to enter the race against Johnson. Ultimately Unruh chose not to run for the U.S. Senate Seat.

Q120: Andrew Jackson had no use for one of his successors, averring: "The Republic may suffer under the present imbecile chief, but the sober second thought of the people will restore it at our next Presidential election." Which President was Andrew Jackson referring to?

Q121: In 1961, George W. Ball, Undersecretary of State for Economic and Agricultural Affairs, advised the President that a continued commitment in Vietnam could rise to 300,000 U.S. troops. Which President characterized Ball as "Crazier than hell"?

Q122: President Lyndon B. Johnson said at this Governor's 51st birthday celebration, "Today you are 51. That's the magic number every man in politics prays for – A simple majority." Whose birthday was it?

Q123: This President was having a conversation about the effects of a book written by Rupert Hughes titled *George Washington: The Human Being and the Hero*. The book put George Washington in a negative light. The President looked out the window and observed: "I see his monument is still there." Which President made this comment?

Q124: This Republican President upbraided conservatives who wanted to abolish the social safety net. He said: "There is a tiny splinter group, of course, that believes you can do these things. Among them are H.L. Hunt, a Texas oil tycoon, a few other Texas oil millionaires, and an occasional politician or businessman from other areas. Their number is negligible and they are stupid." Which President made this statement?

Q125: Which President averred: "Most bad government has grown out of too much government"?

Q126: When U.S. Senator Barack Obama (D-IL) met President George W. Bush for the first time, the first thing Bush said to Obama was: "You know, me and you got something in common." He stated that the two debated which contestant? That guy's a piece of work, isn't he? Who was the candidate?

Q127: Which President said the following: "I've learned that there are only two things necessary to keep your wife happy. First, let her think she's having her way. And second, let her have it."

Q128: This President told sportscaster Frank Gifford: "I have often thought that if I had my life to live over again and did not go into politics, I would like to have your job, you know, be a sportscaster or writer." Which President said this?

Q129: When financier Bernard Baruch advised this President to ask the unpopular Herbert Hoover for help, he responded: "I'm not Jesus Christ. I'm not raising him from the dead." Which President made this statement?

Q130: Which President averred: "If I had five minutes to chop down a tree, I'd spend the first three sharpening my ax?"

Presidential Quotations

A120: William Henry Harrison

A121: John F. Kennedy. However, U.S. troop levels reached 543,00 by 1969.

A122: John Connally (D-TX)

A123: Calvin Coolidge

A124: Dwight D. Eisenhower

A125: Thomas Jefferson

A126: Alan Keys. Bush stated: "That guy's a piece of work, isn't he?" In 2000, Bush and Keyes were both seeking the Republican Presidential nomination. Keyes spoke to a Republican Convention and said of Bush supporters: "I think there are people in this room who will actually go out and stand for the mindless, mediocre equivocators who put our principles on the back burner while promising that they will achieve everything under the sun." In 2004, Keyes was the Republican nominee against Democrat Obama for an open U.S. Senate seat. After Keyes lost in a landslide to Obama, he refused to make a call to concede, declaring, "Obama stood for "a culture evil enough to destroy the very soul and heart of my county. I'm supposed to make a call that represents the congratulations toward that which I believe ultimately stands for and will stand for a culture evil enough to destroy the very soul and heart of my country? I can't do this. And I will not make a false gesture."

A127: Lyndon B. Johnson

A128: Richard M. Nixon

A129: Franklin D. Roosevelt

A130: Abraham Lincoln

Chapter III

Presidential Campaigns

Presidential Campaigns

Q1: Which Democratic Presidential nominee averred: "I can retire with the consciousness that I shall receive from posterity the credit of having been elected to the highest position in the gift of the people, without any of the cares and responsibilities of the office?"

Q2: In 1988, a Republican Presidential candidate was confronted by a heckler who yelled: "You've voted for tax increases 600 times in your career. How can you defend that?" This candidate responded: "Check back into your cave." Who was this Presidential candidate who responded in this fashion to the heckler?

Q3: During his campaign for the 1976 Democratic Presidential nomination, this Democratic Presidential candidate campaigned in a Winnebago and stayed at voters' houses rather than in hotels. He promised those who hosted him that they would be invited to stay in the White House should he win. Which Presidential candidate made this promise?

Q4: Who was the first person to defeat a member of the Kennedy family in an election?

Q5: Which major 2020 Democratic Presidential candidate was not born in a U.S. State?

Q6: Former Massachusetts Governor Joseph B. Ely dropped out of the 1944 race for the Democratic Presidential nomination after losing which state to President Franklin D. Roosevelt?

Q7: Which 2020 Democratic Presidential candidate received his healthcare coverage through the Veterans Administration rather than through the U.S. Congress?

Q8: In 1972, this former Massachusetts Governor ran unsuccessfully for the Democratic Vice Presidential nomination. His memorable slogan was: "The number one man for the number two job." Whose slogan was this?

Q9: In 1979, a Presidential candidate said: "When collective bargaining is forbidden, freedom is lost." Which candidate said this?

Presidential Campaigns

A1: Samuel Tilden. He won a majority of the popular vote but lost by just one vote in the Electoral College to Republican Rutherford B. Hayes following a protracted disputed election in 1876.

A2: Bob Dole

A3: Fred Harris

A4: Eugene McCarthy defeated Robert F. Kennedy in the Oregon Presidential primary. McCarthy garnered 44.7% of the vote. Kennedy mustered 38.8% of the vote.

A5: Tulsi Gabbard. She was born in American Samoa.

A6: Massachusetts. Ely thought Roosevelt was too liberal. Accordingly, he supported Republican Presidential nominee Thomas E. Dewey over Roosevelt in the General Election.

A7: Seth Mouton

A8: Endicott "Chub" Peabody

A9: Ronald Reagan

Presidential Campaigns

Q10: Who is the oldest person to be nominated by a major party on a national ticket?

Q11: Who was the first female to be nominated for President?

Q12: In 1920, this Presidential nominee of the Socialist Party of America ran for President from prison. Who was this Presidential nominee?

Q13: In 2012, while campaigning in Michigan for the Republican Presidential nomination, which Presidential candidate told the Detroit Economic Club: "I love this state. The trees are the right height"?

Q14: These two failed Democratic Presidential nominees believed their Party's President, Franklin D. Roosevelt, had moved too far to the left, Accordingly, they joined the conservative Liberty League and supported Roosevelt's Republican opponents, Alf Landon in 1936, and Wendell Willkie in 1940. Who were these Presidential nominees?

Q15: In 2011, this Republican Presidential candidate dropped out of the race and sought to run for re-election to his congressional seat instead. However, he could not get on the Republican primary ballot, as his signatures were declared invalid. Who was this unsuccessful candidate?

Q16: In 1972, this former President offered the following tepid endorsement of Democratic Presidential nominee George McGovern: "I believe the Democratic Party best represents the people. Therefore, I intend to support the 1972 Democratic nominee." Who was this former Democratic President who was not all that excited about George McGovern's candidacy?

Q17: In 1936, which Republican Presidential nominee made the following profound statement: "Wherever I have gone in America, I have found Americans"?

Q18: During his 2008 Presidential campaign, how much money did Barack Obama raise?

Q19: In 1968, this man, who had unsuccessfully challenged Vice President Hubert Humphrey for the Democratic Presidential nomination, did not endorse Humphrey until the latter days of the General Election Campaign. Even then, his endorsement was tepid at best. He said: "I'm voting for Humphrey, and I think you should suffer with me." Who was this political figure?

Presidential Campaigns

A10: Henry G. Davis: He was a U.S. Senator from West Virginia. At age 80 he garnered the Democratic Party nomination as the runningmate for Alton B. Parker in 1904. The ticket lost in a landslide to Republican President Theodore Roosevelt and his running mate Charles Fairbanks.

A11: Victoria Woodhull. The Equal Rights Party nominated her in 1872. She garnered just over 2,000 popular votes.

A12: Eugene V. Debbs. He was incarcerated for urging Americans to defy the military draft.

A13: Mitt Romney

A14: John W. Davis, who garnered the nomination in 1924 and Al Smith, who mustered the nomination in 1928.

A15: U.S. Representative Thaddeus McCotter (R-MI)

A16: Lyndon B. Johnson. McGovern was a harsh critic of Johnson's handling of the Vietnam War.

A17: Alf Landon

A18: $688 million

A19: Eugene McCarthy. Many Humphrey supporters blame McCarthy's late lukewarm endorsement for costing Humphrey the General Election to Republican nominee Richard M. Nixon.

Q20: In 1904, the Democratic Party nominated New York Appeals Court judge over William Jennings Bryan for President. The populist firebrand Bryan, who had won the nomination in 1896 and 1900, declared: "No self-respecting man would vote for him." Who is this judge turned Presidential candidate that Bryan is talking about?

Q21: In 1992, this Democratic Presidential candidate said: "When I was in England, I experimented with Marijuana a time or two and I didn't like it and didn't inhale and never tried it again." Who was this Presidential candidate?

Q22: Who was the first African-American to garner votes at a national convention of a major political party?

Q23: No Republican has won the Presidency without winning this state since Calvin Coolidge in 1924. Which state has this importance?

Q24: In 1991, this potential Democratic Presidential candidate, an incumbent Governor, declined to run because he could not secure a budget agreement with the Republican controlled State Senate. He had an aircraft ready to take him to New Hampshire to file for a candidacy at the deadline should a deal be reached. Who was this potential Presidential candidate?

Q25: All of this state's 14 counties have voted for the Republican Presidential nominee since 1988. Which state is this?

Q26: When speculating about a possible bid for the 1960 Democratic Presidential nomination, this U.S. Senator jokingly compared himself to the three declared candidates for the nomination: "I'm twice as liberal as Hubert Humphrey, twice as intelligent as Stuart Symington, and twice as Catholic as Jack Kennedy." Who was this Senator?

Q27: In 2000, George W. Bush became the first non-incumbent Republican nominee to win this state since 1928. Which state?

Q28: At a 1992 luncheon at the Democratic National Convention in New York, this Texas Governor drew laughter by commenting: "Well, you can put lipstick on a hog and call it Monique, but it's still a pig." She was referring to feckless government programs. Who was this Governor?

Q29: In 2012, this Republican Presidential candidate called his opponent Mitt Romney "the weakest Republican frontrunner since Leonard Wood in 1920." Americans who looked up the reference found that the now obscure figure was in fact the early front-runner in 1920. He led in Republican delegates, but lost the nomination to U.S. Senator Warren G. Harding (R-OH). Who was the Presidential candidate that came down on Mitt Romney?

Presidential Campaigns

A20: Alton B. Parker

A21: Bill Clinton

A22: Blanche Kelso Bruce: He was a U.S. Senator from Mississippi. A former slave, he mustered eight votes for the Republican nomination for Vice President. The winner was former Collector of the Port of New York, Chester A. Arthur. For his loyalty to the Republican Party, Bruce was appointed Register of the Federal Treasury in 1881 by President James A. Garfield.

A23: Florida

A24: Mario Cuomo of New York

A25: Massachusetts

A26: Eugene McCarthy (D-MN)

A27: West Virginia

A28: Ann Richards

A29: Newt Gingrich

Presidential Campaigns

Q30: In 2003, Ben Cohen, co-founder of the Vermont-based chain Ben & Jerry's Ice Cream, endorsed which candidate for the Democratic Presidential nomination over former Vermont Governor Howard Dean?

Q31: Which Presidential candidate called his airplane *Peanut One*?

Q32: Who was the former Minnesota Governor who ran unsuccessfully nine times for the Republican Presidential nomination?

Q33: In 1912, this Vice President died just one week before he and his running-mate, President William Howard Taft, were up for re-election. Who was this Vice Presidential candidate?

Q34: During the 1992 Democratic Presidential primary, Arkansas Governor Bill Clinton left the campaign trail to be in Arkansas when which prisoner was executed?

Q35: Which state is the only state to vote for Republican Dwight D. Eisenhower in 1952, and for Democrat Adlai Stevenson in 1956?

Q36: What was the only year that California did not vote for the Republican Presidential nominee between 1952 and 1992?

Q37: No Republican has ever won the Presidency without carrying which state?

Q38: Between 1880 and 1920, all 11 states of the "Old Confederacy" voted for the Democratic Presidential candidate. Which state broke this streak in 1920 by voting for Republican Presidential Candidate Warren G. Harding?

Q39: 2008 was the first Presidential election where no incumbent President or Vice President sought the Presidency since which year?

A30: Dennis Kucinich

A31: Jimmy Carter, a renowned peanut farmer

A32: Harold Stassen

A33: James Sherman: Taft chose Columbia University President Nicholas Butler to supplant Sherman on the ticket. The ticket mustered just eight electoral votes, winning only Vermont and Utah

A34: Ricky Ray Rector

A35: Missouri. In 1952, Eisenhower won the state with 50.71% of the vote. In 1956, Stevenson took the state with 50.11% of the vote.

A36: 1964, when the party nominated Barry Goldwater.

A37: Ohio

A38: Tennessee

A39: 1928

Q40: Who was the last incumbent Cabinet Secretary to be elected President?

Q41: Franklin Pierce was a roommate of this writer at Bowdoin College in Brunswick, Maine. This writer wrote a flattering biography of Pierce titled *The Life of Franklin Pierce* when Peirce ran for President in 1852. Who was this writer?

Q42: Which election was the only Presidential election to feature an incumbent President against an incumbent Vice President?

Q43: In 1896, President Grover Cleveland supported which Presidential candidate to succeed him as President?

Q44: Which was the first Presidential election to include Alaska and Hawaii?

Q45: In 1856, which former Whig President pocketed the Presidential nomination of the American Party, aka: The Know Nothing Party?

Q46: In a *Happy Days* episode that depicted the 1956 Presidential election, Richie Cunningham supports which major candidate, while Arthur "Fonzie" Fonzeralli supports the opposing major candidate?

Q47: During the 2016 Presidential election, which Democrat maintained: "Donald Trump is not going to be President of the United States. Take it to the bank, I guarantee it"?

Q48: A 1936 poll taken by *The Literary Digest* predicted that this Presidential candidate would win the election in a landslide with 370 Electoral votes. Who was this Presidential candidate?

Q49: In 1964, Democrat Lyndon B. Johnson won the Presidential election with 60.6% of the vote, yet Republican Barry Goldwater trounced Johnson in which state, mustering 87% of the vote?

A40: Herbert Hoover in 1928. He served as the U.S. Secretary of Commerce.

A41: Nathaniel Hawthorne

A42: 1800. Vice President Thomas Jefferson defeated President John Adams.

A43: John M. Palmer. Cleveland did not support William Jennings Bryan, the Democratic nominee to succeed him. This was because Bryan was opposed to the Gold Standard. Cleveland placed his support with Third Party Candidate, John M. Palmer, of the Pro-Gold Standard National Democratic Party. Palmer garnered less than 1% of the vote in that election. The winner of the election was the Republican nominee William McKinley. The National Democratic Party dissolved in 1900.

A44: 1960: Republican Richard M. Nixon captured Alaska, while Democrat John F. Kennedy took Hawaii.

A45: Millard Fillmore. He won just one state, Maryland, and captured just 21.5% of the popular vote nationally.

A46: Cunningham supports Democrat Adlai Stevenson. Fonzie supports Republican Dwight D. Eisenhower.

A47: U.S. House Minority Leader Nancy Pelosi (D-CA)

A48: Alf Landon. Landon, the Republican, lost in the General Election to Democrat Franklin D. Roosevelt, who garnered a whopping 523 electoral votes. The magazine made the mistake of polling its readers, as well as automobile and telephone owners, who were more likely to be Republicans, as they had more disposable income.

A49: Mississippi

Q50: In 1852, both major party Vice Presidential nominees were native North Carolinians. Who were these North Carolinians?

Q51: In 2008, Barack Obama became the first Democrat to win Salt Lake County, UT since which candidate in 1968?

Q52: In 2008, Barack Obama delivered his last campaign address in Manassas, VA. This municipality was home to which major Civil War battle fought in 1861.

Q53: This man was the Democratic Presidential nominee in 1896, 1900, and 1908. He lost all three Presidential elections. After losing for the third time, he opined: "I'm beginning to think those fellows don't want me in there." Who was this 3-time unsuccessful Presidential candidate?

Q54: In 1920, which state was the home state of both major party Presidential nominees?

Q55: Which state has selected the winner in every Presidential election from 1964 to 2020 (A 56-year stretch)?

Q56: Who was the first third-party Presidential nominee to win a state?

Q57: The four Congressional Districts where Democrat Barack Obama performed the best in 2008 were all in which state?

Q58: In 1960, John F. Kennedy won 80% of the vote of those who defined themselves as members of which religion?

Q59: In a 1952 speech in Indianapolis, Indiana, which Republican Presidential nominee became impatient with the teleprompter, yelling to the operator of the device: "Go ahead! Go ahead! Go ahead! Yah, damn it, I want him to move up [meaning Go Faster]"?

A50: William Rufus King and Alexander Graham: The Democrats nominated William Rufus King (at the time a U.S. Senator from Alabama). The Whigs nominated North Carolina's Graham (a former Governor and U.S. Senator from that state). The Democratic ticket of Franklin Pierce and King defeated the Whig ticket of Winfield Scott and Graham. The only other Native North Carolinian to garner the nomination of a major Party for the Vice Presidency was Democratic U.S. Senator John Edwards in 2004.

A51: Hubert Humphrey

A52: The First Battle of Bull Run. This was the first major battle of the Civil War. The Confederate States of American won the battle.

A53: William Jennings Bryan

A54: Ohio. Republican U.S. Senator Warren G. Harding decisively defeated Ohio's Democratic Governor James M. Cox. Harding garnered 58.47%, while Cox mustered just 38.58%.

A55: Ohio

A56: William Wirt. The former U.S. Attorney General was the nominee of the American Party, a.k.a. the Know Nothing Party, in 1832. He won Vermont, picking up seven electoral votes.

A57: New York

A58: Catholicism

A59: Dwight D. Eisenhower

Q60: In 1992, Independent Presidential Candidate H. Ross Perot's best electoral performance was in which state, where he garnered 30% of the vote?

Q61: In 1924, this former U.S. Solicitor General and past U.S. Ambassador to the United Kingdom won the Democratic Presidential Nomination on a record 103rd ballot. But all was for not, as he lost the general election to Republican President Calvin Coolidge. Who was this Democratic Presidential candidate?

Q62: Since 1956, only one Republican Presidential candidate won Massachusetts in the General Election. Who was he?

Q63: After losing his reelection bid as Governor of Arkansas in 1980, this Governor, and future opponent of Bill Clinton for the 1992 Democratic Presidential nomination, offered Bill Clinton a job, which he turned down. Who was this Governor?

Q64: In which state did Bill Clinton serve as co-chairman of George McGovern's 1972 Presidential campaign?

Q65: What Presidential election recorded the highest voter turnout?

Q66: In 2015, this Republican Presidential aspirant said in an exchange with *CNN* that homosexuality is a choice and that this is proved "Because a lot of people who go into prison, go into prison straight. And when they come out, they're gay. So, did something happen while they were in there? Ask yourself that question." Who made this statement?

Q67: In 1974, this future President told his mother, Lillian, that he would seek the Presidency. She responded: "President of What?" Who was this future President?

Q68: Two Democratic Presidential nominees lost their home state of Tennessee. Who were they?

Q69: In 1976, two former Georgia Governors ran for President. Who were they?

A60: Maine. Interestingly, two years later, the state elected Independent Angus King as its Governor.

A61: John W. Davis

A62: Ronald Reagan. He won the state during his landslide victories in 1980 and 1984.

A63: Jerry Brown of California. In 1992, ironically, Clinton defeated Brown in the Democratic Presidential primary.

A64: Texas. McGovern lost the state to Republican President Richard M. Nixon, garnering just 33.24% of the vote.

A65: 1976, 81.8% voted in the election, which pitted Republican Rutherford B. Hayes against Democrat Samuel Tilden. Hayes was declared the winner.

A66: Ben Carson

A67: Jimmy Carter

A68: James K. Polk in 1844 and Al Gore in 2000

A69: Lester Maddox and Jimmy Carter. Carter was the nominee of the Democratic Party. Maddox was the nominee of the American Independence Party.

Q70: What is the maximum amount a Presidential candidate can spend on his/her campaign if they do not accept federal matching funds?

Q71: In 1896, this Democratic Presidential nominee became the first candidate to campaign in an automobile? Who was this cutting-edge candidate?

Q72: In 1900, New York Republican boss and U.S. Senator Thomas C. Platt (R-NY) successfully urged the Republican Party to select which New York Governor to become the Vice Presidential running mate to William McKinley?

Q73: In 1980, which Republican Presidential candidate spent $11 million and garnered just one delegate, whose name was Ada Mills of Arkansas.

Q74: In the 1976 Republican Presidential primary, only two Republican U.S. Senators supported the failed insurgency candidacy of former California Governor Ronald Reagan over President Gerald R. Ford. Who were these two U.S. Senators?

Q75: In 1908, Theodore Roosevelt endorsed U.S. Secretary of War William Howard Taft to succeed him as President over the incumbent Vice President. Who was this unlucky vice president?

Q76: Who was the first Governor to endorse John McCain in his 2008 bid for the Republican Presidential nomination?

Q77: Which major Party Presidential nominee campaigned in a foreign tongue?

Q78: In the 1984 election, while Ronald Reagan cruised to a 49-state landslide victory, his coattails extended to just one Democratic U.S. Senator losing his seat. Who was the losing Democratic Senator?

Q79: In 1988, this Democratic Presidential candidate bragged about his time as a youth working on a tobacco farm, telling North Carolina voters: "I've raised tobacco . . . I want you to know that with my own hands all my life. I put it in the plate beds and transferred it. I've hoed it. I've chopped it. I've shredded it. I spiked it, put it in the barn and stripped it and sold it." Who was this Presidential candidate?

A70: There is no limit.

A71: William Jennings Bryan. He rode in a Mueller automobile, which was made in Decatur, IL.

A72: Theodore Roosevelt. Senator Platt was hell-bent on getting Roosevelt out of New York and out of the Governorship?

A73: John Connally

A74: Jesse Helms of North Carolina and Paul Laxalt of Nevada

A75: Charles W. Fairbanks

A76: Minnesota Governor Tim Pawlenty

A77: James Garfield: Fluent in German, Garfield delivered a campaign speech to a group of German-Americans in German. This was the first time a major Party Presidential nominee campaigned in a foreign tongue.

A78: Warren Huddleston (D-KY) lost to Republican Mitch McConnell.

A79: Al Gore

Q80: In 2004, The New York Post mistakenly reported that the Democratic Presidential nominee, John Kerry, had selected which man as his Vice Presidential nominee?

Q81: Who was the only President to be unanimously selected by the Electoral College?

Q82: In 1924, twelve Republican members of the U.S. House of Representatives supported which Progressive Party nominee over Republican President Calvin Coolidge? These contrarians were subsequently expelled from their caucus by U.S. House Speaker Nicholas Longworth (R-OH.)

Q83: In the 1992 General Election, Bill Clinton won a majority of the vote in just one state. Which state was it?

Q84: In 1924, former U.S. Solicitor General and U.S. Ambassador to the United Kingdom John W. Davis won the Democratic Presidential Nomination. How many ballots did it take the party to nominate him?

Q85: When this New York Governor announced his support for the Presidential candidacy of Richard M. Nixon in 1960, he mistakenly referred to Nixon as "Richard E. Nixon." Who was this Governor?

Q86: When Republican Calvin Coolidge garnered the Republican Vice Presidential nomination in 1920, this incumbent Vice President telegraphed Coolidge: "Please Accept my sincere sympathy." Who sent this message?

Q87: In 1988, George H.W. Bush became the first sitting Vice President to win the Presidency since when?

Q88: Who was the first U.S. Senator to endorse Barack Obama in his 2008 Presidential run?

Q89: In 1976, Democratic Presidential nominee Jimmy Carter accused Republican opponent Gerald R. Ford of using what strategy to earn free media attention for doing his job?

A80: Dick Gephardt. In actuality, he selected John Edwards as his running mate.

A81: George Washington, in 1792. He won all 68 Electoral votes.

A82: Robert La Follette Sr.

A83: Arkansas. Clinton pocketed 53.21% of the vote in his home state.

A84: A record 103 ballots

A85: Nelson Rockefeller. Nixon's middle initial is "M," not "E."

A86: Thomas Riley Marshall

A87: 1836, when Martin Van Buren secured the Presidency

A88: Dick Durban, of Illinois

A89: The Rose Garden Strategy. This is where the President uses the White House to make public pronouncements rather than campaigning for reelection.

Presidential Campaigns

Q90: In the 1964 Presidential campaign, this Republican Presidential nominee complained about his Democratic opponent, Lyndon B. Johnson: "Every time we raise an embarrassing question, Lyndon leaves town to dedicate a dam." Who was this Republican Presidential candidate?

Q91: During the critical Florida Republican Presidential primary in 1976, President Gerald R. Ford won in part by promising more money for mass transit, prompting his opponent, Ronald Reagan, to deadpan: "If he comes here with the same bag of goodies to hand out that he's been giving away elsewhere, the band won't know whether to play *Hail to the Chief* or" this song? Which other song was this?

Q92: In October of 1972, which National Security Advisor erroneously declared: "Peace is at hand" in Vietnam? This helped President Richard M. Nixon in his upcoming re-election bid.

Q93: In 1987, this former U.S. Senator from Tennessee was contemplating a run for President in 1988. However, he decided not to run when President Ronald Reagan persuaded him to be his Chief of Staff. Who was this former Senator from Tennessee?

Q94: In 2000, this Arizona Governor supported George W. Bush over her home state's U.S. Senator John McCain for the Republican Presidential nomination. Who was this Governor?

Q95: After losing the Democratic Presidential primary in Indiana, which candidate told a crowd in Oregon (the next contest) that supporters of Rival Robert F. Kennedy "were among the less intelligent and less educated people in America"?

Q96: In 1984, Arkansas Governor Orval Faubus (1955-1967), known for sending the Arkansas National Guard to Central High School in Little Rock to prevent nine African-American students from entering the building, endorsed which candidate for the Democratic Presidential nomination?

Q97: In 1992, which major Democratic Presidential candidate refused to accept donations of over $100?

Q98: Which Republican Presidential candidate lost to Donald Trump in the 2020 Republican Presidential primary, winning just one delegate?

Q99: How many electoral votes are required to win the Presidency?

A90: Barry Goldwater

A91: *Santa Claus is Coming to Town*

A92: Henry Kissinger

A93: Howard Baker

A94: Jane Hull

A95: Eugene McCarthy

A96: Jesse Jackson

A97: Jerry Brown

A98: Bill Weld

A99: 270. That is a majority of the possible 538 electoral votes.

Presidential Campaigns

Q100: In 1948, which newspaper prematurely published this brazen headline: "Dewey Defeats Truman"?

Q101: Two candidates for the 1992 Republican Presidential nomination (U.S. Senate Majority Leader Robert J. Dole (R-KS) and Arthur Allan Fletcher, an advisor in Republican Presidential administrations) were alumni of which University located in Topeka, KS?

Q102: The two top vote-getters in the 2000 Republican Presidential contest, George W. Bush and John McCain, supported which Republican Presidential candidate in 2000.

Q103: Who was the first Presidential nominee to run on a platform of opposition to slavery?

Q104: In his 1992 re-election bid, George H.W. Bush did not win a majority of the vote in any state. In what state did he come the closest?

Q105: President Gerald R. Ford developed a close friendship with a former Major League Baseball player and broadcaster. He appeared in advertisements for Ford in his 1976 Presidential campaign and watched election returns with Ford on election night. Who was this sports figure?

Q106: After dropping out of the 2016 Republican Presidential sweepstakes, he endorsed his former rival Jeb Bush for the nomination. About his own effort, he opined: "I got out because I ran out of money. If you want to get money out of politics, you should have joined my campaign." Who was this political figure?

Q107: In 1960, Republican Presidential nominee and Vice President Richard M. Nixon announced his pledge to continue the 90 percent price support for tobacco. However, he was embarrassed when this U.S. Agriculture Secretary announced just hours before that he wanted the program terminated. Who was this Agriculture Secretary?

Q108: In 1952, Democrats who followed the lead of Texas Governor Allan Shivers in supporting Republican Dwight D. Eisenhower over their party's nominee, Adlai Stevenson, earned this moniker?

Q109: Which Presidential candidate employed the campaign slogan "Tippecanoe and Tyler Too?"

Presidential Campaigns

A100: *The Chicago Daily Tribune.* Republican Presidential nominee Thomas E. Dewey was heavily favored to defeat Democrat Harry S. Truman in the 1948 Presidential election. Truman stunned political prognosticators by defeating Dewey handily, garnering 114 more electoral votes than Dewey.

A101: Washburn University

A102: Phil Gramm

A103: U.S. Senator John P. Hale of New Hampshire. He was the nominee of the Free Soli Party in 1853. He garnered just 4.9% of the national popular vote.

A104: Mississippi, where he mustered 49.7% of the vote.

A105: Joe Garagiola

A106: Lindsey Graham

A107: Ezra Taft Benson. Tobacco price supports were wildly popular in the showdown state of Kentucky. Nixon wrote to U.S. Senator John Sherman Cooper (R-KY): "I wholly support the preset tobacco program, and if elected President, I will recommend that it be continued without change." Taft was an unreserved exponent of Free market capitalism, and some questioned if he would fully support Nixon, who was not as Libertarian. Despite the difference, Taft campaigned for Nixon. Nixon won Kentucky in the General Election but lost the General Election to Democrat John F. Kennedy.

A108: Shivercrats

A109: William Henry Harrison, the Whig Presidential nominee in 1840. Harrison, the Governor of the newly established Indiana Territory was the victor at the Battle of Tippecanoe in 1811. John Tyler was his Vice Presidential runningmate. The ticket won the election. The Battle of Tippecanoe was a victory of U.S. forces over the Shawnee Indians in central Indiana.

Presidential Campaigns

Q110: In 1988, the Democratic Presidential nominee Mike Dukakis did not release his medical records. This prominent Republican remarked as he was leaving a press conference: "I'm not going to pick on an invalid," but subsequently remarked that day: "I was kidding . . . I was just trying to be funny and it didn't work." The remarks prompted speculation by some that Dukakis may have had mental health problem. Who was this prominent Republican who made this statement regarding Dukakis?

Q111: In 1964, many down-ballot Republican candidates tried to distance themselves from their party's Presidential nominee Barry Goldwater, who was unpopular in much of the country. The Governor of Michigan's re-election campaign mailed out about 200,000 mock ballots showing voters how to mark their ballots for Democratic President Lyndon B. Johnson for President and for himself for Governor. He won re-election while Goldwater handily lost Michigan. Who was this Michigan Governor?

Q112: In 1995, which Republican Presidential candidate made light of his Southern accent, averring in New Hampshire: "People in New Hampshire talk funny and therefore they think I talk funny"?

Q113: Which Presidential candidate appeared on the hit television show *Rowan and Martin's Laugh-In* and exclaimed: "Sock it to me?"

Q114: This New York Yankees slugger gave speeches for Democratic Presidential nominee Al Smith from the back of the train, which was carrying the championship team home to New York. He was not gracious to hecklers. At one stop, he bellowed: "If that's the way you feel, the hell with you." Who was this slugger who supported Al Smith?

Q115: 1992 Democratic Presidential nominee Bill Clinton and Independent Presidential candidate H. Ross Perot were born just 30 miles from each other in two different states. Where was each man born?

Q116: Which 1960 Presidential candidate refused to speak before segregated audiences?

Q117: Which 1996 Republican Presidential candidate was nicknamed "The Griz" for his bearlike demeanor?

Q118: In 1968, which potential Presidential candidate told a reporter "There is too much dignity in government now. What we need is some meanness"?

Q119: The 1944 Presidential election featured Democrat Presidential nominee Franklin D. Roosevelt and Republican nominee Thomas E. Dewey. Both men once held the same job but at different times. What job did they both once hold?

Presidential Campaigns

A110: Ronald Reagan

A111: George Romney

A112: U.S. Senator Phil Gramm (R-TX) said this while in New Hampshire. However, U.S. Representative Bill Zeliff (R-NH), a supporter of rival Bob Dole, took the remark seriously, and pronounced: "On behalf of every citizen of New Hampshire, I demand a Texas-sized apology from Phil Gramm. We may sound funny to Phil Gramm, but here in New Hampshire our traditions are no laughing matter."

A113: Richard M. Nixon. His opponent, Hubert Humphrey, declined to appear on the comedy show, and later stated that it might have cost him the election.

A114: Babe Ruth

A115: Clinton was born in Hope, AR. Perot was born in Texarkana, TX

A116: U.S. Senator Stuart Symington (D-MO)

A117: Morry Taylor

A118: George Wallace

A119: The Governorship of New York. Democrat Franklin D. Roosevelt was the former Governor of New York. Republican Thomas E. Dewey was the incumbent Governor of New York. Roosevelt defeated Dewey.

Presidential Campaigns

Q120: Which political operative working for the 1980 Jimmy Carter Presidential Campaign wrestled a 260-pound alligator?

Q121: In 1932, William Z. Foster, the nominee of a political party, finished in fourth place in the Presidential election, garnering just 102,000 votes. Which political party did he represent?

Q122: Which Republican Presidential nominee used the inimical catch phrase: "Free Soil, Free Men, Freemont?"

Q123: Which two failed 1976 Democratic Presidential candidates lost their bid to be re-elected to the U.S. Senate in 1980?

Q124: In 1844, the two major party Presidential nominees were both former Speakers of the U.S. House of Representatives. Who were they?

Q125: In 1976, Ronald Reagan announced that if he garnered the Republican Party's Presidential nomination, he would choose which U.S. Senator as his runningmate?

Q126: How many times did 2008 Republican Presidential nominee John McCain mention the name of Republican President George W. Bush during his Acceptance Speech at the Republican National Convention?

Q127: In 1927, while on vacation at his vacation home in the Black Hills of South Dakota, which President personally handed a piece of paper to reporters with the words: "I do not choose to run for President in nineteen-twenty-eight"? He then walked back into the house without answering any questions.

Q128: Which Presidential candidate promised to give land to Western settlers campaigning on the slogan: "Vote yourself a farm?"

Q129: Which Hollywood actor flirted with a bid for the Democratic Presidential nomination in 1999? He chose not to run, later deadpanning: "I will confess to having been flattered at being kicked around as a possibility, but I had seen so many close friends go through such agonies: Gary Hart, George McGovern, Hubert Humphrey, look what happened to Bobby and Jack [Kennedy]! I knew all of them."

Presidential Campaigns

A120: Terry McAuliffe. He did this in return for a $15,000 donation from Seminole Chief Jim Billie. McAuliffe later became Governor of Virginia.

A121: The Communist Party USA

A122: John C. Freemont. He was the first nominee of the newly established Republican Party in 1856.

A123: Birch Bayh of Indiana and Frank Church of Idaho

A124: Whig Henry Clay served as Speaker from 1821-1823. Democrat James K. Polk served as Speaker from 1835-1839. Polk won the race and remains the only former Speaker of the House to become President.

A125: U.S. Senator Richard Schweiker (R-PA). He was a moderate. This was a move to propitiate establishment Republicans, who were afraid Reagan would be too conservative to win the general election. Reagan lost the nomination to President Gerald R. Ford.

A126: 0. Bush's job approval rating hovered below thirty percent.

A127: Calvin Coolidge

A128: Abraham Lincoln, in 1860. As President, he signed the Homestead Act of 1862, which granted all adult citizens who had never fought against the U.S. government 160 acres of government surveyed land.

A129: Warren Beatty

Q130: This President discussed the New Hampshire Presidential Primary this way: "I think New Hampshire is the only place where a candidate can claim 20 percent is a landslide, 40 percent is a mandate and 60 percent is unanimous." Which President made this statement?

Q131: Who were the only two Republican Presidential nominees to lose the General Election between 1860 and 1912?

Q132: Presidential nominee Ralph Nader was a member of which political party in 2000?

Q133: Which failed Republican Presidential candidate told delegates to the Republican National Convention "to vote your conscience" rather than telling them to support their party's presumptive Presidential nominee, Donald Trump?

Q134: Four years before delivering the keynote address at the Democratic National Convention that would effectuate his political stardom, this political figure could not even secure a floor pass entry to the Democratic National Convention in Los Angeles. He instead watched the Convention on a jumbotron (large-screen television set) outside the Staples Center. Who is this future President?

Q135: Franklin D. Roosevelt once praised this man, averring: "He certainly is a wonder, and I wish we could make him President. They're couldn't be a better one." Who was this man Roosevelt spoke so highly of?

Q136: In 1900, this candidate's attempt at winning the Democratic Presidential nomination imploded when he said publicly: "I am convinced that the office of the President is not such a very difficult one to fill." Who was this unfortunate Presidential candidate?

Q137: At the 1940 Republican National Convention, U.S. Senator Gladys Pile became the first female to nominate a Presidential candidate at a major party convention. Who did she nominate?

Q138: From 1812 to 1968, which state harbored the most electoral votes?

Q139: Why was Richard M. Nixon forced off the Presidential campaign trail in 1960 for two weeks?

Presidential Campaigns

A130: Lyndon B. Johnson

A131: James G. Blaine in 1884, and incumbent President Benjamin Harrison in 1892.

A132: None. While he mustered the nomination of the Green Party, he never registered in the political party.

A133: Ted Cruz. He lost a bitter primary to Trump.

A134: Barack Obama

A135: Herbert Hoover. Roosevelt was praising Hoover for his role as U.S. Food Administrator during WWI. Ironically, in 1932, Roosevelt defeated then President Hoover, who was running for re-election.

A136: Admiral George Dewey

A137: Wendell Willkie. He won the Republican Presidential nomination.

A138: New York. It reached its high-watermark at 47 electoral votes in the 1930's.

A139: He suffered from a staph infection after bumping his knee on a car door while campaigning in Greensboro, NC. He was still recovering from it during the first Presidential debate with John F. Kennedy, where he appeared ill. Nixon later blamed this for his loss.

Presidential Campaigns

Q140: Who was the first African-American to be nominated for President?

Q141: When was the last Presidential election where the winner was neither a Democrat nor a Republican?

Q142: From 1920-1944, the Democratic Party nominated a resident of what state to every national ticket save one?

Q143: Before a campaign stop in Milwaukee, this former President was shot in the chest by tavern operator John Schrank. Who was this former President?

Q144: Which state had the largest electoral political party swing at the Presidential level between 2004 and 2008?

Q145: After President Lyndon B. Johnson signed the Civil Rights Act of 1964, which U.S. Senator led a boycott of the Democratic National Convention in Atlantic City, NJ by Southern Democrats?

Q146: Who are the only two brothers to separately be nominated as President or Vice President of a major Party?

Q147: In 1964, who became the first female to have her name placed in nomination for President at a major party convention?

Q148: As the Democratic Presidential nominee in 1952 and 1956, Adlai Stevenson lost his home state, which was his home state twice. Which state was his home state?

Q149: In 1984, Republican President Ronald Reagan was re-elected, winning 49 states. Which sate did he lose?

A140: George Edwin Taylor. He captured the nomination of the National Negro Liberty Party in 1904. The Party advocated for the rights of African-Americans and other minorities.

A141: 1848. The Whig Party ticket of Zachary Taylor and Millard Fillmore was elected.

A142: New York. In 1920, Franklin D. Roosevelt was the Vice Presidential nominee. In 1928, New York Governor Al Smith topped the ticket as the Presidential nominee. Franklin D. Roosevelt topped the ticket in 1932, 1936, 1940, and 1944. The only year a New Yorker failed to make the ticket was in 1924, when the Party nominated John W. Davis of West Virginia and Charles W. Bryan of Nebraska.

A143: Theodore Roosevelt. He gave a ninety-minute oration, opening by telling the crowd " . . . I have just been shot; but it takes more than that to kill a Bull Moose." That was the last campaign event he made, spending the rest of the election season recovering from the wound. The bullet was never dislodged from Roosevelt's chest because the doctors believed the process of removing the bullet could be fatal.

A144: Indiana. Republican George W. Bush won this state with a formidable 60% of the vote in 2004. In 2008, Democrat Barack Obama won it with 50% of the vote.

A145: Richard Russell (D-GA). He had been Johnson's mentor in the U.S. Senate.

A146: William Jennings Bryan and Charles Bryan. William was the Democratic Presidential nominee in 1896, 1900, and 1904. Charles was the Democratic Vice Presidential nominee in 1924. Both brothers lost their respective races.

A147: Margaret Chase Smith of the Republican Party

A148: Illinois

A149: Minnesota. It was the home state of his Democratic opponent, Walter Mondale. Mondale won the state by just 3,761 votes (Mondale also won the District of Columbia).

Presidential Campaigns

Q150: During a campaign rally in 1992, which President said of opponents Bill Clinton and Al Gore: "My dog Millie knows more about Foreign Affairs than these two bozos"?

Q151: Who are the only two Presidents to be re-elected absent opposition?

Q152: In what state did Republican Presidential nominee John McCain win by 13 percentage points in 2008, while at the same time a Democrat won every constitutional office in that same state, and the Democrats gained seats in the Democratically-controlled State Senate?

Q153: Which President lost his wife to Tuberculosis just two weeks before he lost the election?

Q154: Gerald R. Ford maintained that had this person campaigned harder for him in the General Election of 1976, he would have won the Presidency. Who was Ford referring to?

Q155: After waning in the polls, which Democratic Presidential candidate pledged to a town hall in Bedford, NH, that "I'll be with you until the last dog dies"?

Q156: Who was the only President to be elected on his birthday?

Q157: In 1972, which Republican, running mostly on a pledge to end U.S. involvement in the Vietnam War, garnered 20% of the vote in the Republican primary, and just one delegate out of a possible 1,347 which he won in New Mexico?

Q158: In 1968, who served as both the Chairman of the Democratic National Committee and Chairman of Hubert Humphrey's Presidential campaign?

Q159: In 1889, he lost a bid to become Speaker of the U.S. House of Representatives to Thomas Brackett Reed (R-ME). Seven years later, he defeated Reed for the Republican Presidential nomination. Who was this political figure?

Presidential Campaigns

A150: George H.W. Bush

A151: George Washington in 1792 and James Monroe in 1820. In 1820, a New Hampshire elector who had been pledged to Monroe selected Secretary of State John Quincy Adams instead. The New Hampshire elector believed that George Washington should be the only President to sweep the Electoral College.

A152: West Virginia

A153: Benjamin Harrison. His wife was named Mary.

A154: Ronald Reagan. During the summer of 1976, Democratic Presidential nominee Jimmy Carter held a 34-point lead over Republican President Gerald R. Ford. Ford almost closed the gap, just losing the election by two percentage points. Ford believed that had former California Governor Ronald Reagan campaigned for him with conservative Democrats in the South that he would have won the election. Reagan had challenged Ford in the Republican Primary and was popular with the conservative base. To Ford's dismay, Reagan had other commitments and spent limited time on the campaign trail.

A155: Bill Clinton

A156: Warren G. Harding was elected President on November 2, 1920. This was also his 56th birthday.

A157: Pete McCloskey. He asserted: "we've lost the stomach to fight this war on the ground, and yet we think it's appropriate that we can kill people by push-button bombing from 50,000 feet." After visiting Laos, he averred: "what we are doing in Laos is as great a crime as those we executed Japanese and German officials for in World War II." After he made that statement, Republican members of the California Assembly censured him as "an enemy of the American Political process."

A158: Larry O'Brien. He performed both jobs pro bono.

A159: William McKinley

Presidential Campaigns

Q160: What ritual did Barack Obama do on election day in 2008 and 2012?

Q161: In 1896, which Democratic Presidential nominee broke precedent by delivering over 600 speeches in 27 states?

Q162: In 1952, Republican Presidential candidate Robert A. Taft persuaded which General to become his runningmate should he garner the nomination?

Q163: Who was the youngest Presidential nominee of a major party?

Q164: Who did Minnesota Governor Jesse Ventura endorse for President in the 2000 Presidential election?

Q165: In the 1992 Presidential election, all three major Presidential candidates, George H.W. Bush, Bill Clinton, and H. Ross Perot, campaigned in which battleground state?

Q166: Who was the first African-American to be placed on a national ticket?

Q167: Before being tapped by Presidential nominee George W. Bush for his Vice Presidential runningmate in 2000, Dick Cheney moved his official residence from Texas to what state?

Q168: While Green Party Presidential nominee Ralph Nader garnered just 2.4% of the vote in 2000, he mustered 13% of the vote with which ethnic group?

Q169: In 1960, former President Harry S. Truman urged which candidate for the Democratic Presidential nomination to reconsider his bid?

A160: He played a pickup basketball game with friends. Obama won both Presidential elections.

A161: William Jennings Bryan. Prior to that, it was customary for candidates to use surrogates to campaign for them.

A162: Douglas McArthur

A163: William Jennings Bryan in 1896. He was just 36-years-old.

A164: John Hagelin of the Natural Law Party. He was a quantum physicist and an advocate for transcendental meditation.

A165: Texas

A166: Frederick Douglass. He was the Vice Presidential nominee of the Equal Rights Party in 1872.

A167: Wyoming, where he also owned a residence. He did this because: "The Twelfth Amendment reads: "The Electors shall meet in their respective states, and vote by ballot for President and Vice President, one of whom, at least, shall not be an inhabitant of the same state with themselves . . .."

A168: Arab-American voters. Nader is of Lebanese descent.

A169: John F. Kennedy. Truman was supporting his home state senator, Stuart Symington. When asked whom he would support should Symington lose, Truman deadpanned: "I have no second choice. The National Convention was manipulated so that Kennedy would muster the nomination. In protest, Truman refused to attend the Convention as a delegate. However, once Kennedy secured the nomination, Truman became a loyal foot soldier, barnstorming the country campaigning for Kennedy.

Q170: This Speaker of the House and Republican Presidential nominee was nicknamed: "The plumed knight." Who was this plumed knight?

Q171: In 1972, former President Lyndon B. Johnson remained neutral in the Democratic Presidential primary, even though his former Vice President Hubert Humphrey was running. However, one of the candidates, visited him at the ranch, and the former President gave him a copy of his autobiography, *Vantage Point* with a $500 donation tucked in it. Who was this lucky candidate?

Q172: In what year was the popular vote for a Presidential election decided by just 7,368 votes?

Q173: Who was the first African-American female to deliver the keynote address at a major party national convention?

Q174: In June of 1996, which Republican Presidential candidate was disallowed from attending the Washington State Republican Convention because he did not endorse the prospective nominee, former U.S. Senate Majority Leader Bob Dole (R-KS)? Accordingly, he held a convention of his own with his supporters in San Diego and stated: "We're going to fight until Hell freezes over. You all come down to San Diego [Where the Republican National Convention was scheduled to be held] and bring your ice skates."

Q175: Who was the winner of the 1976 Democratic Iowa Caucuses?

Q176: Which 36-year-old U.S. Senator from Massachusetts turned down Democratic Presidential nominee Hubert Humphrey's offer to be his Vice Presidential runningmate in 1968?

Q177: In all except for one election between 1856 and 1960 Maine voted for the Republican Presidential nominee? In what year did this anomaly occur?

Q178: Who became the first Vice President to win the nomination of his party since Democrat Martin Van Buren in 1836?

Q179: During the 2008 General Election Presidential campaign, how many states received no campaign appearances by a major campaign Presidential candidate?

A170: James G. Blaine. Former Illinois Attorney General Robert F. Ingersoll granted him the nickname for the way he battled against adversity.

A171: Terry Sanford, the President of Duke University, in Durham, NC, and the former Governor of North Carolina. Sanford was amazed that Johnson, once President of the United States was now making picayune decisions. Sandford averred: "There is a great big fellow with overalls on, old time gallus overall. He is standing there chewing tobacco, and Johnson stopped, and the man says: "Why I had the cultivator out there and it brook, and I was trying to plant some peas. Now, I don't know whether to plant the peas or fix the cultivator. There was Johnson making those decisions." Sanford finished in fifth place for the nomination. The nomination went to U.S. Senator George McGovern (D-SD.)

A172: 1880. Republican James Garfield defeated Democrat Winfield S. Hancock by just 7,368 popular votes. In the Electoral College the margin was much wider with Garfield garnering 214 votes and Hancock mustering just 155 votes.

A173: U.S. Representative Barbara Jordan at the Democratic National Convention in 1976.

A174: Pat Buchanan

A175: Uncommitted. Jimmy Carter came in second.

A176: Ted Kennedy

A177: In 1912, the state voted for Democrat Woodrow Wilson.

A178: Richard M. Nixon

A179: 35

Q180: In the 1992 Presidential campaign, Independent Candidate H. Ross Perot garnered 18.9% of the popular vote. How many Electoral votes did he pocket?

Q181: In 1996, the Republican Presidential nominee, Bob Dole, spent the last 96 hours of the campaign on a non-stop 96-hour campaign tour of the country. His last stop was in which hometown of a former President?

Q182: In the 2000 race for the Republican Presidential nomination, George W. Bush raised record amounts of money, much of it from well-heeled benefactors, often derisively referred to as "fat cats." An opponent quipped: "George Bush has fat cats. I want skinny cats." After Bush raised $36 million, which Presidential contender asked and received donations of just $36 dollars?

Q183: In 2012, Barack Obama became the first Democratic Presidential nominee to win an outright majority in two election cycles since whom?

Q184: The 2012 Republican Iowa Caucuses were the closest in history. The winner won by just 34 votes. Who was the winner?

Q185: In 1872, which nominee of the Democrat and Liberal Republican Party died before the Electoral College met to cast their votes?

Q186: In 1924, four progressive Republican U.S. Senators and 14 Republican U.S. House members abandoned their party's Presidential nominee, Calvin Coolidge, supporting instead which nominee of the Progressive Party? This resulted in their being expelled from the Republican Caucus.

Q187: At the 1948 Democratic National Convention, this Minneapolis Mayor delivered an address in support of the "minority plank" which would commit the party to oppose racial segregation?

Q188: In the 1960 Presidential election, Richard M. Nixon pledged to campaign in all fifty states. What was the last state he touched down in?

Q189: In what place did Vice President George H.W. Bush come in during the 1988 Republican Iowa Caucuses?

A180: 0

A181: Independence, MO, the hometown of President Harry S. Truman.

A182: Orrin Hatch. He raised just $2 million, and dropped out of the race to endorse Bush.

A183: Franklin D. Roosevelt, in 1944

A184: Rick Santorum

A185: Horace Greeley. Greeley had lost the election, mustering just 66 electoral votes. Four non-candidates received the votes of the electors pledged to Greeley. The leading vote-getter was the newly inaugurated Governor of Indiana, Thomas Andrews. Ulysses S. Grant was re-elected to a second term.

A186: Robert La Follette Sr.

A187: Hubert Humphrey. The plank was narrowly ratified by the convention.

A188: Alaska

A189: Third, behind U.S. Senate Minority Leader Bob Dole (R-KS) and Televangelist Pat Robertson.

Presidential Campaigns

Q190: Which political party held the first political convention to establish its Presidential nominee?

Q191: What is the requirement to get one's name on the New Hampshire Presidential Primary Ballot?

Q192: In 1948, in what was the hottest summer in this city since it held the Constitutional Convention of 1787, the Democratic Party, the Progressive Party, and the Republican Party held their National Conventions in this city. What city was this?

Q193: Who won the 1992 New Hampshire Democratic Presidential Primary?

Q194: Which Chicago Mayor, speaking at a Cook County political dinner in 1975, said in introducing the keynote speaker, U.S. House Speaker Henry "Scoop" Jackson: "And with God's help, Scoop Jackson will lead this nation in 1960!"?

Q195: Who was the first Asian-American to seek the Republican Presidential nomination and to garner votes at their national convention?

Q196: In 1940, entrepreneur and statistician Roger W. Babson (who predicted the stock market crash of 1929), the founder of Babson College in Wellesley, MA, was the nominee of which political party?

Q197: Which Presidential candidate received the moniker "Norwegian Wood" because of his Norwegian heritage and boring demeanor?

Q198: Comparing himself to two of his opponents (Vice President George H.W. Bush and U.S. Senate Majority Leader Bob Dole (R-KS)), which 1988 Republican Presidential candidate told voters incessantly: "Shake a leg for Haig, beware of Dole and Dole - it's only watered-down pineapple juice - and, above all, don't get Bush-whacked"?

Q199: On January 6, 1969, Vice President Hubert Humphrey was not available to preside over a joint session of the U.S. Congress in his role as President of the U.S. Senate. At the time, he was in Oslo, Norway attending the funeral of Trygve Lie, the first elected Secretary General of the United Nations. Had he been able to preside over the Senate on that day, he would have had the unceremonious task of announcing his own Presidential electoral loss to Richard M. Nixon. Which Senator, in his role as Senate pro tempore, presided over the joint session of Congress in Humphrey's place?

Presidential Campaigns

A190: The American Party, a.k.a. The Know Nothing Party. The party nominated former U.S. Attorney General William Wirt as its Presidential nominee in the 1832 election. Wirt garnered 7.8% of the popular vote, winning just one state, Vermont.

A191: One must be constitutionally eligible to serve as President, and must pay a $1,000 fee.

A192: Philadelphia, PA

A193: Paul Tsongas. Although Bill Clinton dubbed himself "The Comeback Kid" after his strong showing in the New Hampshire Presidential Primary, he actually came in second to former U.S. Senator Paul Tsongas (D-MA).

A194: Richard J. Daley

A195: U.S. Senator Hiram Fong (D-HI), in 1964

A196: The Prohibition Party. Babson garnered just 57,903 popular votes. After losing, Babson sent a congratulatory note to the victor, Democrat Franklin D. Roosevelt, which read: "Hearty congratulations. A defeated statistician, however, humbly reminds you that 1 per cent of the vote properly allocated would have elected [Republican Nominee] Wendell Willkie. Therefore, I know you will work for coalition, both with Republicans and minority parties. Please keep well. Four great years are ahead." However Roosevelt handily defeated Willkie by almost ten percentage points, winning 38 states and garnering 449 electoral votes.

A197: Walter Mondale

A198: Alexander Haig

A199: Richard Russell (D-GA)

Presidential Campaigns

Q200: This Governor rose to national prominence for declaring during the Boston Police Strike: "There is no right to strike against the public safety by anyone, anywhere, any time." This statement made him a national figure and rocket-launched him to the 1920 Republican Vice Presidential nomination. Who was this Governor?

Q201: When Mitt Romney ran for the Republican Presidential nomination in 2012, one of his rivals, Newt Gingrich, mentioned that Romney voted for which Democrat in the 1992 Presidential primaries?

Q202: In 1948, fearing that President Harry S. Truman would lose in the General Election, James Roosevelt, the son of Franklin D. Roosevelt, tried to draft this prominent American to run against Truman for the Democratic nomination?

Q203: Which Republican political consultant coined the term: "Soccer mom?"

Q204: In 1972, as U.S. Senator George McGovern (D-SC) was winning vital Democratic Primaries, a concerned Democratic politician disclosed anonymously to Columnist Robert D. Novak that: "The people don't know McGovern is for amnesty, abortion and legalization of pot. Once Middle America - Catholic middle America, in particular - finds this out, he's dead. Amnesty, Acid, and Abortion." Who disclosed this information?

Q205: Which two states close their polls the earliest on Presidential election nights?

Q206: After the bitter 1960 West Virginia Democratic Presidential primary, Robert F. Kennedy, the campaign manager for his brother John F. Kennedy, approached the wife of his Democratic opponent with a handshake. She later averred that she didn't know whether to shake his hand or punch him. Who was the losing candidate and his wife?

Q207: In 1988, Democratic Presidential candidate Al Gore questioned why one of his rivals, Michael Dukakis, was not trying to distinguish himself politically from which other Democratic Presidential candidate?

Q208: What future Republican Texas Governor supported Democrat Al Gore's 1988 Presidential campaign?

Q209: In the 1972 election and in the 1984 election, the Republican Presidents Richard M. Nixon and Ronald Reagan respectively, were re-elected, scoring 49-state landslide victories over their Democratic opponents. How many seats did their parties pick up in the U.S. Senate both times?

A200: Calvin Coolidge

A201: Paul Tsongas. This statement came back to haunt Romney when he ran for President in 2012. He danced around the subject, making the following opaque statement: "I've never voted for a Democrat when there was a Republican on the ballot. And in my state of Massachusetts, you could register as an Independent and go vote in (whichever) primary happens to be very interesting. And any chance I got to vote against Bill Clinton or Ted Kennedy I took. . . . I have always voted for a Republican any time there was a Republican on the ballot." However, in 1992, there was both a Democratic primary and a Republican primary between President George H.W. Bush and Pat Buchanan. The Democratic primary was not seriously contested, as Tsongas was the heavy favorite and won the state with a whopping 67% of the vote.

A202: Dwight D. Eisenhower. The General turned down the overtures. In 1952, he won the Republican Presidential nomination, and the Presidency.

A203: Alex Castellans. He was a senior media advisor to Republican Presidential nominee Bob Dole. He told *Washington Post* political columnist E.J. Dionne that Democratic President Bill Clinton was appealing to this demographic. A Soccer Mom was defined as: "the overburdened middle-income working mother who ferries her kids from soccer practice to scouts to school?"

A204: U.S. Senator Allen Eagleton (D-MO). Without knowing that Eagleton was the originator of that quote, McGovern selected Eagleton to be his running mate. After just 18 days on the ticket, McGovern bowed to public pressure to "Dump Eagleton" when it was revealed that Eagleton had gone through electroshock therapy to cure a bout of clinical depression. Nixon would go on to trounce McGovern in the General Election. Novak did not reveal the source of the quote until 2008, after Eagleton's death.

A205: Indiana and Kentucky. They both close the polls at 6:00 PM EST.

A206: Hubert and Muriel Humphrey

A207: Reverend Jesse Jackson. Gore maintained that Dukakis was too trepidatious to attack Jackson, an African-American, because some might perceive that as racism. Gore averred: "He's scared to death he'll be misinterpreted. He's very uneasy with the whole subject. It's just ludicrous. He is absurdly timid when it comes to uttering the slightest sound that might somehow be interpreted as containing an unfavorable view of one of Jesse Jackson's positions."

A208: Rick Perry

A209: Zero. In fact, the Democrats actually picked up two seats both times.

Q210: Which 1940 Presidential nominee asserted: "The doctrinaires of the opposition have attempted to picture me as an opponent of liberalism, but I was a Liberal before many of those men heard the word"?

Q211: Where was the only place where Michael Bloomberg won in the 2020 Democratic Presidential primary?

Q212: Urging voters to stay the course, which Republican Presidential nominee ran on the campaign slogan: "Don't swap horses when crossing stream?"

Q213: After being the Republican Vice Presidential nominee in 1976, this candidate garnered less than 1% of the vote in the New Hampshire Presidential primary in 1980, forcing him to egress from the race. Who was this candidate?

Q214: Which state was the only state where Bill Clinton finished in third place in 1992?

Q215: At an address before the United Conference of Mayors in Philadelphia, Democratic Presidential candidate Jesse Jackson took a back-handed swipe at the frontrunner for the nomination, former Vice President Walter Mondale, a Minnesota native, by stating that another politician was "The last significant politician out of the St. Paul-Minneapolis area." Who was this other politician from Minnesota?

Q216: Which Presidential candidate used the following campaign slogan: "Why not the best?"

Q217: In 1912, which incumbent President mustered just eight electoral votes, and just 23.2% of the popular vote (the poorest showing for an incumbent President in history)?

Q218: After the grueling last days of the 1976 Presidential campaign, Republican President Gerald R. Ford lost his voice and was unable to concede to the winner, Democratic nominee Jimmy Carter. Who delivered Ford's concession speech?

Q219: In 1974, which outgoing Governor told his mother that he would seek the Presidency. His mother responded: "President of what?'

A210: Republican Wendell Willkie

A211: American Samoa. He spent over $500,000,000 on his entire campaign, and all he won was five delegates from American Samoa. Bloomberg won in American Samoa in part by hiring seven paid staffers on the island. He won 175 votes there (49.9%.).

A212: Abraham Lincoln, in 1864. He won the election.

A213: Bob Dole

A214: Utah

A215: Hubert Humphrey

A216: Jimmy Carter

A217: William Howard Taft

A218: Betty Ford

A219: Jimmy Carter

Q220: When Lyndon B. Johnson was offered the Vice Presidential nomination with U.S. Senator John F. Kennedy, he consulted with which former Vice President who advised him: "The Vice Presidency isn't worth a bucket of warm spit"?

Q221: The 1964 Republican Presidential nominee was once blackballed when he applied for membership in a Country Club because his father was Jewish. At the time, he responded: "Since I'm only half-Jewish, can I play only nine holes?" Ironically, he won the nomination, wresting it away from the hegemonic country club bloodline of the Republican Party. Who was this Presidential nominee?

Q222: At the 1988 Democratic National Convention, this Texas State Treasurer delivered the keynote address, mocking Republican Presidential nominee George H.W. Bush with this line: "Poor George, he can't help it. He was born with a silver foot in his mouth." Who was this Texas politician?

Q223: This 2008 Democratic Presidential candidate told students at Phillips Exeter Academy in Exeter, NH: "Go get yourself a fifth of Scotch or a fifth of gin and chug-a-lug it down and you'll find you lose your senses a lot faster than you would smoking some marijuana." Who made this odd statement?

Q224: Which Presidential candidate made the statement: "Governor Reagan and I do have one thing in common: We both played football. I played for Michigan. He played for Warner Brothers"?

Q225: In 2011, which Republican Presidential candidate, in referring to the nation's founding documents, said: "The very founders that wrote those documents worked tirelessly until slavery was no more"?

Q226: When asked by a reporter to name one decision which his Vice President (who was running to succeed him) had participated in, this President answered: "If you give me a week, maybe I'll think of one"?

Q227: This 2020 Democratic Presidential candidate came in fourth place in the state where she grew up and third place in the state she represents in the U.S. Senate. Who was this candidate?

Q228: Breaking with Democratic orthodoxy, which 1992 major Democratic Presidential candidate called for the elimination of the U.S. Department of Education?

Q229: This Republican Vice Presidential nominee mocked Democratic Vice President and Presidential nominee Hubert Humphrey for his relationship with President Lyndon B. Johnson. He averred: "After playing Tonto for so long, apparently Mr. Humphrey isn't comfortable playing The Lone Ranger." Who made this mocking statement?

A220: John Nance Garner. Johnson ignored the advice and accepted the nomination.

A221: Barry Goldwater

A222: Ann Richards

A223: Mike Gravel

A224: Gerald R. Ford, who defeated Ronald Reagan for the Republican Presidential nomination. Reagan was a former actor and played George Gipp, a famous Notre Dame football player in the Warner Brothers Movie: *Knute Rockne—All American.* Ford was a Center for the University of Michigan Wolverines.

A225: Michele Bachmann. Actually, many of the founders were slave owners, and slavery did not end until the Civil War.

A226: Dwight D. Eisenhower, in referring to Richard M. Nixon.

A227: Elizabeth Warren

A228: Jerry Brown

A229: Spiro Agnew

Q230: In what year was the first Presidential nominating convention held?

Q231: This Republican Presidential nominee made fun of his Democratic opponent for his record as Governor of Massachusetts. He stated, "My opponent ranks first in spending increases -- Second in tax hikes. If this were the Olympics, his composite score would make him the gold medal winner in the tax-and-spend competition." Which Presidential Nominee made this statement about his Democratic opponent?

Q232: While campaigning for Democratic Presidential nominee George McGovern, this Rhode Island Governor asserted: "Nixon has been sitting in the White House while George McGovern has been exposing himself to the people of the United States." Who made this rather odd, accidental statement?

Q233: At the high-water mark of the Vietnam War, which Presidential candidate averred: "Why does the Air Force need expensive new bombers? Have the people we've been bombing over the years been complaining?"

Q234: When was the last time a major political party Presidential candidate allowed his party's national convention to decide on the Vice Presidential nominee?

Q235: After garnering just 3.5% of the vote in the 1984 New Hampshire Presidential primary, which South Carolina U.S. Senators told reporters and supporters: "Well: Nothing happened to me on the way to the White House?"

Q236: In 2011, former President Bill Clinton mocked this Republican Presidential candidate by calling him "A good looking rascal." Who was Clinton referring to?

Q237: On the campaign trail, this Arizonan would joke: "Arizona may be the only state where mothers don't tell their children they can grow up to be President. I want to change that." Who was this Presidential candidate?

Q238: Which Republican Presidential nominee joked: "How can a President not be an actor?"

Q239: Which former Massachusetts Governor remarked about one of his Gubernatorial successors, Mitt Romney (who happened to be the Republican Presidential nominee): "He's Smart, he's slick, he's a fraud, simple as that . . . I think he'd be a disaster in the White House. I'm trying to be as subtle as I possibly can here?"

Presidential Campaigns

A230: In 1831. The Anti-Masonic Party, a.k.a. the Know Nothing Party, nominated William Writ for President. Ironically, Writ was a former Mason.

A231: George H.W. Bush, in referring to Michal Dukakis

A232: Frank Licht

A233: George Wallace

A234: 1956. Adlai Stevenson opened the choice of selecting a Vice Presidential nominee to the Democratic National Convention. The Democratic Conventioneers chose U.S. Senator Estes Kefauver (D-TN).

A235: Ernest "Fritz" Hollings

A236: Rick Perry

A237: John McCain. He was referring to the losing Presidential bids of Barry Goldwater, Mo Udall, and Bruce Babbitt.

A238: Ronald Reagan, in 1980

A239: Michael Dukakis

Presidential Campaigns

Q240: This Presidential candidate tells a story of a friend of his who was campaigning for him in the Massachusetts Democratic Primary. The friend saw that his cab driver had literature in the cab supporting a candidate from Oklahoma. The friend asked, "Where's he from?" The Boston Cab Driver responded: "Oklahoma." The friend then jokingly asked: "Where is Oklahoma?" The Cab Driver responded: "Well I think you go west on Commonwealth Avenue" (A popular major Street in the City of Boston). Who was this Massachusetts Presidential candidate who told this funny story?

Q241: Speaking before a Chamber of Commerce Luncheon in Charleston, WV, the brother of this Democratic Presidential candidate joked that he was in the state "to help my brother get a job." Who was this campaign helper?

Q242: Who won the New Hampshire Republican Presidential primary in 1964 as a write-in candidate, without entering the primary, and not even living in the country?

Q243: In 1988, William Carrick, the campaign manager for Democratic Presidential candidate Richard Gephardt, minced no words about his disdain for which rival, averring: "It's blood lust. Let me at him. I hate him. I hate all of them. I think they are the phoniest two-bit bastards that ever came down the pike, starting with Al Gore, moving through boy wonder ex-wordsmith, the mosquito who roared {Fred Martin, Gore's manager}. They are just a {expletive} bunch of meddlesome bastards."?

Q244: Which 1996 Presidential candidate opined: "War has rules. Mud wrestling has rules. Politics has no rules"?

Q245: Who used the Presidential campaign slogan: "Nevertheless, she persisted"?

Q246: Which 2008 Republican Presidential candidate said: "It isn't rocket science. Diets fail because you lose weight and then it's, oh, thank goodness this is over. I did every diet: Atkins. Cabbage-soup diet. Dean Ornish. But I couldn't live the rest of my life like a rabbit"?

Q247: After the death of Republican Gerald R. Ford, which former Democratic Presidential nominee told *CNN*'s Larry King that he voted for Ford in 1976 over Democratic nominee Jimmy Carter

Q248: This 1928 Democratic Presidential nominee became a vociferous opponent of Democratic President Franklin D. Roosevelt. During the 1936 campaign cycle, he supported Republican nominee Al Smith. However, he conceded that many voters would support Roosevelt because they benefited from his domestic New Deal. He remarked: "You don't shoot Santa Clause." Which nominee made this statement?

Q249: When asked why Democratic Presidential nominee Hubert Humphrey did not win Illinois, which Illinois politician responded: "He didn't get enough votes"?

A240: U.S. Senator Fred Harris (D-OK)

A241: Robert F. Kennedy, in 1960

A242: Henry Cabot Lodge Jr. He was serving as U.S. ambassador to South Vietnam under Democratic President Lyndon B. Johnson

A243: Al Gore

A244: H. Ross Perot

A245: Elizabeth Warren

A246: Mike Huckabee

A247: George McGovern, the 1972 Democratic Presidential nominee. He said: "At Thanksgiving dinner that year, I never said anything about this to Eleanor or to her five children. But I told them at Thanksgiving time I had voted for President Ford, even though he lost. And I told them why, because I thought he had come in at a difficult time. I didn't know President Carter very well then. And I just felt more comfortable somehow with Jerry Ford. Whereupon my wife Eleanor said, so did I vote for him. We went around that table -- this is hard to believe -- all five of my kids voted for him [Ford]."

A248: Al Smith

A249: Richard J. Daley

Presidential Campaigns

Q250: In 1876, after the Republican National Convention selected U.S. Representative William Wheeler (R-NY) as their Vice Presidential nominee, the Republican Party's Presidential nominee replied: "I am ashamed to say: "Who is Wheeler?" Who was the Presidential nominee who had never heard of his runningmate?

Q251: In explaining the lack of drama at the 1924 Republican National Convention, which political humorist deadpanned: "The only excitement occurred when a delegate lost his hotel room key"?

Q252: Responding to an advertisement which questioned his support for abortion rights, which 1992 Democratic Presidential candidate referred to opponent Bill Clinton as: "The prince of sleaze"?

Q253: In 1976, Republican Presidential candidate Ronald Reagan announced that if he were to garner the nomination, he would select U.S. Senator Richard Schweiker (R-PA) as his Vice Presidential runningmate. This inflamed conservative U.S. Senator Jesse Helms (R-NC), an early backer of Reagan. In response, Helms encouraged a movement to draft which conservative U.S. Senator to run for the Presidential nomination?

Q254: Donald Trump said that this Democratic Presidential candidacy failed because: "People don't like her. She's a very mean person. And people don't like her. They don't want that." Who was Trump denouncing?

Q255: When asked about the possibility that football Quarterback Peyton Manning would join the Denver Broncos, this 2012 Republican Presidential candidate responded: "Well, you know I'm surprised to hear that Denver is thinking about him. They're — I don't want him in our neck of the woods [New England]. Let's put it that way. I don't want him to go to Miami or to the Jets. But I've got a lot of good friends, the owner of the Miami Dolphins and the New York Jets — both owners are friends of mine." Who made this rambling statement?

Q256: Which Presidential candidate informed an Ohio crowd: "It's no exaggeration to say the undecideds could go one way or another?"

Q257: This *New Yorker Magazine* film critic and resident of Berkeley, CA told an audience: "I live in a rather special world. I only know one person who voted for [Republican Richard M.] Nixon. Where they are I don't know. They're outside my kin. But sometimes when I'm in a theater I can feel them." Who said this?

Q258: In announcing his support for George H.W. Bush to become President in 1988, which prominent Republican mispronounced Bush's name.

Q259: At a $1,000-a-plate fundraiser for his re-election campaign in Houston, which President told attendees: "Probably there are people in this room still mad at me at that budget because you think I raised your taxes too much. It might surprise you to know that I think I raised them too much, too"?

A250: Rutherford B. Hayes. At the time, the party convention, not the Presidential nominee selected the Vice Presidential runningmate.

A251: Will Rogers

A252: Jerry Brown. He told a crowd in New York City: "He's always smiling and saying 'ah don't attack, don't attack, don't go negative. Yet just before an election on the last weekend he [Clinton] unleashes a vicious attack."

A253: James Buckley (Conservative Party-NY)

A254: Elizabeth Warren

A255: Mitt Romney

A256: George H.W. Bush

A257: Pauline Kael

A258: Ronald Reagan. He pronounced the name Bush, as rhymes with rush.

A259: Bill Clinton. Republican National Committee Chairman Haley Barbour responded: "Americans have grown accustomed to Bill Clinton taking great liberties with the truth. But the whopper he told in Houston last night qualifies him for an award in fiction."

Presidential Campaigns

Q260: In 2011, this Republican Presidential candidate made the following misstatement: "Those of you that will be 21 by November the 12th, I ask for your support and your vote. Those of you who won't be, work hard." This is a misstatement because the legal age for voting is 18, not 21, and the election was scheduled for November 6, not November 12. Who was this candidate?

Q261: In 2007, this Democratic Presidential candidate told an Indian-American supporter "In Delaware, the largest growth in population is Indian-Americans moving from India. You cannot go to a 7-11 or a Dunkin Donuts unless you have a slight Indian accent. I'm not joking." Who made this odd statement?

Q262: In 1984, Mississippi Agricultural Secretary Jim Buck Ross asked this Vice Presidential candidate if she could bake a blueberry muffin. She replied: "Sure can, can you?" Ross answered: "Down here in Mississippi the men don't cook." Who was this Vice Presidential candidate who could bake a blueberry muffin?

Q263: After finishing a distant third place with just 12% of the vote in the 1980 Wisconsin Primary, this California Governor aborted his bid for the Democratic Presidential nomination. Who was this Governor who dropped out of the race?

Q264: When his Chief of Staff, Tom D'Amore, told a meeting of local New Hampshire reporters that his boss, a Liberal Republican, was considering seeking the Republican Presidential nomination in 1980, one reporter told him: "Mr. D'Amore, let me tell you something. We've got Communists here in New Hampshire, and believe me, 'our' Communists don't even like 'your' Communists." Who was the Liberal Republican who made this statement?

Q265: Which Democratic Presidential nominee charged that: "The working class is subsidizing the $50 martini lunch"?

Q266: When a reporter asked this Republican Presidential nominee how many homes he and his wife owned, he answered: "I think – I'll have my staff get back to you." Who was this Presidential nominee?

Q267: During the 1928 Presidential campaign, radio was becoming a vital medium for political candidates to get their messages out. This Republican nominee reluctantly used it. When he was asked if he got a thrill from using it, he responded: "The same thrill I get when I rehearse an address to a doorknob." Who made this rather unusual statement?

Q268: The day Bill Clinton accepted the 1996 Democratic Presidential nomination, which advisor resigned after it was revealed that he was involved with Prostitute Sherry Rowlands?

Q269: In the 1992 Democratic Presidential primaries, which was the only state won by Bob Kerrey?

A260: Rick Perry

A261: Joe Biden

A262: Geraldine Ferraro

A263: Jerry Brown

A264: U.S. Senator Lowell Weicker (R-CT)

A265: Jimmy Carter

A266: John McCain. The couple owned seven properties.

A267: Herbert Hoover

A268: Dick Morris

A269: South Dakota

Presidential Campaigns

Q270: In 1968, Republican Presidential nominee Richard M. Nixon asked U.S. House Minority Leader Gerald R. Ford (R-MI) if he would accept the Vice Presidential nomination if offered. Ford told Nixon that he believed there was a good chance the Republicans would take control of the U.S. House, and that he would rather be Speaker. Who did he recommend Nixon select?

Q271: In 1884, this Republican Presidential nominee sat silently while Presbyterian Minister Samuel Burchard excoriated the Democratic Party as the party of "Rum. Romanism, and Rebellion." Many Irish-American voters took umbrage at the remark, believing that the word "rum" was a thinly veiled reference to the stereotype that the Irish were alcoholics. In response, the Irish Americans went to the polls to vote for Democrat Grover Cleveland in protest. Who may have lost the election based on his reluctance to confront the minister about his characterization of the Irish?

Q272: Which 2004 Democratic Presidential candidate told a crowd in De Moines, IA: "Many years ago doctors would bleed patients with leeches. Today, the insurance companies do that"?

Q273: In 1958, former New York Governor Averell Harriman told a Democratic rally that he wants the Democrats to nominate which former President for the Democratic Presidential nomination in 1960? He told the crowd of more than 2,500 Democratic supporters: "He is the man to get us back on the rails."

Q274: Campaigning for a full four-year term, which President mistakenly read words in the margins of his written speech ("with emphasis"): "I say to you this is nonsense with emphasis"?

Q275: This Democratic Presidential nominee was chided as too intellectual. He wore that moniker with pride, declaring: "Eggheads of the world unite, you have nothing to lose but your yolks." Who was this candidate?

Q276: In 1975, this Democratic Presidential candidate introduced himself in a New Hampshire barbershop and told a barber he was running for President. The barber responded: "Yeah, I know, we were just laughing about that yesterday." Who was this candidate the barbershop customers were laughing about?

Q277: In his famous 1992 appearance on *The Arsenio Hall Show*, what song did Democratic Presidential candidate Bill Clinton play on his saxophone?

Q278: After a mass exodus of campaign consultants, David Carney, an advisor to the Presidential candidate in 2011, described the overspending campaign as: "living a Cadillac campaign on a Bud Light budget." Who was the candidate?

Q279: After losing the Presidential election, which Republican nominee joked: "Tomorrow will be the first time in my life I don't have anything to do"?

A270: John Lindsay, the Mayor of New York City. Lindsay, at the time was a staunch Nixon ally, was seriously considered, but in the end, Ford selected Maryland Governor Spiro Agnew. When Agnew resigned the office in 1973, Nixon asked Ford to succeed him as Vice President, and with U.S. Senate confirmation, he assumed the position. In 1969, Lindsay lost the Republican nomination for re-election as Mayor, but remained on the ballot as the nominee of the Liberal Party, and won the Mayoral election. No longer a Republican, Lindsay became a thorn in the side of Nixon and New York Republican Governor Nelson Rockefeller. Nixon told a Rockefeller friend that he would offer to use his office to wiretap Lindsay's telephone. "If he needs any help from the FBI, or money, or anything else, you have him let me know." There is no evidence that Rockefeller accepted the offer. Lindsay became a vociferous critic of Nixon, and even unsuccessfully ran for the Democratic Presidential nomination in 1972.

A271: James G. Blaine

A272: Dennis Kucinich

A273: Harry S. Truman. Truman responded at the rally: "I don't deserve what Harriman says, but I like to hear him say it." Truman had endorsed Harriman for the nomination in 1956. Harriman lost to former Illinois Governor Adlai Stevenson. Harriman said he was "deadly serious" in wanting Truman to be the nominee. Truman was 74-years-old at the time.

A274: Gerald R. Ford

A275: Adlai Stevenson

A276: Mo Udall

A277: *Heartbreak Hotel* by Elvis Pressley

A278: Newt Gingrich

A279: Bob Dole

Q280: Which Democratic Presidential nominee told an audience: "The Republicans have a 'me too' candidate running on a 'yes but' platform, advised by a 'has-been' staff."?

Q281: In 1940, this Presidential candidate campaigned for delegates at the Republican National Convention. He did not participate in the Republican primaries, viewing them as inconsequential. He said: "Imagine killing yourself for Vermont." He lost the nomination to fellow Republican Wendell Willkie. Who was this Presidential candidate?

Q282: In 1979, Jimmy Carter said that if this Presidential candidate challenged him for the Democratic Presidential nomination, he would "whip his ass." Whose ass was Carter going to whip?

Q283: In which Presidential election were both the Democratic and Republican nominees born in Massachusetts?

Q284: While campaigning for a full term as President, an audience member bellowed: "Give him hell." This President retorted: "I don't give them hell. I just tell the truth about them and they think it's hell." Which President made this comment?

Q285: In 1856, this Democratic President lost his own Party's nomination for reelection to James Buchanan who was serving as Ambassador to the United Kingdom. When he found out that he had lost, he deadpanned: "There's nothing left to do but get drunk." Which President made this remark?

Q286: During the last days of the 1932 Presidential campaign, Franklin D. Roosevelt called this man a: "fat timid capon." Who was Roosevelt referring to?

Q287: Which Presidential nominee, who lost three Presidential elections, commented: "I would rather be right than President"?

Q288: In 2008, she told the Republican National Convention: "I guess a small-town mayor is sort of like a community organizer, except that you have actual responsibilities." Who made this remark?

Q289: Up Until 1957, Maine held its Gubernatorial and Congressional elections in September. During Presidential years, the state became a bellwether for the pending election in November. If the state voted for a member of one party for Governor, the thinking was that the nation would vote for the Presidential nominee of the same party in the Presidential election. In 1936, Maine voted overwhelmingly for Republican candidates in the September election. However, in the Presidential election, only Maine and staunchly Republican Vermont voted for the Republican nominee Alfred Landon over Democrat Franklin D. Roosevelt. This Postmaster General and Roosevelt's Campaign Manager joked: "As Maine Goes, So Goes Vermont." Who made this remark?

A280: Adlai Stevenson

A281: Arthur Vandenberg

A282: Ted Kennedy. Kennedy replied: "I always knew the White House would stand behind me, but I didn't realize how close they would be."

A283: The 1988 Presidential election. Democrat Michael Dukakis was born in Brookline, Massachusetts. He lived most of his life in the Bay State and won three terms as the state's Governor. Republican George H.W. Bush was born in Milton, Massachusetts. His family moved to Connecticut before his first birthday, but Bush came back to the state for his high school years, where he attended the prestigious prep school Philips Academy in Andover, Massachusetts.

A284: Harry S. Truman

A285: Franklin Pierce

A286: Herbert Hoover

A287: Henry Clay

A288: Sarah Palin. She was comparing her experience as the Mayor of Wasilla, AK with Democratic Presidential Nominee Barack Obama, who had been a community organizer.

A289: James Farley

Presidential Campaigns

Q290: 2012 was the first election when both major Vice Presidential nominees were Catholic. Who were these Vice Presidential candidates?

Q291: Which Republican President running for re-election told voters that he had tried to extend "a hand of friendship, and these old mossbacks bit it off"?

Q292: This U.S. Senator, who saw many of his colleagues run for President, observed: "When the Presidential bug gets in your veins, the only thing that will get it out is embalming fluid." Which Senator made this comment?

Q293: This Vice Presidential runningmate called himself "a warmonger in the battle against the dissipation of natural resources." He then suggested he favored abortion as a means of birth control. Who was this VP candidate?

Q294: In the 1900 Presidential campaign, Democratic activists convinced this enormously popular U.S. Navy Admiral to seek their party's Presidential nomination. The Admiral's candidacy imploded when he said publicly: "I am convinced that the office of the President is not such a very difficult one to fill." Who was the Admiral who made this statement?

Q295: Which Democratic Presidential nominee told a heckler in Battle Creek, Michigan: "Listen, you son of bitch, why don't you kiss my ass"? His supporters subsequently manufactured campaign buttons with the acronym "KMA" emblazoned on them.

Q296: This Presidential candidate considered former Major League Baseball Commissioner and Kentucky Governor Happy Chandler as his Vice Presidential runningmate. Who was this Presidential candidate?

Q297: In 1988, Vice President George H.W. Bush was sitting next to Tom Brokaw of *NBC NEWS,* in New York. The next person to be interviewed was his election opponent. Brokaw asked Bush if he had anything to say to his opponent. Bush answered: "Just wish him well and we'll see him in the South." When Bush's opponent was asked if he had anything to say to Bush, he deadpanned: "Yeah, tell him to stop lying about my record." Who was this Bush opponent?

Q298: In referring to the 1992 Democratic Presidential ticket of Bill Clinton and Al Gore, which Presidential candidate commented: "My dog Millie knows more about foreign affairs than these two bozos"?

Q299: When asked if Mitt Romney would select this political figure as his Vice Presidential runningmate in 2012, this former Governor of Arkansas responded: "I think there is a greater likelihood that I'll be asked by Madonna to go on tour as her base player than I'll be picked to be on the ticket." Who made this comment?

A290: Republican Paul Ryan and Democrat Joe Biden

A291: George H.W. Bush, in 1992. "Mossback" refers to someone too conservative to seek progress.

A292: George Aiken (R-VT)

A293: Curtis Lemay. He ran on the Independent Party ticket with George Wallace. To get this gaffe-prone, politically tone-deaf candidate out of the news cycle, the Wallace campaign sent him on a "fact-finding mission" to Vietnam.

A294: George Dewey. After dropping out of the race, Dewey supported the successful re-election campaign of Republican President William McKinley.

A295: George McGovern. U.S. Senator James Eastland (D-MS) later told him: "That was the best line of the campaign."

A296: George Wallace, in 1968. The offer never came to fruition, as his segregationist supporters were apoplectic that Chandler was supportive of the Brooklyn Dodgers signing African-American Jackie Robinson in 1947.

A297: Bob Dole. Dole was one of Bush's Republican primary opponents.

A298: George H.W. Bush

A299: Mike Huckabee

Presidential Campaigns

Q300: This manager of William McKinley's 1896 Presidential campaign commented: "There are two things that are important in politics. The first is money and I can't remember what the second one is." Who was this campaign manager?

Q301: In 1928, this New York Gubernatorial candidate and supporter of Al Smith, the first Catholic Presidential nominee of a major party, received a letter from a voter stating that he heard that "If Governor Smith is elected president, the Pope's son will be his secretary." Who was the Gubernatorial candidate who received this letter?

Q302: In 1964, which Republican Presidential candidate was dogged by his divorce and remarriage?

Q303: This convicted felon and member of the U.S. Congress, endorsed Newt Gingrich's 2012 Presidential campaign. His endorsement came from the Federal Penitentiary in Tucson, AZ. It read: "Newt, a voice out of the past. Down but not out and still fighting. First, I do not want anything from you but have been watching the debates. I have 80% of inmates that would vote for you. They might not be able to but their extended families will." Who was this felon?

Q304: Trying to contrast himself from Republican Ronald Reagan, who at 76 years of age was the oldest President, this 40-year-old U.S. Senator announced his Presidential candidacy from the Senate Caucus Room where John F. Kennedy, at age 43 became the youngest person ever elected President, announced his candidacy in 1960?

Q305: In 1976, which U.S. Senator announced he would not seek the Democratic Presidential nominations because: "I don't want to spend the next few years at Holiday Inns?"

Q306: In 1936, a newspaper column helped to derail which frontrunner from garnering the Vice Presidential nomination with Presidential nominee Alfred Landon?

Q307: In 1992, this Democratic Presidential candidate concluded: "The Cold War is over. Japan won." Which candidate made this misstatement?

Q308: This Vice Presidential candidate was asked if the use of nuclear weapons would be necessary to win the war in Vietnam. He answered: "We can win this war without nuclear weapons." However, he then added, "But I have to say, we have a phobia about nuclear weapons. I think there may be times when it would be most efficient to use nuclear weapons." Who made this comment?

Q309: During a 2007 interview with Radio Talk Show Host Don Imus, which Republican Presidential candidate quipped: "I may not be the expert as some people on foreign policy, but I did stay at a Holiday Inn Express last night."?

Presidential Campaigns

A300: Mark Hanna

A301: Franklin D. Roosevelt

A302: Nelson Rockefeller. Rockefeller married New York Socialite Margaretta Large "Happy" Rockefeller. At the time, Rockefeller was the frontrunner. The Rockefellers were recently divorced, and at the time, divorce and infidelity were a near taboo in American politics. Nelson was nearly 18 years older than his new bride, and news that the two were having an extra-marital affair prior to the divorce permeating the American body politic. Nelson was the father of five children with his first wife, and Happy had four children, all of whom she surrendered to her first husband just five weeks before marrying Mr. Rockefeller. Rockefeller's campaign was garnering momentum as the critical California primary was looming. However, news then trickled out that Happy birthed a baby boy, and Republican voters were reminded of the infidelity. Accordingly, the momentum then shifted to his opponent, U.S. Senator Barry Goldwater (R-AZ). Goldwater won the state by 3% and eventually won the nomination.

A303: Randy "Duke" Cunningham (R-CA)

A304: Al Gore. He averred: "After eight years under Ronald Reagan, the oldest president, Americans may well feel as they did in 1960, that it is time to turn to youth, vigor and intellectual capacity."

A305: Walter Mondale

A306: Styles Bridges. The morning of the Republican National Convention, which was held in Cleveland, OH, James E. Doyle, the highly acclaimed sports columnist for *The Cleveland Plain Dealer* ended his column giving this unsolicited advice to the GOP: "If they should nominate Gov. Bridges of New Hampshire for vice president, the Democrats would go to town – EVERY town – with the ready-made slogan of the century 'Landon-Bridges falling down.'" Many in the party feared this unfortunate slogan would come to fruition, and newspaper publisher Frank Knox became Landon's running mate instead. Supporters bellowed: "Off the Rocks with Landon and Knox." The ticket lost the General Election in an electoral landslide to Democrats Franklin D. Roosevelt and John Nance Garner.

A307: Paul Tsongas. He was referring to the fact that the Japanese automotive industry was on the rise, while the U.S. automotive industry was experiencing a nosedive.

A308: Curtis Lemay. Lemay was the runningmate of George Wallace of the American Independent Party.

A309: Mike Huckabee

Q310: In 1976, Democratic Presidential nominee Jimmy Carter told a magazine journalist: "I've looked at a lot of women with lust. I've committed adultery in my heart many times." Which magazine carried this quote from Carter?

Q311: In 1976, members of the news media were saying that the Iowa caucuses would "winnow out" candidates who performed poorly. After this candidate finished ahead of expectations, coming in fourth place, he one-upped the media, telling them "The winnowing-out process has begun and we have just been winnowed in." Who was this candidate who was winnowed in?

Q312: Leading in the polls, this Republican Presidential nominee was trepidatious to say anything controversial. Accordingly, he told a rally: "The future, like yours in Arizona, is still ahead of us." Who was this Presidential nominee?

Q313: While heaping praise on Governors for the way they responded to the Corona virus, presumptive Democratic Presidential nominee Joe Biden mistakenly referred to Massachusetts Governor Charlie Baker by the name of which jazz legend?

Q314: In 1920, this Republican Presidential nominee ran on the campaign slogan: "America First."

Q315: When this Pennsylvania Governor decided to enter into the 1976 sweepstakes for the Democratic Presidential nomination, he stated that he thought he could do a better job than his fellow contestants. He averred: "I saw the caliber of these people, and I said, 'What the hell." Who was this Governor?

Q316: In 1964, Barry Goldwater, the Republican Presidential nominee, told reporters that he chose this Republican National Committee Chairman and U.S. Representative from New York as his vice Presidential runningmate because "he drives [his opponent President Lyndon B.] Johnson nuts." Who did Goldwater choose?

Q317: At the 1948 Democratic National Convention, this keynote address was so captivating that he garnered the party's Vice presidential nomination. His famous quote from the speech was: "What is a bureaucrat? A bureaucrat is a Democrat who holds an office a Republican wants." Who delivered this speech?

Q318: In 2008, this Democratic Vice President nominee said of Republican Presidential nominee John McCain: "Look, John's last-minute economic plan does nothing to tackle the number one job facing the middle class, and it happens to be, as Barack [Obama] says, a three-letter word: jobs. J-O-B-S." Who made this comment?

Q319: This 2008 Republican Presidential candidate told *MSNBC*'s Morning Joe: "When we were in college, we used to take a popcorn popper -- because that was the only thing they would let us have in the dorms -- and fry squirrels in the popcorn popper." Who made this funny statement?

A310: *Playboy Magazine*. Republican Vice President Nelson Rockefeller joked: "I never thought I'd see the day when Christ's teachings were discussed in *Playboy* and I'm a Baptist, ladies and gentlemen." The remark by Carter began a precipitous decline of his commanding lead over President Gerald R. Ford.

A311: Fred Harris

A312: Thomas E. Dewey

A313: Charlie Parker

A314: Warren G. Harding

A315: Milton Shapp. He skipped the New Hampshire Primary, focusing on other Northeastern states. However, he failed to garner much traction. After winning just 3% of the vote in the Massachusetts primary, and 3% in Florida, he withdrew from the race.

A316: William Miller

A317: Alben Barkley

A318: Joe Biden

A319: Mike Huckabee

Presidential Campaigns

Q320: This former President urged John F. Kennedy to drop his bid for the 1960 Democratic Presidential nomination. In announcing his support for U.S. Senator Stuart Symington (D-MO), this former President stated publicly to Kennedy: "I hope someone with the greatest possible maturity and experience may be available at this time. May I urge you to be patient?" Who made this comment?

Q321: Which Presidential candidate was nicknamed: "The Rail-splitter?"

Q322: In 1960, Richard M. Nixon made an agreement with this prominent New York Republican, the titular head of the party's liberal bloodline, adding language to the GOP platform in return for his unequivocal endorsement of his Presidential nomination. This pact came to be known as "The treaty of Fifth Avenue." Who was this prominent New York Republican?

Q323: In 2007, this Republican Presidential aspirant told a voter: "I purchased a gun when I was a young man. I've been a hunter pretty much all my life." It was later revealed that this Presidential contender had only hunted twice in his life. He later said: "I'm not a big-game hunter. I've made that very clear. I've always been a rodent and rabbit hunter. Small varmints, if you will." Who was this non-hunter Presidential aspirant?

Q324: This 1988 Democratic Presidential candidate's television appearances were flat and uncharismatic. However, he worked on trying to improve his charisma by reviewing his past television performances. He told *The New York Times*: "If they can teach Mr. Ed to talk on television, they can teach me" (Mr. Ed was a 1950s TV sitcom featuring a talking horse). Who was this dull speaker?

Q325: Drawing sharp contrasts with his Democratic opponent, this Republican Presidential nominee pledged to offer: "a choice, not an echo." Who made this pledge?

Q326: In 2003, this Democratic Presidential aspirant told Democratic voters: "I'm going to slap the donkey until the donkey kicks and we are going to kick George [W.] Bush out of the White House." Who made such an unusual statement?

Q327: At the 1992 Republican National Convention, this failed candidate joked: "Bill Clinton's foreign policy experience stems mainly from having breakfast at the International House of Pancakes." Who made this witty statement?

Q328: In 1992, which Vice Presidential candidate began his opening statement with the existential question: "Who am I? Why am I here?"

Q329: In 1984, after losing the Presidency in a 49-state landslide, Democrat Walter Mondale asked the only other Democratic Presidential nominee to lose 49 states (in 1972): "When does it stop hurting?" He replied: "When it does, I'll let you know." Who also lost in a 49-state landslide?

Presidential Campaigns

A320: Harry S. Truman

A321: Abraham Lincoln. During his Presidential campaign in 1860, two of his mother's first cousins, Richard J. Oglesby and John Hanks, found a split-rail fence they thought Lincoln had built in 1830. Lincoln himself was not sure if that was the actual rail he had split. However, a poster of a young Lincoln splitting rails with a drawing of the White House in the background, eventually emerged.

A322: Nelson Rockefeller, the Governor of New York

A323: Mitt Romney

A324: Bruce Babbitt

A325: Barry Goldwater, the 1964 Republican Presidential nominee, running against Democrat Lyndon B. Johnson

A326: Al Sharpton

A327: Pat Buchanan

A328: James Stockdale, runningmate of Independent Presidential Candidate H. Ross Perot

A329: George McGovern

Presidential Campaigns

Q330: This Michigan Governor told a campaign rally for the re-election of President George H.W. Bush: "My friends, it's with a great deal of pride that I present to you a President who wants to cut jobs, who wants to cut taxes and cut jobs, who wants to stop the regulations and cut the jobs." Who made these comments?

Q331: This former Democratic President excoriated the 1960 Republican Presidential nominee, saying: "Richard Nixon is a no-good lying bastard. He can lie out of both sides of his mouth at the same time, and if he ever caught himself telling the truth, he'd lie just to keep his hand in." Who was this former President?

Q332: U.S. Senator Boise Penrose (R-PA) knew that his 1920 Republican Presidential nominee was prone to making gaffes. Accordingly, he suggested to his campaign team: "Don't let him make any speeches. If he goes out on tour, somebody's sure to ask him questions." Who was this Presidential nominee?

Q333: After winning the 1840 Presidential election, U.S. Senator John C. Calhoun (D-SC) commented: "He seems to enjoy the election as a mere affair of personal vanity." Which President-elect was this statement geared toward?

Q334: At the 1940 Republican National Convention, former U.S. Senator Majority Leader James E. Watson (R-IN) said to this Republican Presidential aspirant who had recently converted from the Democratic Party to the Republican Party: "I may welcome a repentant sinner into my church, but I wouldn't want him to lead the Choir." Who was Watson speaking to?

Q335: During the 1948 Presidential election, which young U.S. Representative made the following statement in support of Democratic President Harry S. Truman and against the Republican Party: "They use the Hitler Line – no matter how big the lie: repeat it often enough and the masses will regard it as true."?

Q336: In 1991, this Democratic Presidential candidate posed next to a horse. He then pointed to it and averred: "Here you have a horse's head." He then pointed to himself and commented: "and here you have a horse's ass." Who was this orator?

Q337: In 1968, this Presidential candidate told a coterie of heckling hippies: "You come up when I get through and I'll autograph your sandals for you. That is, if you got any on . . . . You need a good haircut. That's all that's wrong with you . . . . There are two four-letter words I bet you folks don't know: work and soap." Who made these statements?

Q338: In 1976, President Gerald R. Ford mocked which Republican challenger by suggesting he "doesn't dye his hair, he's just prematurely orange"?

Q339: In 2012, this Republican Presidential candidate told a crowd at the Peterborough, NH Town Hall: "I would restore your right to drink raw milk anytime you like." Who made this statement?

Presidential Campaigns

A330: John Engler

A331: Harry S. Truman

A332: Warren G. Harding

A333: William Henry Harrison

A334: Wendell Willkie

A335: John F. Kennedy

A336: Bob Kerrey

A337: George Wallace

A338: Ronald Reagan

A339: Ron Paul

168

Presidential Campaigns

Q340: This New York City Mayor told reporters that he welcomed protestors to the Republican National Convention slated to be held in the city. He even said protestors who sport badges reading: "Peaceful Activist" will qualify for hotel and restaurant discounts. He stated at a Press Conference: "It's no fun to protest on an empty stomach . . . They will still get a discount, even the anarchists." Which New York Mayor made these statements?

Q341: In 1880 he became the first former President to seek a third term in office?

Q342: Which two former political allies ran against Franklin D. Roosevelt when he sought an unprecedented third term in 1940?

Q343: In 2008, this Republican Presidential nominee declared: "I will veto every single beer." Who said this?

Q344: In 1995, this Republican Presidential aspirant told a Republican crowd: "I'll be another Ronald Reagan if that's what you want me to be." Who made this interesting statement?

Q345: This Republican Presidential candidate averred: "I know how hard it is for you to put food on your family." Who was this Presidential candidate?

Q346: In his address announcing he was dropping out of the 1992 race for the Democratic Presidential nomination, he told supporters: "I feel a little like the Jamaican bobsled team. We had a lot of spirit, but unfortunately, we didn't get a lot of medals." Who made this Jamaica bobsled analogy?

Q347: Which Presidential nominee flew to the Democratic National Convention to announce his choice for Vice President to the delegates?

Q348: This person, who competed thrice for the Republican Presidential nomination with Republican Thomas E. Dewey, commented: "You really have to get to know Dewey to dislike him." Which Republican made this comment?

Q349: In 1991, this Democratic Presidential candidate mocked Republican President George H.W. Bush this way: "Bush's recovery program can be summed up in three words: Cut Capital Gains. That's his answer to everything. Give more tax cuts to the rich. You've got eight million unemployed: Cut capital gains. Stagnant economy: Cut capital gains: Trade deficit: Cut capital gains. Got a tooth ache: Cut capital gains." Which Democrat made this statement?

A340: Michael Bloomberg

A341: Ulysses S. Grant. Though he never declared himself a candidate, he pushed his surrogates to advance his name as a candidate in 1880 for the Republican Presidential nomination. Grant lost the nomination to U.S. Representative James Garfield (R-OH).

A342: Vice President John Nance Garner and James Farley (the former Democratic National Committee Chairman and Post Master). Gardner, a business-oriented conservative Democrat from Texas, thought that Roosevelt had veered too far to the left ideologically. Farley asserted that no President should serve more than two terms. Roosevelt easily won the nomination and went on to win his third term.

A343: John McCain. He meant to say that he would veto "every single bill."

A344: Bob Dole

A345: George W. Bush. He most likely meant to say: "I know how hard it is for you to put food on your family's dinner table."

A346: Bob Kerrey

A347: Lyndon B. Johnson. He flew to Atlantic City, NJ in 1964 to announce his choice of Hubert Humphrey as his Vice Presidential runningmate.

A348: Robert A. Taft

A349: Tom Harkin

Q350: In 1963, this prospective Republican Presidential candidate, in discussing the use of nuclear missiles, deadpanned: "I don't want to hit the moon. I want to lob one into the men's room of the Kremlin and make sure I hit it." Who made this statement?

Q351: Which 2008 Democratic Presidential candidate said of Republican candidate Rudy Giuliani: "[He] is probably the most underqualified man since George W. Bush to seek the Presidency. Rudy Giuliani – there's only three things he [needs] to make a sentence: a noun and a verb, and 9/11"?

Q352: In 1888, this successful Republican Presidential nominee told Republican National Committee Chairman Mathew Stanley Quay: "Providence has given us a victory." Who made this statement?

Q353: This California Governor broke his pledge to California voters while running for re-election in 1994 not to seek the Republican Presidential nomination in 1996. His campaign failed to garner traction, and in September of 1995, he became the first major Republican to drop out of the race. Who was this Governor?

Q354: In 1940, this long-time U.S. Senate Majority Leader and new Vice Presidential runningmate for Republican Presidential nominee Wendell Willkie, gave Willkie, new to electoral politics, the following advice: "In politics you'll never get into trouble by not saying too much." Who gave this sage advice?

Q355: During the 1952 Presidential election, an enthusiastic supporter approached this Democratic Presidential nominee, and said: "Governor, every thinking person will be voting for you." The Governor replied: "Madam that is not enough. I need a majority." Which Governor made this funny reply?

Q356: After winning his home state of Illinois in the1988 Democratic Presidential primary, this U.S. Senator declared: "The victory is one of the most gratifying in my years of public life. The ancient god of Greek mythology Antilles received his strength by touching the ground. I have renewed my strength by touching the ground of Illinois." Who was this Senator?

Q357: In 1979, the rock and roll band *Chicago* endorsed and held a concert for which Democratic Presidential candidate?

Q358: In 1992, Democratic Presidential nominee Bill Clinton said of this Republican U.S. Representative from California: "He looks like he needs a rabies shot." Who was he referring to?

Q359: This Presidential candidate took heat for his statement regarding an $87 billion appropriation to pay for the wars in Afghanistan and Iraq: "I actually did vote for the $87 billion [appropriation] before I voted against it." Who made this unusual statement?

A350: Barry Goldwater

A351: Joe Biden

A352: Benjamin Harrison. Republican National Committee Chairman Mathew Stanley Quay later said to a news reporter: "He ought to know that Providence didn't have a damn thing to do with it. Harrison will never know how many men were compelled to approach the penitentiary to make him President."

A353: Pete Wilson

A354: Charles L. McNary

A355: Adlai Stevenson

A356: Paul Simon

A357: Jerry Brown. However, Larry Lamb, the keyboardist for the group, supported the way that one of his opponents, President Jimmy Carter, was dealing with the Iranian Hostage situation. When he was asked about Brown's statement that Carter was politicizing the issue, Lamb said that Brown "sat at the feet of a real politician all his life [His father, Edmund G. Brown] and politics is second-nature to him. When he makes a statement like that, he's being a politician." As for Brown's other major opponent, U.S. Senator Ted Kennedy (D-MA), Lamb averred: "Frankly, I think he's incompetent." Interestingly, many concertgoers came simply for the music, and not for Brown. In fact, when Brown addressed the crowd, he was booed. He made a brief statement: "Your presence here will help protect the earth, serve the people and explore the universe." That line soon became his campaign slogan.

A358: Bob Dornan

A359: John Kerry

Presidential Campaigns

Q360: Who is the only person to deliver the Keynote Address at both a Democratic and Republican National Convention?

Q361: In 2011, which Republican Presidential candidate told a group of unemployed Americans in Tampa, FL: "I should tell you a story. I too am unemployed."?

Q362: In 2007, this Republican Presidential candidate answered a telephone call while addressing the National Rifle Association (NRA) by saying: "Hello, dear. I'm talking to the members of the NRA right now. Would you like to say hello? I love you, and I'll give you a call as soon as I'm finished, O.K? O.K, have a safe trip. Bye-bye. Talk to you later, dear. I love you." He was met with uproarious laughter from the audience. Who was this Presidential candidate?

Q363: In 1976, former President Richard M. Nixon visited China. This reminded Republican primary voters that President Gerald R. Ford had pardoned him. Which Republican U.S. Senator, a Ford supporter, averred: "As far as I'm concerned, Nixon can go to China and stay there."?

Q364: At the 1940 Republican National Convention, on the sixth ballot, conventioneers yelled: "We want Willkie!" The U.S. House Minority Leader could not control the convention, and bellowed: "Well, if you'll be quiet long enough, maybe you'll get him." Who was the House Minority Leader?

Q365: This 2008 Presidential candidate discussed a hotel he stayed at on the campaign trail: "It was so bad, I called my wife and said I'm the only guy in this hotel that has sleeves on his shirt and is not completely tattooed from head to toe. It was that bad." Who was this complaining Presidential candidate?

Q366: This President, appearing on *The Tonight Show with Jay Leno*, joked about a week before his successful re-election bid: "If anybody comes from Ohio, they can expect a Hershey bar 'this' big [moving his hands outward.] Ohio was a critical showdown state that year, which he won. Which President said this?

Q367: In 2011, this New Jersey Governor was often questioned about running for President in 2011. He told a reporter bluntly: "Short of suicide, I don't really know what I'd have to do to convince you people that I'm not running." Which New Jersey Governor made this statement?

Q368: In 2008, this former U.S. Senator and Presidential candidate, while serving as an advisor to Republican Presidential nominee John McCain, told *The Washington Times*: "We have sort of become a nation of whiners. You just hear this constant whining, complaining about a loss of competitiveness, America in decline despite a major export boom that is the primary reason that growth continues in the economy." Who made this comment?

Q369: After this Republican suffered the worst electoral defeat for an incumbent President, pocketing just 23.2% of the vote, he said: "I have one consolation. No candidate was ever elected ex-president by such a large majority." Which President made this astute observation?

A360: Zell Miller. In 1992, Georgia Governor Zell Miller was the keynote speaker at the Democratic National Convention, which nominated Arkansas Governor Bill Clinton for President. In 2004, Miller, at the time a U.S. Senator, was the Keynote Speaker at the Republican National Convention, which nominated President George W. Bush for re-election. Miller was a rare Democrat who crossed party lines, endorsing Republican Bush for re-election.

A361: Mitt Romney

A362: Rudy Giuliani

A363: Barry Goldwater

A364: Joe Martin (R-MA)

A365: Mike Huckabee

A366: Barack Obama

A367: Chris Christie

A368: Phil Gramm of Texas. McCain disavowed the remarks, averring: "I think Senator Gramm would be in serious consideration for ambassador to Belarus, although I'm not sure the citizens of Minsk would welcome that."

A369: William Howard Taft

Q370: In defending 2012 Republican Presidential nominee Mitt Romney's holdings in offshore tax havens, which U.S. Senator averred: "It's really American to avoid paying taxes legally"?

Q371: In 1992, which Democratic Presidential contestant averred that should Bill Clinton muster the Democratic Presidential nomination, "he will not be able to win. I think he's going to be opened up like a soft peanut in November of 1992"?

Q372: This 1968 Presidential candidate asserted: "Well if I get to become President, I'm gonna call in a bunch of bureaucrats and take away their briefcases and throw'em in the Potomac River. And if any demonstrator ever lays down in front of my car, it'll be the last car he'll ever lay down in front of." Who was this Presidential candidate?

Q373: When asked if he had ever used cocaine, this 2000 Reform Party Presidential candidate answered: "No to marijuana. No to cocaine, and a question mark over Jack Daniels." Who was this candidate?

Q374: In 1992, Democratic Presidential candidate Jerry Brown promised that he would choose this Civil Rights Leader as his Vice Presidential nominee should he pocket the nomination. Who was this Civil Rights Leader?

Q375: During the 1992 campaign for the Democratic Presidential nomination, this candidate held up a panda bear, telling supporters that Bill Clinton was a "Pander bear." Unfortunately for him, many voters watching the event thought he was saying: "panda bear" and did not understand the significance. Who was this candidate who held up the panda bear?

Q376: In 1980, Massachusetts Governor Ed King endorsed President Jimmy Carter over which Massachusetts candidate?

Q377: Which Republican Presidential nominee lost his home state by the widest margin ever recorded?

Q378: Who was the first Governor to endorse Mitt Romney for President in 2012?

Q379: Which Presidential candidate joked: "Being lectured by the President on fiscal responsibility is a little bit like Tony Soprano [who played Mafia member James Gandolfini] talking to me about law and order in this country"?

A370: Lindsey Graham (R-SC)

A371: Bob Kerrey made these remarks in an address before the 1992 Georgia Presidential Primary. Candidate Bob Kerrey argued that the parry frontrunner, Bill Clinton, would lose to Republican President George H.W. Bush, chiefly because of his lack of service in the Vietnam War, and his actions protesting against the war. Kerrey was introduced by Georgia State Representative Mabel Thomas, who told the crowd: "We want a President to be Commander-in-Chief, not commander-in-chicken" (Kerrey won a Medal of Honor in the Vietnam War). When he came home from Vietnam, he was a vocal opponent of the War." Accordingly, Clinton responded: "I hope that he'll wake up as his old self, remind himself that he came home as an opponent of the Vietnam War." Clinton secured the nomination, and handily defeated Bush.

A372: George Wallace

A373: Pat Buchanan

A374: Jesse Jackson

A375: Paul Tsongas

A376: Ted Kennedy. Carter won the nomination.

A377: John C. Freemont. He lost California to Democrat James Buchanan by 29.6%.

A378: Dave Heinemann of Nebraska

A379: John Kerry

Presidential Campaigns

Q380: In 1888, the Republican Presidential nominee went to bed before the final election results were in. He explained: "I knew that my staying up would not change the election result if I were defeated, while if elected I had a hard day ahead of me. So, I thought a night's rest was best in any event." Who made this practical statement?

Q381: Which Republican joked: "I don't know many people who run for Vice President and President and lose both"?

Q382: At the 1968 Democratic National Convention, which Chicago Mayor told members of the media: "Gentlemen – get this straight once and for all – the policeman is not there to create disorder, the policeman is there to preserve disorder"?

Q383: During and after the Watergate Affair, bumper stickers were printed in Massachusetts exclaiming: "Don't blame me. I'm from Massachusetts". Which President was Massachusetts proud not to support for re-election?

Q384: At the 2012 Democratic National Convention, this Ohio Governor declared: "Mitt Romney has so little economic patriotism that even his money needs a passport." Which Ohio Governor made this statement?

Q385: In 2004, when this Republican U.S. Senator was asked by talk show host Conan O'Brien if he would consider being the runningmate on a bipartisan ticket with Democrat John Kerry, he deadpanned: "I spent several years in a North Vietnamese prison camp, in the dark, fed with scraps. Do you think I want to do that all over again as Vice President of the United States?" Who said this?

Q386: At the 1968 Democratic National Convention, which U.S. Senator delivering a speech nominating George McGovern for President, and bellowed: "And with George McGovern as President of the United States, we wouldn't have the Gestapo tactics on the streets of Chicago"?

Q387: In 1952, which host Governor delivered a speech welcoming the delegates to the Democratic National Convention?

Q388: The day after being elected to the U.S. Senate from Illinois in November of 2004, this new Senator exclaimed: "I can unequivocally say I will not be running for national office in four years, and my entire focus is making sure that I'm the best possible Senator on behalf of the people of Illinois." However, in February of 2007 he announced his candidacy for the Presidency of the United States. Who was this Senator who made this not so unequivocal statement?

Q389: Who was the first major party Presidential nominee to actually appear at his party's national convention, which unexpectedly nominated him for President?

Presidential Campaigns

A380: Benjamin Harrison. He won the election.

A381: Bob Dole. He was the losing Vice Presidential nominee in 1976 and the losing Presidential nominee in 1996.

A382: Richard J. Daley

A383: Richard M. Nixon. Nixon got caught up in the Watergate Affair which resulted in his ignominious resignation. Massachusetts was the only state to vote for Nixon's Presidential Democratic opponent George McGovern (McGovern also won the District of Columbia).

A384: Ted Strickland

A385: John McCain

A386: Abraham Ribicoff (D-CT)

A387: Adlai Stevenson. He became the Democratic nominee for President.

A388: Barack Obama

A389: James Garfield. Garfield was there to nominate Ohio favorite-son John Sherman for President, but in a deadlocked convention, he landed up becoming the dark horse nominee himself, on the 36th ballot.

Q390: After the Boston Red Sox won the World Series in 2004, this hurler appeared with his wife Shonda on *ABC's* *Good Morning America*. At the end of the broadcast, he told host Charles Gibson: "And make sure you tell everyone to vote, and vote [George W.] Bush next week." Who was this baseball figure?

Q391: At a campaign rally in Ames, Iowa in 2011, this Republican Presidential candidate made the following statement about government waste: "No greater example of it than this administration sending millions of dollars into the solar industry, and we lost that money. I want to say it was over $500 million that went to the country Solyndra." Which Presidential candidate thought Solyndra was a country?

Q392: In 1988, which Democratic Presidential nominee mocked George H.W. Bush for playing "Santa Claus to the wealthy and Ebenezer Scrooge to the rest of us."?

Q393: Evelyn Lincoln, President John F. Kennedy's personal secretary, claimed that the President told her that he would not select Vice President Lyndon B. Johnson to be his running mate when he sought re-election in 1964. Evelyn Lincoln said that Kennedy was leaning toward choosing which North Carolina Governor instead?

Q394: After a long day of campaigning, which successful Presidential nominee would have his campaign staff massage his head?

Q395: Who are the only Presidents to be elected twice without winning a majority of the popular vote?

Q396: In 1972, which future First Couple, who were both law students at Yale University, spent a semester in Texas working on George McGovern's failed Presidential campaign? The couple never attended class, came in to take the final exams, and both aced them.

Q397: In 1992, after this Democratic Presidential candidate, exhibiting his " fitness" for office appeared in a television advertisement swimming in a pool, Texas Governor Ann Richards averred: "I won't endorse any presidential candidate that looks better than me in a bathing suit?"

Q398: In 1952, which Democratic Presidential nominee said: "Man does not live by words alone; despite the fact that sometimes he has to eat them"?

Q399: This 2004 Democratic Presidential candidate told astronaut Jay C. Buckley: "I would like to see mankind get off this planet. I'd like to know what's out there beyond the solar system. I still believe in $E = mc^2$. But I can't believe that in all of human history we'll never ever be able to go beyond the speed of light to reach where we want to go. I happen to believe that mankind can do it. I've argued with physicists about it. I've argued with best friends about it. I just have to believe it. It's my only faith-based initiative"?

A390: Curt Schilling

A391: Rick Perry. He misspoke. Solyndra is not a "country." It is a failed renewable energy company, which won $535 million in federal stimulus funding before it went broke.

A392: Michael Dukakis

A393: Terry Sanford

A394: Benjamin Harrison

A395: Democrats Grover Cleveland, Woodrow Wilson, and Bill Clinton. Cleveland garnered 48.5% of the vote in 1884 and 46.0% in 1892 (Cleveland served two non-consecutive terms). Wilson mustered 41.8% of the vote in 1912 and 49.2% in 1916. Clinton collected 43.0% of the vote in 1992 and 49.2% of the vote in 1996.

A396: Bill and Hilary Clinton

A397: Paul Tsongas

A398: Adlai Stevenson

A399. Wesley Clark

Presidential Campaigns

Q400: In 1999, this Democratic Presidential candidate bragged: "During my service in the United States Congress, I took the initiative in creating the Internet." Opponents claimed he was taking credit for inventing the Internet." Which candidate made this assertion?

Q401: In 1956, Democratic Presidential nominee Adlai Stevenson poked fun at this Vice President, averring: he "is the kind of politician who would cut down a redwood tree, then mount the stump for a speech on conservation." Who was Stevenson speaking about?

Q402: At the 2004 Republican National Convention, this Vice President said: "People tell me that Senator John Edwards got picked [to run as a Democratic Vice Presidential nominee] for his good looks, his sex appeal, and his great hair. I say to them, 'How do you think 'I' got the job?' Who said this?

Q403: In 1936, which Republican Presidential nominee said in a campaign speech: "Wherever I have gone in this country, I have found Americans."?

Q404: At a 1992 luncheon at the Democratic National Convention in New York, this Texas Governor drew laughter by commenting: "Well, you can put lipstick on a hog and call it Monique, but it's still a pig." She was referring to feckless government programs. Who made this comment?

Q405: After raising $4.1 million at a fundraiser for his 1996 bid for the Republican Presidential nomination, this candidate boasted: "I have the most reliable friend you can have in American politics, and that is 'ready money.'" Which candidate made this statement?

Q406: In 1992, which Democratic Governor told Democratic Presidential candidate Bill Clinton to "save himself the quarter"?

Q407: At the 1896 Republican National Convention, which U.S. House Speaker was asked if the Republican Party would nominate him for President? His reply was: "They could do worse, and they probably will."

Q408: Before the New Hampshire Presidential Primary in 1988, this Republican Presidential candidate was confronted by a heckler who said: "You've voted for tax increases 600 times in your career. How can you defend that?" The candidate responded: "Check back into your cave." Who was this candidate?

Q409: *The Associated Press* asked the 2008 Republican Presidential aspirants the one thing they would want if they were ever stranded on a desert island. Which candidate adroitly answered: "A boat"?

A400: Al Gore. He was referring to his role as the lead sponsor of the 1991 High-performance Computing and Communications Act, which appropriated $600 million for high-performance computing and co-sponsored the Information Infrastructure and Technology Act of 1992.

A401: Richard M. Nixon

A402: Dick Cheney

A403: Alf Landon

A404: Ann Richards

A405: Phil Gramm

A406: Mario Cuomo. Cabriolet Lounge singer Gennifer Flowers alleging that she had a 12-year sexual relationship with Clinton, made public a secret tape recording of a conversation between herself and Clinton. At one point in the tape, Flowers says of New York Governor Mario Cuomo: "I wouldn't be surprised if he didn't have Mafioso major connections." Clinton responded: "Well, he acts like one." Also on the tape, Clinton referred to Cuomo as "a mean son of a bitch." While denying the affair with Flowers, Clinton did apologize for the remark about Cuomo. He averred: "I fumed in private and said things about Mario I regret. Wounds were caused. I want to apologize again for any hurt that was caused to any Italian-American in this region, state or country or anyone else offended." When told Clinton was going to call him to personally apologize, an inflamed Cuomo shot back: "he ought to save himself his quarter. If you're not capable of understanding what was said, then don't try apologizing." When asked if Clinton's remarks would disqualify him from becoming President, Cuomo stated: "The people of the United States of America will decide who the president should be." The two Democratic Governors had a rapprochement, and Cuomo delivered the address nominating Clinton for President at the Democratic National Convention in New York City.

A407: Thomas Brackett Reed. The party nominated former Ohio Governor William McKinley instead.

A408: Bob Dole

A409: Tom Tancredo

Q410: Which former First Lady appeared in an advertisement for Richard M. Nixon in his 1972 re-election campaign?

Q411: U.S. Representative Tom Delay (R-TX) defended the lack of military service during the Vietnam War of the Republican Vice Presidential because: "So many minority youths had volunteered for the well-paying military positions to escape poverty and the ghetto that there was literally no room for patriotic folks like himself." Who was this Vice Presidential nominee that Delay is referring to?

Q412: This 1968 Democratic Presidential candidate stated: "Being in politics is like being a football coach. You have to be smart enough to understand the game, and dumb enough to think it's important." Who made this sports analogy?

Q413: This candidate for the 2008 Democratic Presidential nomination was revealed to be the eighth cousin of Vice President Dick Cheney. He joked: "The truth is, I am ok with it. You know, now I don't want to be invited to the family hunting party." (In 2006, Cheney accidently shot attorney Harry Whittington on a quail hunt in Kennedy County, Texas). Who was Dick Cheney's eighth cousin?

Q414: In 1999, which two Presidential candidates joined forces in a rare bipartisan appearance in support of campaign finance reform?

Q415: In 2007, this Democratic Presidential aspirant mistakenly said: "I want every caucus-goer to know I've been fighting these people and winning my entire life. And if we do this together, rise up together, we can actually make absolutely certain, starting here in Iowa, that we make this country better than we left it." Who made this rather unusual statement?

Q416: This losing Democratic Presidential nominee commented: "Every once in a while, I run into somebody who tells me that she met her husband in my campaign or a husband who says I met my wife. I have to tell you, I caused a few divorces too." Who made this funny comment?

Q417: In 1976, this future U.S. Senator from New York announced his support for Democratic Presidential aspirant Henry "Scoop" Jackson. When asked if his wit would counter Jackson's dullness, he commented: "Don't give me that. The most exciting thing you encounter in government is competence, because it's so rare. The man [Jackson] knows his business." Who was this future Senator?

Q418: In 2011, this Republican Presidential aspirant commented on his opposition to gay marriage: "It's like going out and saying 'That tree is a car.' Well, the tree's not a car. A tree's a tree. Marriage is marriage." Who made this comment?

Q419: In 1975, a reporter asked this Democratic Presidential aspirant how he would feel if his daughter Amy participated in a premarital affair. The candidate responded: "I would be deeply shocked and disappointed – because our daughter is only seven years old." Who was the candidate?

A410: Mamie Eisenhower. Nixon had served as Vice President under her husband, President Dwight D. Eisenhower.

A411: Dan Quayle

A412: Eugene McCarthy

A413 Barack Obama

A414: Democrat Bill Bradley and Republican John McCain. The event was held in Claremont, NH, where President Bill Clinton and U.S. House Speaker Newt Gingrich (R-GA) had shaken hands, agreeing to establish a blue-ribbon commission on campaign finance reform. That commission never came to fruition.

A415: John Edwards. He corrected himself and averred: "Leave it better than we started."

A416: George McGovern

A417: Daniel Patrick Moynihan

A418: Rick Santorum

A419: Jimmy Carter

Presidential Campaigns

Q420: Which Republican Presidential candidate told a rally in Saginaw, MI: "I know human beings and fish can coexist peacefully." Who made this comment?

Q421: In 1988, this Democratic Presidential candidate lambasted opponent Michael Dukakis: averring "Dukakis had an on-air ad in which he basically blamed American workers for the trade problems. I have a motto in my campaign: 'It's your fight too.' I wonder if his (campaign) has a motto, 'It's your fault too.'" Which candidate made this statement?

Q422: In 1928, which opponent of the Republican Presidential candidate described his chief rival, Herbert Hoover, as "a man for whom the party will be on the defensive from the day he is named until the close of the polls on election day"?

Q423: At a campaign stop in Missouri In 1896, this Democratic Presidential nominee noticed that there was no platform from which to deliver his stump speech. A supporter found a manure spreader and rolled it out for him to stand on. The Democratic candidate remarked: "This is the first time I have ever spoken from a Republican Platform." Who made this witty remark?

Q424: In 1980 there was speculation that Independent Presidential candidate John Anderson would select which former U.S. Health, Education, and Welfare Secretary as his Vice Presidential runningmate. The former Secretary told Civil Liberties attorney Mitchell Rogovin: "Vice Presidents are candidates for castration." Who made this remark?

Q425: In 2003, U.S. Senator Tom Harkin (D-IA) hosted each of the major Democratic Presidential candidates in Iowa as part of his "Hear it from the Heartland Series." Just ten days prior to the pivotal Iowa Caucuses, Harkin endorsed which candidate, calling him: "The Harry [S.] Truman of our generation?"

Q426: In 1944, Alice Roosevelt Longworth, the daughter of President Theodore Roosevelt, observed that this Republican Presidential nominee "looks like the little man on the wedding cake." Who was she referring to?

Q427: This 1996 Republican Presidential candidate joked: "President Clinton zigs and zags. He gets up on both sides of the bed every morning. He's the only President we've ever had who feels it's necessary to act out his midlife crisis in public." Who made this joke at President Clinton's expense?

Q428: In 1932, Democratic Vice Presidential nominee John Nance Garner said the policies of Republican President Herbert Hoover were leading _____?

Q429: In 1988, which Democratic Presidential candidate "blindly accepted" an invitation by six outdoorsman he met while campaigning for the New Hampshire Presidential primary to join them in climbing Tuckerman Ravine, a glacial cirque (a valley) in the White Mountains?

A420: George W. Bush

A421: Richard Gephardt

A422: Charles Curtis. He became Hoover's Vice Presidential runningmate that year.

A423: William Jennings Bryan

A424: Joseph Califano

A425: Howard Dean

A426: Thomas E. Dewey

A427: Lamar Alexander

A428: "Down the path of Socialism"

A429: Bruce Babbitt. He later told *The New York Times*: "I learned that it's one of the most terrifying precipices there is -- a sheer 5,000-foot vertical drop off the top of Mount Washington. Dozens of people are rescued there every year. Falling people and their equipment are a common occurrence. The guidebooks helpfully note." He felt that he could not cancel the trip, despite his extreme trepidation: "because that's life on the road in New Hampshire. You go to extreme lengths to win those votes -- all six of them."

Presidential Campaigns

Q430: In 1987, which U.S. Labor Secretary left his department to become the campaign manager for the ultimately unsuccessful 1988 campaign of Bob Dole for the Republican Presidential nomination?

Q431: At the 2004 Democratic National Convention, keynote speaker Zell Miller said to this *MSNBC* Talk Show Host: "Get out of my Face. If you are going to ask me a question, step back and let me answer. I wish we lived in the day where you could challenge a person to a duel. Now, that would be pretty good." Who was Miller fantasizing dueling with?

Q432: Years after losing to John F. Kennedy in his bid for the 1960 Democratic Presidential nomination, which candidate deadpanned: "as a professional politician, I was able to accept and indeed respect the efficacy of the Kennedy campaign. But underneath the beautiful exterior, there was an element of ruthlessness and toughness that I had trouble either accepting or forgetting"?

Q433: In 1984, this esteemed boxer, who had supported Jesse Jackson in the Democratic Presidential primary, switched his allegiance to Republican President Ronald Reagan in the General Election, telling reporters: "He's keeping God in the schools. That's enough." Who was this boxer?

Q434: This Presidential candidate, who has abnormally large ears, said in his closing statement: "We've got to clean this mess up, leave this country in good shape, and pass on the American dream to them [Our Children]. We've got to collect the taxes to do it. If there's a fairer way, I'm all ears." Who was his candidate?

Q435: In 1951, this Democratic President was asked if he would embark on a whistle-stop campaign for the 1952 Democratic Presidential nominee if he were not the nominee. He answered: "I will answer that in a negative way. I will not say that I would not." Who made this statement?

Q436: In 2004, this Independent Presidential nominee did not obtain the requisite 15% in the polls to be allowed on the Presidential debate stage. He told the members of the University of Miami's Faculty Club: "If I could go through the ducts and leap out in a cape - - - that's my dream." Who was this Independent candidate?

Q437: Which Democratic Presidential Candidate said to an Ohio store owner: "Can I get me a hunting license here?"

Q438: Which major party Presidential nominee briefly left the country the day he lost the Presidential election?

Q439: 1924 was the last time that a third-party Presidential nominee won a non-Southern state? What was that state?

A430:   Chris Mathews

A431:   Richard M. Nixon

A432:   Hubert Humphrey

A433:   Muhammad Ali

A434:   H. Ross Perot

A435:   Harry S. Truman

A436:   Ralph Nader

A437:   John Kerry

A438:   Harry S. Truman

A438:   Richard M. Nixon. In 1960, after voting in Whiter, CA, Nixon got into a convertible automobile with a few aides, and traveled to Tijuana, Mexico to eat lunch at Old Heidelberg Restaurant.

A439:   Wisconsin. This was the home state of Robert F. Lafollette Sr., the nominee of the Progressive Party.

Presidential Campaigns

Q440: In 1980, this former Watergate Prosecutor became the honorary chairman of "Democrats for Ronald Reagan." When asked if he thought Reagan was too extreme, he responded: "I would rather have a competent extremist than an incompetent moderate." Who was this Watergate Prosecutor?

Q441: Which Green Party nominee ran twice against Mitt Romney?

Q442: In 2012, which U.S. Representative, who led the Republican Presidential race at one point, was re-elected to her Congressional seat by just 4,298 votes?

Q443: The term "Children's Crusade" was a nickname for which Presidential candidacy?

Q444: This candidate ran for the Republican Presidential nomination as a stalking horse (a stocking horse is a candidate put in place to help another candidate win) for Dwight D. Eisenhower. Forty-one Republican luminaries supported his candidacy until Eisenhower entered the race. Who was this stalking horse?

Q445: The unsuccessful re-election campaign of this President popularized the word "OK." Who was this President who is associated with the term "OK?"

Q446: In 2008, this Democratic U.S. Representative who represented the Western part of Pennsylvania, was asked by a member of *The Pittsburg Post-Gazette's* Editorial Board if Barack Obama could carry his blue-collar Congressional District in the Presidential race. He exclaimed: "There's no question West Pennsylvania is a racist area." After this remark went viral, he apologized. Who made this statement?

Q447: In 1964, the campaign of Republican Presidential aspirant Nelson Rockefeller sent out mailers about an opponent, asking: "Who do you want in the room with an H bomb button?" Who was this campaign opponent?

Q448: In which five Presidential elections were both major Presidential nominees residents of the same state?

Q449: This Democratic Presidential nominee began his speech by accepting his party's nomination by stating: "I'm reporting for duty." Who was this Presidential nominee?

A440: Leon Jaworski

A441: Jill Stein. In 2002, Stein ran against Romney for Governor of Massachusetts. She garnered 3.49% of the vote. In 2012, Stein captured 0.36% of the vote in the Presidential sweepstakes.

A442: Michelle Bachmann

A443: Eugene McCarthy, in 1968. His message of withdrawing U.S. troops from Vietnam struck a resonant chord with scores of young Americans.

A444: Harold Stassen

A445: Martin Van Buren. His was nicknamed "Old Kinderhook" simply because he hailed from Kinderhook, New York. Van Buren became known as "OK" for short. During his 1840 re-election campaign, his supporters created OK clubs. Although the expression OK had been around for some time, Van Buren's Campaign popularized the expression. Van Buren's political adversaries mendaciously claimed that OK originated from his predecessor and ally Andrew Jackson. They alleged that Jackson was a poor speller, and that Jackson believed that OK was the abbreviation for "all correct."

A446: Jack Murtha. Interestingly, Obama lost the District in November. It was the only District where John Kerry won in 2004 and Obama lost in 2008.

A447: Barry Goldwater

A448: 1) 1860. Republican Abraham Lincoln defeated Democrat Steven A. Douglas in 1860. Both candidates were residents of Illinois, 2) 1904. Republican Theodore Roosevelt defeated Democrat Alton B. Parker. Both candidates were residents of New York, 3) 1920. Republican Warren G. Harding defeated Democrat James M. Cox. Both candidates were Ohio Residents, 4) 1944. Democrat Franklin Roosevelt defeated Republican Thomas E. Dewey. Both candidates were New York residents, and 5) 2016. Republican Donald Trump defeated Democrat Hillary Clinton. Both candidates were residents of New York.

A449: John Kerry, in 2004

Presidential Campaigns

Q450: Who were the only five Presidents to win re-election with a smaller percentage of the popular vote than in their first election?

Q451: In 2016, the Libertarian Party fielded a national ticket of two former Governors, Gary Johnson of New Mexico for President and Bill Weld of Massachusetts for Vice President. When was the last time before this that two Governors were on the same ticket?

Q452: In 1988, this Democratic Presidential candidate joked: "Vice President Bush and Senator Dole have been saying some rather nasty things about each other. Senator Dole says the Vice President is not much of a leader, and the Vice President says Senator Dole is not much of a leader. I don't ordinarily agree with those guys but in this case, I agree with both of them. Neither of them is much of a leader." Who made this comment?

Q453 In 1992, Democratic Presidential candidate Tom Laughlin said of this contender: "I think he's a sleazebag. I despise him." Who was Laughlin referring to?

Q454: In 1948, Republican Presidential nominee Thomas E. Dewey was the favorite to win the election. Members of the media were already speculating on his Presidential cabinet. Many agreed that a President Dewey should choose a particular individual to become U.S. Secretary of State. However, Democratic President Harry S. Truman upset Dewey. The next day, the individual to be picked for Dewey's Secretary of State told a reporter: "I'm the former future [U.S.] Secretary of State." Who was this unfortunate individual?

Q455: In 1912, this former President, running as the nominee of the Progressive Party, was shot in the chest by tavern operator John Schrank, a manic-depressive. The former President continued the address, telling the crowd: "I have just been shot; but it takes more than that to kill a Bull Moose." Who was the President who was shot but continued his speech?

Q456: In 2012, Barack Obama became the first Democratic President to win an outright majority in two election cycles, since whom?

Q457: In 1960, this actor wrote a letter to Republican Presidential nominee Richard M. Nixon, suggesting: "Shouldn't someone tag Mr. [John F.] Kennedy's bold new imaginative program with its proper age? Under the tousled boyish haircut is still old Karl Marx - first launched a century ago." Who made this comment?

Q458: Which 1976 Democratic Presidential candidate was fond of saying: "If you are a United States Senator and are not under indictment or in detoxification, you automatically consider yourself as a potential candidate for the Presidency"?

Q459: Which failed Vice Presidential candidate appeared in a commercial for Diet Pepsi?

Presidential Campaigns

A450: James Madison in 1812, Andrew Jackson in 1832, Grover Cleveland in 1892, Franklin D. Roosevelt in 1940 and 1944, and Barack Obama in 2012.

A451: In 1948, the Republicans nominated New York Governor Thomas E. Dewey for President and Earl Warren of California for Vice President.

A452: Michael Dukakis

A453: Tom Harkin

A454: John Foster Dulles

A455: Theodore Roosevelt

A456: Franklin D. Roosevelt, in 1944

A457: Ronald Reagan

A458: Mo Udall

A459: Geraldine Ferraro

Presidential Campaigns

Q460: In 1966, this Republican Vice Presidential nominee ridiculed President Franklin D. Roosevelt calling him "a blundering visionary and fanatic," and said that the New Deal contained "something of Karl Marx equally as much as Groucho Marx." (Karl Marx was the author of *The Communist Manifesto*. Groucho Marx was a comedian). Who ridiculed President Roosevelt?

Q461: In 1940, this Republican Presidential nominee told a crowd in Kansas City, Missouri: "I'm the cockiest fellow you ever met. If you want to vote for me, fine. If you don't, go jump in a lake." Who was this Republican Presidential nominee?

Q462: In 2008, this U.S. Representative with the last name of Edwards was on Barack Obama's shortlist for a Vice Presidential runningmate. Edwards failed to secure the nomination in part because his last name was the same as this disgraced former Democratic Vice Presidential and Presidential candidate. Edwards averred: "I would have to think that a bumper sticker that said 'Obama/The Other Edwards' would be difficult." Who was this "other" Edwards?

Q363: On Election night in 1948, this campaign manager for Republican Presidential nominee Thomas E. Dewey told a crowd at Dewey headquarters: "We now know that Governor Dewey will carry New York by at least 50,000 votes and that he will be the next President of the United States." Dewey did win New York, but lost the election. Who was the campaign manager that made this mistake?

Q464: In 2003, U.S. Senator Joe Lieberman (D-CT) excoriated which opponent for the Republican Presidential nomination for becoming a Democrat "as a matter of political convenience, not conviction?"

Q465: An early edition of *The Milwaukie Journal and The Sentinel* mendaciously said that this man had upset Jimmy Carter in the 1976 Wisconsin Presidential primary. Which candidate "supposedly" had beaten Carter?

Q466: In a 1975 interview, this First Lady said it would be "perfectly normal" if her 18-year-old daughter Susan was having a premarital affair. Her husband joked: "Honey, there goes twenty million votes, but we'll get over it." Who was this First Lady?

Q467: While campaigning for the 1960 Democratic Presidential nomination, who averred: "*Time, Look and Life* [Popular magazines at that time] don't give a damn about dairy prices. They don't know the difference between a corn cob and a ukulele."?

Q468: In 2012, Barack Obama became the first Democratic President to win an outright electoral majority in two election cycles since which other President?

Q469: In 1976, which member of the Democratic high command, and former New York Governor and U.S. Commerce Secretary, said of Democratic Presidential candidate Jimmy Carter: "He can't win the Presidency. I don't even know him."?

A460: Frank Knox. Knox later became U.S. Secretary of the Navy under Roosevelt.

A461: Wendell Willkie

A462: Chet Edwards (D-TX)

A463: Herbert Brownell

A464: Wesley Clark. Clark had voted for President Ronald Reagan and had said "I tremendously admire and think we all should, the great work done by our commander-in-chief, our President, George Bush, and the men and women of the United States Armed Forces. "Lieberman averred: "I was fighting (Bush's) reckless economic strategy while Wes Clark was working to forward the Republican agenda by raising money for the Republican Party." Just two years later, Lieberman lost his bid for renomination to the U.S. Senate, as his opponent, Ned Lamont, tethered him to Bush, for his staunch support for the Iraq War. Bush kissed Lieberman on the cheek after his State of the Union Address. Lieberman subsequently formed "The Connecticut for Lieberman Party" and won re-election. In 2008, Lieberman supported Republican Presidential nominee John McCain. In 2020, he appeared in a television advertisement supporting U.S. Senator Susan Collins (R-ME.)

A465: Mo Udall. Udall made a speech declaring the victory "a very good win." However, the late-night vote then came in, and Jimmy Carter eked out a victory.

A466: Betty Ford

A467: Hubert Humphrey

A468: Franklin D. Roosevelt, in 1944

A469: Averill Harriman

Presidential Campaigns

Q470: In 1976, this comedian said of Democratic Presidential nominee Jimmy Carter at a Hollywood fundraiser with supporters from the entertainment industry: "You've probably never met with people of this level, to which Carter retorted: "No, that's how I got the nomination." Who was the comedian?

Q471: In 2008, this New Mexico Governor endorsed Barack Obama over Hillary Clinton for President. Hillary's husband Bill had nominated this Governor to the posts of U.S. Ambassador to the U.N. and to the position of U.S. Secretary of Energy. Political Consultant James Carville, a supporter of Hillary, observed: "his endorsement came right around the anniversary of the day when Judas sold out for 30 pieces of silver, so I think the timing is appropriate, if ironic." Who was this New Mexican Governor who endorsed Obama over Hillary Clinton?

Q472: On July 14, 1987, this 40-year-old Southern Governor announced that he would not seek the Democratic Presidential nomination, telling a press conference: "I hope I will have another opportunity to seek the Presidency when I can do it and be faithful to my family, my state and my sense of what is right." Who said this?

Q473: In 1940, after Republican Presidential nominee Wendell Willkie bragged about his humble roots, this former first daughter commented that Willkie has: "grassroots in every country club in America." Who made this comment?

Q474: In 1916, this Republican Presidential nominee went to bed believing he had been elected President. When a reporter called his butler to get a reaction to the fact that he had lost the election, the butler responded: "The President is asleep." The reporter retorted: "When he wakes up, tell him he isn't the President." Who is this Presidential nominee who thought he was President?

Q475: Donald Trump said that this candidate would: "take away your guns, destroy your second amendment. No religion, no anything. Hurt the Bible, hurt God." Who was Trump referring to?

Q476: After a bitter rivalry, Republican Presidential candidate George W. Bush garnered the endorsement of this former rival. Bush told *The Dallas Morning News*: "The past is over." Who was the political rival Bush was referring to?

Q477: In 1844, a deadlocked Democratic National Convention nominated former Tennessee Governor James K. Polk for President. This Whig Presidential nominee mused: "Who is James K. Polk?" Who made this comment?

Q478: Which are the only two states Barack Obama carried in the General Election in 2008, but lost in 2012?

Q479: In 1960, John F. Kennedy clinched the Democratic Presidential nomination with electoral votes from which state?

A470: Tony Randall. Randall starred in the hit television sitcom *The Odd Couple.*

A471: Bill Richardson

A472: Bill Clinton

A473: Alice Roosevelt Longworth

A474: Charles Evans Hughes

A475: Joe Biden, his Democratic opponent

A476: John McCain

A477: Henry Clay

A478: Indiana and North Carolina

A479: Wyoming, the last state in the roll call

Q480: In 2012, Mitt Romney and Barack Obama were the major Presidential nominees. Both of their fathers were born outside of the U.S. Where were they born?

Q481: Carroll O'Connor, who played a conservative in the hit series *All in the Family*, was a liberal off the screen. In fact, he appeared in an advertisement for which Democratic Presidential candidate in 1980?

Q482: This state, now a Republican citadel, was once Democratic territory. When it first entered the Union in 1896, the Democratic Presidential nominee, William Jennings Bryan, pocketed 83% of the vote. The record still stands. Which state made such a radical transformation?

Q483: Which 2012 Republican Presidential candidate called for a "9-9-9 Plan?" The proposal supported supplanting the current economic system with a 9-percent tax on business transactions, a 9-percent personal income tax, and a 9-percent federal income tax.

Q484: Who was the first member of the U.S. Congress to endorse Donald Trump for President?

Q485: This Governor broke tradition by traveling to the Democratic National Convention to accept his party's Presidential nomination in person. Who was this Presidential nominee?

Q486: Which Republican Presidential nominee alienated many moderate voters by declaring in his acceptance speech: "Extremism in the defense of liberty is no vice. Moderation in the pursuit of justice is no virtue."?

Q487: In 1991, Democratic Presidential candidate Paul Tsongas proposed a phased-in 50-cents per gallon gasoline tax increase. Playing on his last name, critics gave him what moniker?

Q488: In 1940, this 33-year-old boy-wonder delivered the keynote address at the Republican National Convention. Who was this boy-wonder?

Q489: Who was the first Governor to endorse Mitt Romney for President in 2012?

Presidential Campaigns

A480: George Romney was born in Mexico. Barack Obama Sr. was born in Kenya.

A481: Ted Kennedy

A482: Utah

A483: Herman Cain

A484: U.S. Representative Chris Collins (R-NY)

A485: Franklin D. Roosevelt, in 1932

A486: Barry Goldwater

A487: Paul Taxongas (Paul Tsongas, who ran for President in 1992.)

A488: Harold Stassen, the Governor of Minnesota

A489: Dave Heinemann of Nebraska

Q490: There were three Presidents who lost their re-election bids for another term and who subsequently ran for President again. Interestingly, all three were from New York. Who were these three Presidential nominees?

Q491: In 2020, Joe Biden became the first person to win the Presidency without carrying Florida and Ohio since when?

Q492: Theodore Roosevelt called which Republican Presidential nominee (who faced off against Democrat Woodrow Wilson), "that Whiskered Wilson?"

Q493: In 1996, which Republican Presidential candidate told a crowd in Des Moines, IA: "We've got the worst of the law profession running our country. Somebody has got to go in and cut Washington." He pledged to cut a third of the government bureaucrats: "especially the dummies." He called his critics "a bunch of nuts," and averred: "I don't care. They can all become [Bob] Dole supporters as far as I am concerned." Who made this comment?

Q494: In 1987, which Democratic Presidential candidate ran as "a centrist realist?"

Q495: Which was the only state Wesley Clark won in the 2004 Democratic Presidential primary?

Q496: Which Republican Presidential nominee, known for his taciturn demeaner, similar to President Calvin Coolidge, earned the moniker: "The Kansas Coolidge?"

Q497: In 2007, New Mexico Governor Bill Richardson, running for the Democratic Presidential nomination, averred: "I'm the first Latino – we checked this – to run for President." Who was the actual first Latino to seek a major party Presidential nomination?

Q498: Which Democratic Presidential candidate labeled rival Al Gore: "a Democratic in Republican clothing"?

Q499: What was the term delegated to a Republican who broke party ranks to support Democratic Presidential nominee Grover Cleveland over Republican James G. Blaine in the 1884 Presidential election?

Presidential Campaigns

A490: Democrat Martin Van Buren, Whig Millard Fillmore, and Democrat Grover Cleveland. Van Buren lost re-election in 1840. He split with his party over slavery. Van Buren was an abolitionist. He lost the election, pocketing just 10.1% of the vote. Fillmore (who succeeded to the Presidency after the death of Zackary Taylor in 1850), and lost a bid for a full Presidential term in 1852, was the nominee of the American Party a.k.a. The Know Nothing Party in 1856. He garnered 21.5% of the vote, and won Maryland. Grover Cleveland lost his bid for re-election in 1888. He actually won the popular vote, but lost in the Electoral College. He came back in 1892, and won the Democratic Party nomination again, then upended President Benjamin Harrison in the General Election campaign.

A491: 1960, when John F. Kennedy accomplished that feat.

A492: Charles Evans Hughes. Theodore Roosevelt mocked Hughes as being similar to Woodrow Wilson politically, and that the only difference between Hughes and Wilson was a shave. Hughes had a beard. Roosevelt did however vote for Hughes over Wilson.

A493: Morry Taylor

A494: Al Gore. He excoriated his opponents as being to the left of the mainstream, He stated that the biggest difference between himself and his opponents was that the others would not defend our vital interests in the world when they are challenged. He averred: "Retreat, complacency and doubt are labels that I believe characterize a view in part of the Democratic Party that all five of my opponents have come close to subscribing to." Gore was the most hawkish candidate when it came to the use of military force and the most conservative in the race.

A495: Oklahoma. He mustered 30% in the state, and said: "I leave Oklahoma full of hope."

A496: Alf Landon

A497: In 1980, Ben Fernandez, a Republican fundraiser, co-founder of the Republican National Hispanic Council, and the former U.S. Special Envoy to Paraguay, ran for the Republican Presidential nomination. He appeared on the ballot in 18 primaries garnering 25,520 votes and three delegates to the Republican nomination. He based his campaign on a formidable showing in the Puerto Rico Primary, which effectuated lackluster results. He then dropped out of the race. He also ran in 1984 and 1988.

A498: Jesse Jackson

A499: A Mugwump. They were Republicans who viewed their party's Presidential nominee, James G. Blain, as unethical, and instead, supported Cleveland. *New York Sun* Editor Charles Anderson Dana wrote: "Their mug sat on one side of the fence and their womp sat on the other."

Presidential Campaigns

Q500: In 2004, the daughter of which Democratic Presidential candidate promised that if her father (who was opposed to Gay rights) was elected President, she would be "a live-in lobbyist" for Gay rights?

Q501: 2020, Democrat Joe Biden won both Arizona and Georgia. Who was the last Democratic Presidential nominee to win both states?

Q502: In 1960 which Racial Segregationist won 14 unpledged electors?

Q503: In 1992, a news reporter asked Democratic Presidential candidate Bill Clinton what he thought about the report that the Reverend Jesse Jackson had endorsed which contestant for the Democratic Presidential nomination over him?

Q504: When this General was told by a political aide that the Whig Party had nominated him for President, he replied: "Stop your nonsense and drink your whiskey"? Who was this General?

Q505: Who was re-elected as a Republican to the at-large U.S. House from North Dakota the same day that he lost the Presidential election in 1936 as the nominee of the populist-oriented Union Party?

Q506: Which newly minted Los Angeles Lakers Basketball coach became a surrogate for Bill Bradley's unsuccessful bid for the Democratic Presidential nomination in 200?

Q507: The first selection of a Democratic Vice Presidential nominee since 1944 has always been a U.S. Senator except for which year?

Q508: In 1999, who told *CNN* talk show host Larry King that he would be forming an exploratory committee to run for the Reform Party Presidential nomination?

Q509: Although many consider this four-time Presidential candidate to be a conservative, he held some liberal positions. He began his political career as a populist, known for his early support of Civil Rights and increased funding for Social programs. He also sat on the Board of Trustees of the Tuskegee Institute. Some even called him a Socialist. Who was this four-time candidate?

Presidential Campaigns

A500: Dick Gephardt. His daughter, Chrissy stated: "I want my dad to understand why this is so important to me," she said. "Why should I not be able to marry if my brother and sister can? I'm working on him with this issue. And I can assure you he's listening."

A501: Harry S. Truman in 1948.

A502: U.S. Senator Harry Byrd (D-VA). He won 8 votes in Mississippi, 5 from Alabama, and a faithless elector in Oklahoma. All opposed the Democratic Presidential nominee John F. Kennedy because of his support for civil rights for African-Americans.

A503: Tom Harkin. Clinton's answer took news headlines away from Clinton's message, as the news media focused like a laser beam for the next few days on Clinton's statement. Jackson replied: "I am disturbed by the tone of the blast at my integrity, my character. I feel blind-sided by what I saw and heard him say." The report was later proved inaccurate. Jackson had not endorsed any Presidential candidate. Believing the camera was not on, an incensed Clinton responded: "It's an outrage, a dirty, double-crossing, back-stabbing thing to do. For him to do this, for me to hear this on a television program, is an act of absolute dishonor.

A504: Zachary Taylor

A505: William Lemke

A506: Phil Jackson

A507: 1984. U.S. Representative Geraldine Ferraro (D-NY). She was chosen by Democratic Presidential nominee Walter Mondale (In 1972, Democrat George McGovern's first chose was U.S. Senator Thomas Eagleton (D-MO)). However, he left the ticket after it was revealed that he had been treated with electroshock therapy to treat bouts of clinical depression. McGovern's second choice was former U.S. Ambassador to France Sargent Shriver.

A508: Donald Trump. He averred: "I'm quite liberal and getting much more liberal on health care and other things. I really say: What's the purpose of a country if you're not going to have defense and health care? If you can't take care of your sick in the country, forget it, it's all over. I mean, it's no good. So, I'm very liberal when it comes to health care. I believe in universal healthcare. I believe in whatever it takes to make people well and better." The campaign never got past the exploratory phase, as Trump concluded that he could not unify the fractured party.

A509: George Wallace. While he became a racial segregationist after losing his first run for Governor primarily on economic issues, he had some liberal stances. He called for a National Health Insurance Program, increases in education funding, and Social Security benefits. He made no moves to vitiate his progressivism, averring: "I'm not against spending money – I believe in spending money."

Q510: This 1992 Democratic Presidential candidate, bemoaning the role of emotion in American politics, averred: "I'd be very surprised if Jesus Christ, when he delivered his *Sermon on the Mount*, screamed and shouted. And I suspect it was very moving." Who was this Presidential candidate?

Q511: In 1980, Republican Presidential candidate Bob Dole called on which Democrat to "apologize for bashing Georgia bunnies?"

Q512: Who was the first major candidate for President who was openly Gay?

Q513: In 1976, U.S. Senator Joe Biden (D-DE), a supporter of Democratic Presidential candidate Jimmy Carter, announced that if a certain opponent were to garner the Democratic nomination, he would cross the aisle and support President Gerald R. Ford, should he muster the Republican nomination?

Q514: Leonard "Live-Forever" Jones was a perennial Presidential candidate, running every year from 1840-1864 as the nominee of "The High-Moral Party." He was the only member of this Party. What was his flagship issue?

Q515: The first selection of a Democratic Vice Presidential nominee since 1944 has always been a U.S. Senator with one exception. What is the one exception?

Q516: When Bill Clinton chose Al Gore as his Vice Presidential runningmate, which former Democratic Presidential candidate was critical, averring: "It takes two wings to fly and here you have two of the same wing. When you look at the Clinton-Gore ticket, it's basically conservative"?

Q517: When U.S. Senator Kamala Harris (D-CA) announced her bid for the Democratic Presidential nomination, which California U.S. Senate colleague endorsed former Vice President Joe Biden, instead, stating of Harris: "She's brand new [in the Senate] . . .It takes a little time to get to know somebody"?

Q518: In 2011, *The Daily Caller* reported that this Republican Presidential candidate suffers from migraine headaches? Who was this candidate?

Q519: Who was the first member of a Democratic national ticket to hail from a state west of Texas?

Presidential Campaigns

A510: Bob Kerrey

A511: Jimmy Carter. As the story goes, In 1976, then Democratic Presidential nominee Carter was interviewed by *Playboy Magazine*, and commented: "I've looked on a lot of women with lust. I've committed adultery in my heart many times." This stupefied and stunned many voters, and precipitated a downward spiral in the polls. In 1980, then President Carter swatted with his paddle a rabid rabbit which came onto his boat while on vacation in his hometown of Plains, GA. This is when Dole called upon Carter to apologize for bashing a Georgia bunny. Dole also commented: "This is not the first time President Carter has gotten in trouble with bunnies. It seems to me he had a problem back in the fall of 1976 as well."

A512: Fred Karger. The Republican political consultant and former actor ran for the Republican Presidential nomination in 2012. His best showing was in the Puerto Rico primary, where he came in fourth place.

A513: George Wallace. He was a past supporter of racial segregation. Wallace lost the nomination to Carter.

A514: Immortality. He contended that human beings could achieve this simply by saying prayers and fasting. After Abraham Lincoln was assassinated in 1865, Jones maintained that the act was "retributive justice" for the USA not electing Jones. His orations would attract large crowds, as Jones would jump up and down and whack the table with his cane.

A515: In 1984, Walter Mondale selected U.S. Representative Geraldine Ferraro (D-NY). The first selection in 1972 by George McGovern was U.S. Senator Thomas Eagleton (D-MO). He was dropped from the ticket when it was revealed he had had electroshock therapy for clinical depression. He was supplanted on the ticket with Sargent Shriver, the former U.S. Ambassador to France.

A516: Jesse Jackson

A517: U.S. Senator Diane Feinstein (D-CA)

A518: Michelle Bachmann. She gets treated by medication, and stated: "I'd like to be abundantly clear: My ability to function effectively will not affect my ability to serve as commander-in-chief."

A519: Kamala Harris. She was the Democratic Vice Presidential nominee with Presidential nominee Joe Biden in 2020. She is from California.

Presidential Campaigns

Q520: In accepting the Democratic Vice Presidential nomination, who commented: "We choose hope over despair, possibilities over problems. Optimism over cynicism. We choose to do what's right even when those around us say: "you can't do that"?

Q521: This 1968 this Independent Presidential candidate explained his reasoning for running for President this way: "Why not, I can't dance. Besides, the job has a good pension plan and I'll need a lot of money when I retire." Who made this statement?

Q522: In 1904, which city hosted the Democratic National Convention (which nominated Alton B. Parker for President), the Summer Olympics, and the World's Fair?

Q523: In 1972, which nominee of the American Independent Party commented after Republican President Richard M. Nixon went to China: "I'm not opposed to his visit to China. I'm only opposed to his coming back"?

Q524: In 2000, which esteemed musician ran for the Green Party Presidential nomination?

Q525: In 1984, Notre Dame Football Coach Brian Kelley helped run the Massachusetts campaign of which Democratic Presidential candidate?

Q526: Bill Clinton was introduced by Jimmy Lou Fisher at his initial speech announcing his 1992 Democratic Presidential campaign. What position did Jimmy hold?

Q527: In 1980, this Presidential candidate said of opponent Ronald Reagan: "He's promising to cut taxes by thirty percent, and balance the budget, and increase defense spending, and stop inflation all at the same time. It just isn't gonna work. What I call a voodoo economic policy." Which candidate made this statement?

Q528: Which Democratic Presidential nominee had declined to offer his views on issues prior to his nomination while a New York Appeals Court Judge?

Q529: In their 1976 bid for their respective party's nomination, Republican Ronald Reagan and this Democrat fought for the same conservative voters. After the Democrat lost his Party's Primary in Florida, and his chances at securing his party's nomination were dim, the Reagan campaign ran a television advertisement urging his supporters to cross over and vote for Reagan in the Republican Primary. Who was this Democrat?

A520: John Edwards, in 2004

A521: Pat Paulson

A522: St. Louis, MO

A523 John G. Schmitz. He also averred: "Nixon is the living embodiment of the old political adage that if you get the reputation of being an early riser, you can sleep till 11.... [He] used to rant against Keynesian economics. Now he's bumbling and fumbling in the same policies as the people he threw out. Now, Keynes said he was a Marxist and Nixon says he's a Keynesian. You figure it out....If there were two Gods, Richard Nixon would pray to both of them."

A524: Eric Reed Boucher, a.k.a., Jello Biafra, lead singer of the punk rock band "The Dead Kennedys." His flagship issue was the institution of a maximum wage, telling MTV News: "You can live pretty well on a hundred thousand bucks." He proposed using the accrued tax money collected from those who make over a hundred thousand dollars a year to fund free health care, education and transportation, which would include ground and air travel. Biafra called it "nonviolent extermination of the rich." Biafra lost the election to consumer advocate Ralph Nader.

A525: Gary Hart. Kelley drove Hart around the state in a 1980 Ford Escort.

A526: Arkansas State Treasurer

A527: George H.W. Bush. Bush changed his tune when Reagan selected him as his Vice-Presidential Runningmate, after losing the Republican nomination to him.

A528: Alton B. Parker

A529: George Wallace. A Democratic voter appearing in the advertisement intones: "I've been a Democrat my whole life, a conservative Democrat. As much as I hate to admit it, Wallace can't be nominated, Ronald Reagan can. Both men lost their respective primaries that year.

Presidential Campaigns

Q530: During an interview with *Telemundo,* which two Democratic Presidential candidates could not name the President of Mexico, Lopez Obrdor?

Q531: In 1968, Elvis Presly sported a sign in front of Graceland for which Presidential candidate, who was a personal friend?

Q532: Who was the first African-American woman to be nominated for Vice President?

Q533: In 1920, it appeared imminent that the Nineteenth Amendment to the U.S. Constitution would be ratified in time for women voters to go to the polls. Which Democratic Presidential nominee put on a full-court-press to cultivate the female vote?

Q534: Jo Jorgensen, the 2020 Libertarian Presidential nominee, skipped a campaign rally after being bitten by which winged creature?

Q535: Which Democratic Presidential nominee garnered the label: "The Little Giant?"

Q536: He was one of five finalists to become Jimmy Carter's Vice Presidential runningmate. His grandfather was a Vice President, and his father was twice the Democratic Presidential nominee. Who is this political individual?

Q537: This former Chairman of the Republican National Committee joined the Lincoln Project, which opposed the re-election of Donald Trump in 2020. Who was the Chairman?

Q538: Which successful Republican Presidential candidate ran on the slogan: "A chicken in every pot, a car in every garage"?

Q539: In 1960, which Democratic Los Angeles Mayor endorsed Republican Presidential nominee Richard M. Nixon over Democratic nominee John F. Kennedy?

Presidential Campaigns

A530: Amy Klobuchar and Tom Steyer. Pete Buttigieg could name the Mexican President.

A311: George Wallace, the nominee of the American Independent Party

A532: Charlotte Bass. She was the nominee of the Progressive Party in 1952.

A533: James Cox. In fact, Cora Wilson Stewart, a suffragette who headed the literacy commission for the National Education Association was selected to second the nomination of Cox for President. In addition, the day he was nominated, Cox sent a telegram to the head of the Louisiana Democratic State Committee, beseeching him to reconsider his past opposition to the ratification. Cox lost the election in a landslide to his fellow Ohioan, U.S. Senator Warren G. Harding.

A534: A bat

A535: Stephan A. Douglas, the unsuccessful Democratic nominee in 1860. He stood at 5"4.

A536: Adlai Stevenson III

A537: Michael Steele

A538: Herbert Hoover, in 1928. He was President during the Great Depression.

A539: Sam Yorty

Q540: Where was the first Democratic Presidential primary Robert F. Kennedy entered in 1968?

Q541: Which major Democratic Presidential candidate for President in 1968 supported Republican Ronald Reagan for President in 1980?

Q542: In his 1992 campaign for the Democratic Presidential nomination, which liberal stalwart was the only Democrat in the U.S. Senate to endorse his liberal colleague, Tom Harkin?

Q543: Who was the only Presidential candidate to win the outright majority of the popular vote, but lost the election?

Q544: In his speech announcing his Presidential candidacy, he said: "I believe that together we can make American great again." Who stated this?

Q545: Which Democratic Presidential candidates founded a media conglomerate, now located in Atlanta GA, with over 55,000 employees?

Q546: Which two Presidential nominees were domiciled in Libertyville, IL at some point in their lives?

Q547: During the 1952 Presidential campaign, which Democratic Presidential nominee was photographed with his legs crossed with a hole on his shoe?

Q548: In 2000, which Republican Florida Secretary of State certified George W. Bush as the winner of her state by 537 votes?

Q549: In 1992, Robert Reiner, the actor who portrayed the ultra-liberal "Mike," and Carol O'Conner, who played his ultra conservative father-in-law Archie Bunker in the popular TV sitcom *All in the Family*, appeared in a television advertisement promoting which Democratic Presidential candidate?

A540: Indiana. Kennedy's first campaign stop was at the University of Notre Dame in South Bend. He won the primary, with 42% of the vote.

A541: Eugene McCarthy

A542: Paul Wellstone (D-MN)

A543: Samuel Tilden, in 1876

A544: Bill Clinton, in 1991

A545: James Cox, the 1920 nominee. He founded Cox enterprises.

A546: Adlai Stevenson, the Democratic Presidential nominee in 1952 and 1956 and Jo Jorgensen, the Libertarian Vice Presidential nominee in 1996 and the Libertarian Presidential nominee in 2020.

A547: Adlai Stevenson. The campaign consequentially used the slogan: "I'd rather have a man with a hole in his shoe than a hole in everything he says." There is a statue of Stevenson with the hole in the shoe at the Central Illinois Regional Airport.

A548: Katherine Harris

A549: Jerry Brown. In the advertisement, the duo sings the praises of Brown's proposal for a thirteen percent flat tax. Reiner later said he regretted appearing in the advertisement, after Brown announced that Reverend Jesse Jackson would be his Vice Presidential runningmate should Brown garner the Democratic nomination.

Presidential Campaigns

Q550: In which state did Republican Bill Weld do best in his bid for the 2020 Republican Presidential nomination?

Q551: Which Presidential candidate used the campaign slogan: "Why not the best?"

Q552: Donald Trump won 2,348 delegates for the Republican nomination. How many delegates did his Republican opponent Bill Weld muster?

Q553: When was the last time a candidate, who was not an official candidate at the start of a major party's convention, won the Presidential nomination?

Q554: This California Governor ran for re-election in 1994, promising his constituents that he would not run for President in 1996, declaring definitively: "I'll rule it out." However, just a year later, he broke that pledge and declared his Presidential candidacy. Who was this Governor who had a change of mind?

Q555: In 1980, Democratic Presidential candidate Ted Kennedy suffered a setback when he gave a nebulous answer to Journalist Roger Mudd on the question: "Why do you want to become President?" However, few voters saw the interview live because it was up against the first television showing of what hit movie?

Q556: Which 1984 Democratic Presidential contestant appeared with his wife before supporters in the Bel Air neighborhood of Los Angeles, where he averred: "The deal is that we campaign separately. That's the bad news. The good news for her is she campaigns in California, and I campaign in New Jersey." She then said: "I got to hold a koala bear." He then retorted: "I won't tell you what I got to hold – samples from a toxic waste dump." Who was this Presidential contestant?

Q557: This 1880 Presidential nominee stated that: "the tariff question is a local question." He meant to state that voters would select members of the U.S. Congress to take positions on the issue. However, critics pounced, charging that he was an ignoramus who did not know that this was a national issue. Who was this Presidential nominee?

Q558: In 1988, which Republican California Governor asked Republican Presidential nominee George H.W. Bush not to consider him for Vice President because Democrat Leo T. McCarthy would succeed him as Governor?

Q559: When asked what he would have done differently in his failed quest for the Democratic Presidential nomination, which candidate asserverated: "Have Ross Perot adopt me?"

A550: Vermont, where he mustered 10.1% of the vote

A551: Jimmy Carter, in 1976

A552: One. The delegate representing this vote hailed from Iowa.

A553   In 1952, Adlai Stevenson, the Governor of Illinois, gave an oration welcoming the delegates to the Democratic National Convention. He landed up mustering the nomination.

A534: Pete Wilson. At a press conference announcing the formation of a presidential exploratory committee, Wilson said of his pledge: "When I said it, I meant it."

A555: *Jaws*

A556: Gary Hart. Hart had to backtrack, telling news reporters: "The people of New Jersey know very well that I deeply admire the progress that state has made." His main challenger for the nomination, Walter Mondale, pounced. He said: "The good news is that Gary Hart is coming back to New Jersey. The bad news is that the people of New Jersey are going to vote on June 5." Mondale won New Jersey, while Hart won California.

A557: Winfield Hancock

A558: George Deukmejian

A559: Paul Tsongas. Tsongas lost the primary to Bill Clinton. Perot, a billionaire industrialist ran for President as an Independent that year, garnering 18.9% of the popular vote.

Presidential Campaigns

Q560: Which failed Republican Vice Presidential nominee appeared in a 1979 American Express Commercial averring: "Do you remember me? I ran for Vice President, so I shouldn't have trouble charging a meal. Should I? But I do, that's why I carry an American Express Card"?

Q561: When contemplating a run for the Democratic Presidential nomination in 1987, this Governor averred: "The people who are urging me to run believe I've done all I can for the state – that I can't squeeze blood out of a turnip. But I need to convince myself that things are left in good enough shape so, should I run, they can be managed at a long distance." Which Governor made this statement?

Q562: In 2020, this Wrestler made his first political endorsement, supporting the Democratic Presidential ticket of Joe Biden and Kamala Harris. He called Harris: "A certifiable badass." Who was this wrestler?

Q563: This man, who ran the campaign of his rival for the Republican Presidential nomination, George H.W. Bush, became Chief of Staff to Ronald Reagan. Who was this man?

Q564: Which former New York Yankees Closer, who recorded a record 652 saves, endorsed Donald Trump in his 2020 re-election bid?

Q565: In 1952, U.S. Senator Milton Young (R-ND) stunned the political establishment by announcing that he would support this Democratic Presidential candidate should he win his party's Presidential nomination, labeling him: "superbly qualified." Who was this superbly qualified political individual?

Q566: Which President, who signed the Independent Treasury Act into law, ran for re-election on the slogan: "Independent Treasury and Liberty"?

Q567: In 2020, Republican Governor Wanda Vazquez Garced endorsed Donald Trump for President? Which American territory was she from?

Q568: In 2016, John Zaccaro Jr. was elected by 21 votes as the Mayor of Saltaire LI, located on Fire Island. He is the son of which Democratic Vice Presidential nominee?

Q569: Which Democratic Presidential candidate, who attacked opponent Bill Clinton during the primary campaign as "unprincipled' and "a panderbear," endorsed him after losing, subsequently averring: "Bill Clinton is a healer by instinct and that skill will be critical as we come to understand the pulls and tugs of our multi-cultural society"?

Presidential Campaigns

A560: William Miller, who ran as the Vice Presidential runningmate with Barry Goldwater in 1964.

A561: Bill Clinton. Ultimately, he chose not to run. He ran for re-election as Governor in 1990, and then ran for President in 1992 while governing Arkansas from a distance. Lieutenant Governor Jim Guy Tucker served by law as Governor when Clinton was out of state.

A562: Wayne "The Rock" Johnson

A563: James Baker

A564: Mariano Rivera. He served on Trump's Opioid Drug Abuse Commission and as the co-chair of the President's Council on Sports, Fitness, and Nutrition.

A655: Richard Russell. Some prominent North Dakota Republicans called on Young to resign from the party. He did not.

A566: Martin Van Buren. He lost his 1840 re-election bid to William Henry Harrison.

A567: Puerto Rico

A568: Geraldine Ferraro. Vermont Governor Peter Shumlin pardoned Zaccaro, who had been convicted for selling a quarter of a gram of cocaine to an undercover police officer while a student at Middlebury College in Middlebury, VT, when he was a student there in 1988.

A569: Paul Tsongas. As for Tsongas' earlier statement, he averred: "It was a campaign. Campaigns are tough. People make tough statements and I did, and others did as well."

Q570: The mother of which Republican Presidential nominee died at age 108?

Q571: Which 2008 Democratic Presidential candidate was often referred to as "Grandpa Mike?"

Q572: With major protests expected at the Democratic National Convention in Chicago in 1968 over his expected nomination, Vice President Hubert Humphrey wanted to move the convention to which city?

Q573: On December 24, 1979, this outgoing Mississippi Governor announced he would run for the Democratic Presidential nomination. He said: "I will be the next President of the United States." Who made this bold statement?

Q574: Which Democratic Presidential candidate averred: "I don't know who created Pokémon Go, but I am trying to figure out how we get them to have "Pokémon Go' to the polls"?

Q575: During election night coverage in 1996, this *ABC News* commentator, believing he was not on air, was caught saying: "Americans could expect four more years of "goddamned nonsense from [Bill} Clinton." He commented that Clinton "has not a creative bone in his body. Therefore, he is a bore –and always will be a bore." Who was this *ABC News* commentator who made these inappropriate remarks?

Q576: On his way to a Presidential election night event in 1996, which Mississippi Governor was critically injured when his sport utility vehicle hit an embankment?

Q577: Which New York Governor was nominated for President at the Democratic Presidential nomination in 1920, 1924, 1928, and in 1932?

Q578: In 2000, which 18-year-old high school student, and future Democratic Presidential candidate won the Profiles in Courage Award from the John F. Kennedy Presidential Library and Museum for his essay on Bernie Sanders?

Q579: When was the first Presidential election where all 50 states and the District of Columbia were counted in the Electoral College?

A570: John McCain, the 2008 Republican Nominee. His mother was Roberta. She died in 2020, more than two years after John McCain died.

A571: Mike Gravel

A572: Miami. President Lyndon B. Johnson opposed this idea, as he had promised Chicago Mayor Richard M. Daley that the convention would be held in his city.

A573: Cliff Finch. Finch said the late announcement was "because I was visiting with my family to make sure I got their permission before I announced." A news reporter asked Finch how many of the requisite 1,000 signatures he had garnered to get his name placed on the ballot for the New Hampshire Primary. He replied: "I don't have a single one." (The primary was just two months away). Finch then went on to say: "I'm going to win. You're looking at the next President of the United States. I waited in the wings hoping that some other candidate of either party would answer the country's cries in the wilderness, but no one has. So, it's up to me." To his chagrin, Finch mustered just 0.25% of the vote in the primaries. His best showing came in Arkansas, where he pocketed just 4.3% of the vote. No major Presidential candidate has run for the Presidency from Mississippi since.

A574: Hillary Clinton, in 2016

A575: David Brinkley. He apologized to Clinton when he interviewed him on the last episode of *This Week with David Brinkley*. Former *CBS News* anchor Walter Cronkite took exception to the apology, averring: "Why shouldn't he have an opinion if he thinks the president is boring? If he's not going to apologize, then the nice thing would have been if he had said: 'Mr. President, you know now that I think you're boring. You've got ten minutes to prove me wrong.'"

A576: Kirk Fordice

A577: Al Smith. He secured the nomination in 1928, but lost the Presidency to Republican nominee Herbert Hoover.

A578: Pete Buttigieg. He was a Senior at South Bend High School in South Bend, Indiana. Ironically, Buttigieg ran against Sanders for the Democratic Presidential nomination in 2020. Both candidates lost to Joe Biden.

A579: 1964, after the passage of the Twenty-third Amendment to the U.S. Constitution was passed, which awarded three electoral votes to the District of Columbia.

Q580: In the 2020 Presidential election, Zapata County, with a population of less than 15,000 denizens, was the only county in the Southern part of which state where Republican Donald Trump lost in 2016, but won in 2020?

Q581: This candidate came in fourth in Iowa, and fifth in New Hampshire, but came back to win in South Carolina, then won the nomination. Who was this Presidential candidate?

Q582: In 1852, Franklin Pierce won the state of Delaware by the smallest margin of any Presidential nominee in any state in Presidential election history. How many votes did he win by?

Q583: The first licensed radio station was *KDKA* in Pittsburg, PA. It debuted on November 2, 1920, broadcasting results of which Presidential election?

Q584: In 2020, 66.9% of eligible voters turned out for the Presidential election. This is the highest rate since what year?

Q585: Which are the only two of the original 13 colonies to have never elected a President?

Q586: This Republican Presidential nominee bragged about how he had balanced the state budget as Governor of Kansas. However, his Democratic opponents pointed out that he did this with revenue allocated from the New Deal program created by his Democratic opponent, Franklin D. Roosevelt. Who was this Kansas Governor?

Q587: Who was the only Democratic Presidential nominee to win Alaska?

Q588: Lenora Fulani, an exponent of Marxist ideology and former Presidential nominee of the New Alliance Party and the Peace and Freedom Party, stunned the political establishment by endorsing which ultra conservative candidate for the Reform Party Presidential nomination?

Q589: When asked what political philosopher or thinker he identified with most, which 2000 Republican Presidential candidate answered: "Christ, because he changed my heart"?

A580: Texas. Many feared Democrat Joe Biden would put them out of work. This largely Tejano area (Hispanic residents of Texas descended from Spanish speaking settlers of Tejas, Coahuila) is largely dependent on the natural gas industry. The area is also socially conservative and opposes most gun control measures.

A581: Joe Biden, in 2020

A582: 27

A583: The Presidential election in which Republican Warren G. Harding upended Democrat James Cox. Only about 100 people listened. For the first time, listeners were able to hear the results live, rather than having to wait to read the results in the newspaper.

A584: 1900, when the voter turnout was 73.7%.

A585: Maryland and Rhode Island

A586: Alf Landon

A567: Lyndon B. Johnson, in 1964. Johnson won the state in a landslide, garnering 65.91% of the vote.

A588: Pat Buchanan. The commonality between Fulani and Buchanan is that they both were economic populists, which included vociferous opposition to international Free Trade deals.

A589: George W. Bush. When pressed by journalist John Bachmann about his answer, Bush responded: "When you turn your heart and your life over to Christ, when you accept Christ as the savior, it changes your heart. It changes your life. And that's what happened to me."

Q590: What does the acronym MATH, used by Democratic Presidential candidate Andrew Yang, stand for?

Q591: In 1984, which Democratic Presidential candidate made political hay by labeling the Democratic frontrunner Walter Mondale as "an agent of Soviet influence" under the tutelage of "an international grain control"? His campaign aired 14 television spots making this case. This resulted in complaints to the local *CBS* affiliates that aired it. Who made these false accusations?

Q592: In 1992, which U.S. Representative labeled Democratic Presidential nominee Bill Clinton: "a goddamned, womanizing draft-dodging son of a bitch."?

Q593: During the 2008 Presidential campaign, at what school did Jill Biden, the wife of Democratic Vice Presidential nominee Joe Biden, teach English four days a week before hitting the campaign trail for the other three days?

Q594: Which 2020 Republican Presidential candidate mocked opponent Donald Trump for having "small hands?"

Q595: Which Republican Presidential candidate ran on the slogan: "Hope, Growth, and Opportunity"?

Q596: Rudy Giuliani, Donald Trump's Attorney, used a landscaping company for a backdrop to discuss his strategy for challenging the 2020 Presidential election? What was the name of this business?

Q597: In 1964, Republican Presidential nominee Barry Goldwater derided the policies of this former President as: "a dime-store new deal." In response, this former President said of Goldwater: "Now I'm convinced he is just plain dumb." Who was this former President?

Q598: In 1975, this dissident, the author of *The Gulag Archipelago,* was suspended from the Soviet Union? President Gerald R. Ford was urged by conservatives, including U.S. Senator Jesse Helms (R-NC), to meet with him. However, Ford was promoting *Detente* with the Soviet Union, and averred that a meeting would not be in the "spirit of *detente*." Ronald Reagan mounted a challenge against Ford for the Presidential nomination, using Ford's failure to meet with the dissident as *causes belie* for a challenge. Who was this Soviet dissident?

Q599: Which U.S. Senator considered running for President in 2020, going on a "Dignity of Work Tour "but chose not to run?

A590: Make America Think Harder

A591: Lyndon LaRouche

A592: Bob Dornan (R-CA). Clinton's Communications Director George Stephanopoulos branded Doran "a lying lunatic - - but entertaining. We don't spend a lot of time worrying about what he's saying." Dornan retorted: "Stephanopoulos is the lunatic, because he's a misguided young jerk. What does that young punk know?"

A593: Delaware Technical and Community College in Dover, DE

A594: Marco Rubio

A595: Steve Forbes, in 1996 and 2000.

A596: Four Seasons Total Landscaping, located in Philadelphia, PA.

A597: Dwight D. Eisenhower

A598: Aleksandr Solzhenitsyn. According to historian Douglas Brinkley, Ford privately viewed the Solzhenitsyn visit to the U.S. as a vehicle: "primarily to publicize his books and drum up lecture dates." In addition, Ford tattooed Solzhenitsyn as "a God Damn Horse's Ass."

A599: Sherrod Brown (D-OH)

Q600: Who was the first First Lady to engage on a whistle stop tour for her husband, as he sought a full term as President?

Q601: Which Presidential candidate at his birthplace in Middlesex PA told the assembled audience: 'Wherever I have gone in this country, I have found Americans."?

Q602: In 1951, U.S. Senator Milton Young (R-ND) stupefied the political establishment by endorsing which Democrat for the Democratic Presidential nomination?

Q603: During the 1988 Democratic Presidential nomination battle, which opponent was the first candidate to excoriate Massachusetts Governor Michael Dukakis for the prisoner furlough program for criminals in Massachusetts?

Q604: Which future Democratic Presidential nominee once averred: "You know, I would like to see more successful business people run for office. I really would like to see that because I do think, you know, you don't have to have 30 billion, but you have a certain level of freedom"?

Q605: In 1972, the Left-Wing People's Party nominated which famed pediatrician as its Presidential nominee?

Q606: Which future Republican President campaigned for the re-election of Democrat Harry S. Truman in 1948?

Q607: Which former Republican Governor garnered just 12 votes in the 2016 Iowa Caucus, then just 133 votes in the New Hampshire primary?

Q608: In October of 1964, both major Presidential candidates, Democrat Lyndon B. Johnson and Republican Barry Goldwater, agreed to a moratorium on campaigning out of respect for the death or which former President?

Q609: In 2016, this Republican Presidential candidate lampooned opponent Donald Trump for his New York pedigree, telling conservative Boston talk show host Howie Carr: "Look I think he may shift in his new rallies to playing 'New York, New York' because you know Donald comes from New York and he embodies New York values. And listen, the Donald seems to be a little bit rattled." Who was this Presidential candidate?

Presidential Campaigns

A600: Lady Bird Johnson. She traveled to eight states in the South on a train called "The Lady Bird Special."

A601: Alf Landon, the unsuccessful Republican Presidential nominee in 1936.

A602: Richard Russell. He designated Russell as: "superbly qualified to become President." Senator Young commented: "No member of Congress knows more about the intricate farm problem or is more sympathetic to them." Interestingly, Young also endorsed U.S. Senator Robert A. Taft (R-OH) for the Republican nomination. Some prominent North Dakota Republicans were appalled that Young would cross the partisan line in supporting a Democratic for President, and called on Young to resign from the party. He did not resign.

A603: Al Gore. He branded them as "weekend passes for criminals."

A604: Hillary Clinton

A605: Benjamin Spock. His platform included an end to U.S. military intervention overseas, and an end to all victimless crime laws, the legalization of abortion and homosexually, and a guaranteed income. His campaign garnered just a tenth of one percent of the popular vote.

A606: Ronald Reagan. Reagan was a Democrat at the time. He became a Republican after the 1960 Presidential election.

A607: Jim Gilmore

A608: Herbert Hoover. Both candidates attended his funeral.

A609: Ted Cruz. When *Fox News'* Megyn Kelly asked what he meant by that statement, Cruz averred: "The rest of the country knows exactly what New York values are." This statement infuriated U.S. Representative Peter King (R-NY) who said: "Memo to Ted Cruz: New York Values are the heroes of 9/11; the cops who fight terror; and people you ask for campaign donations. Go back under a rock." Moreover, King branded Cruz as "a carpetbagger," and when asked if he would support Cruz should he garner the nomination, responded that he "would jump off that bridge when we come to it." King voted for rival John Kasich, and contended: "I hate Ted Cruz, and I think I'll take cyanide if he gets the nomination."

Presidential Campaigns

Q610: At a campaign event in Beaverton, Oregon, a Democratic Presidential candidate meant to say that he had visited 47 states. Instead, he said he visited 57 states. His political opponents had a field day with this, suggesting that he legitimately thought there were 57 states in the U.S. The actual quote is: "It is wonderful to be back in Oregon. Over the last 15 months, we've traveled to every corner of the United States. I've now been in 57 states. I think [I have] one left to go. Alaska and Hawaii. I was not allowed to go to even though I really wanted to visit, but my staff would not justify it." Which Presidential candidate made this statement?

Q611: In 1999, when contemplating a run for the Reform Party Presidential nomination, this individual told Maureen Dowd of The New York Times: "To be blunt, people would vote for me. They just would. Why? Maybe because I'm so good looking. I don't know. [Talk Show Host] Larry King calls and says, 'Do my show. I get my highest ratings when you're on.'" Who made this comment about himself?

Q612: This Democrat delivered the Keynote address at the Republican National Convention, excoriating his Party's Presidential nominee, John Kerry: "Listing all the weapon systems that Senator Kerry tried his best to shut down sounds like an auctioneer selling off our national security, but Americans need to know the facts . . . This is the man who wants to be the Commander in Chief of our U.S. Armed Forces? U.S. forces armed with what? Spitballs?" Who made this comment about candidate John Kerry?

Q613: In 2003, former Vice President Al Gore endorsed which candidate over his 2000 Vice Presidential runningmate Joe Lieberman for the Democratic Presidential nomination, without first telling Lieberman?

Q614: Which former New York Mets slugger appeared on *Celebrity Apprentice*, and served on the Evangelicals for Trump Advisory Board?

Q615: Who are the only two major party Presidential nominees to earn a Ph.D?

Q616: Which 2011 Presidential candidate criticized the Paul Ryan Budget plan as "rightwing social engineering"?

Q617: During his speech announcing his candidacy for the Democratic Presidential nomination, which candidate averred: "Let's be bold – let's join the world and go metric?"

Q618: What was the name of the train Harry S. Truman used during his 1948 whistle-stop campaign for a full term as President?

Q619: What was the campaign slogan that William McKinley used in his successful 1896 Republican Presidential campaign?

A610: Barack Obama

A611: Donald Trump

A612: Zell Miller

A613: Howard Dean. Lieberman told *The Today Show* that he found out about the news: "reading it on a crawl on a television screen. Lieberman had been a loyal Vice Presidential running mate to Gore in 2000. Lieberman had said he would not run in 2004, if Gore chose to run. Lieberman said of Gore "I don't have anything to say today about Al Gore's sense of loyalty, I really don't, and I have no regrets about the loyalty that I had to him when I waited until he decided whether he would run to make my decision because that was the right thing to do." Both Lieberman and Dean lost the nomination to U.S. Senator John Kerry (D-MA).

A614: Daryl Strawberry

A615: Woodrow Wilson earned a PhD in The History of Government from John Hopkins University in 1885. George McGovern garnered a Ph.D. in History from Northwestern University in 1953.

A616: Newt Gingrich

A617: Lincoln Chafee

A618: *The Ferdinand Magellan*

A619: A Full Dinner Pail. It refers to the economic recovery, which occurred under the McKinley administration.

Q620: In 1992, Jacques Barzaghi, a quixotic advisor to a certain Democratic Presidential candidate, offered the following remark: "We are not disorganized. Our campaign transcends understating." He branded rival Bill Clinton as "the groom on the top of the wedding cake. He looks like he slept with a hairnet." However, Barzaghi heaped accolades on his counterpart, James Carville, from the Clinton campaign, commenting that he is: "brilliant, very funny, so messy. He is very real." Which Presidential candidate was Barzaghi working for?

Q621: Which candidate was the first choice of Democratic consultant James Carville and conservative columnist George Will for the 2020 Democratic Presidential nomination?

Q622: In 2007, U.S. Representative Tom Tancredo (R-CO), a candidate in the Republican Presidential nomination sweepstakes, challenged which opponent to drop out if his hometown team loses the World Series?

Q623: Vendors compensated by the 1976 Presidential campaign of President Gerald R. Ford effectuated a button with Ford dressed as which television character?

Q624: In 1960, which Democratic Presidential candidate allocated funds he had saved for his daughter's college education to pay for his last television advertisement?

Q625: It is customary for the delegates from the home state of the Prospective Presidential nominee to stay at the same hotel as him/her. George H.W. Bush afforded this honor to delegates in the state in which he resided, Texas; where he had a summer house, Maine; where he grew up, Connecticut; and which other state?

Q626: Though this U.S. Treasury Secretary was exonerated of charges of taking $10,000 in bribes for influencing a price-support decision, this incident dogged him in his 1980 bid for the Republican Presidential nomination. Who was this Presidential candidate?

Q627: In 1964, which Civil Rights Activist led the Mississippi Freedom Democratic Party (MFDP), which challenged the all-white Democratic delegation to the Democratic National Convention? She gave a noted address on the need for racial equality and about the Mississippi Democratic Party's efforts to block blacks from participating as delegates to the Convention?

Q628: What was the theme song of Franklin D. Roosevelt's 1932 Presidential campaign?

Q629: In 1992, which Democratic Presidential candidate, who was a Governor, announced in his State-of-the-State Address that he was liquidating his Presidential campaign?

Presidential Campaigns

A620: Jerry Brown

A621: Michael Bennett. He dropped out after garnering just 958 votes in the New Hampshire Presidential Primary.

A622: Mitt Romney, the former Massachusetts Governor. Tancredo had challenged him earlier to a clay pigeon shooting contest, but Romney did not agree. That year, the Colorado Rockies, Tancredo's home team, was playing Romney's hometown team, the Boston Red Sox, in the World Series. Accordingly, Tancredo offered a wager with Romney. He issued a statement averring: "I will agree to drop out of the race if the Red Sox win on the condition that you agree to drop out if the Rockies win. Romney declined the offer. His spokesman Kevin Madden maintained: "Governor Romney got in the race for the Republican nomination to win." As an aside, The Boston Red Sox won the World Series four games to zero. If Romney had accepted the bet, Tancredo would have had to drop out of the Presidential race.

A623: Arthur Herbert Fonzeralli, a.k.a., The Fonz. The slogan: "Happy Days are here again" emblazoned over his head, and the name "Fordzie" was placed underneath him. Fordzie is sporting a WIN button on his chest, which is an abbreviation for Whip Inflation Now, a campaign he supported to encourage personal savings, which in turn would curtail inflation.

A624: Hubert Humphrey. In addition to failing to inoculate himself from the draft dodging charges, Humphrey could not overcome the infinite campaign spending of his major opponent, John F. Kennedy.

A625: New Hampshire. After finishing an embarrassing third place in Iowa, Bush's campaign was sputtering. Then, he won New Hampshire, effectuating a juggernaut, and eventually garnering the nomination. The delegates from the state were awarded with "Thank you, New Hampshire rooms." When bush was elected, in his speech, he also bellowed: "Thank you, New Hampshire."

A626: John Connally. He tried to make the scandal a political asset rather than a political liability. While campaigning in Iowa, he told a coterie of dairy farmers: "Let me tell y'all something. None of you have made the sacrifices for the dairy industry that I have. I got indicted because of it. If you think I don't know anything about milk production and milk prices, you're crazy."

A627: Fannie Lou Hammer. Her speaking event was not covered live. President Lyndon B. Johnson was holding a live television press - conference. However, the networks covered it later that day.

A628: *Happy Days are here again*

A629: Douglas Wilder of Virginia. He averred: "Long before I announced for President, I said that if it became difficult for me to govern the commonwealth and conduct a presidential campaign, I would terminate one endeavor." This move was a political masterstroke, in that it allowed him to egress from the race gracefully, as his poll numbers were sagging. Concomitantly it made him seem attuned to the needs of his constituents.

Q630: Which 2020 Democratic Presidential candidate met his future spouse on the Dating App named Hinge?

Q631: Who was the first incumbent U.S. Senator to support the long-shot bid of former Georgia Governor Jimmy Carter for the Democratic Presidential nomination in 1976?

Q632: Which 2012 Republican Presidential candidate tried to distinguish between himself and wealthy Republicans, by calling himself: "A Sam's Club Republican?"

Q633: Donald Trump deliver his last campaign speech in both 2016 and 2020 in which battleground city?

Q634: In 2016, why did Republican Ted Cruz tattoo Donald Trump, his opponent for the Republican Presidential nomination, as: "a sniveling coward?"

Q635: In 1984, Republican President Ronald Reagans offered praise for Bruce Springsteen. What did his staffers say was his favorite Springsteen song?

Q636: Who was the head of the Vice Presidential search committee in 2000 for George W. Bush (which eventually chose Dick Cheney)?

Q637: On what day did President Donald Trump file for re-election?

Q638: What was the campaign theme song for 2012 Republican Presidential nominee Mitt Romney?

Q639: Which 2000 Republican Presidential candidate (a staunch conservative), endorsed Democratic Presidential nominee John Kerry over Republican Presidential nominee George W. Bush in 2004?

A630: Pete Buttigieg. He met Chasten Glezman, then a Master's degree student, at DePaul University in Chicago.

A631: Joe Biden. He was just 33 years old at the time, and said: "I'm not eligible to run, so I will support Jimmy. He told *The New York Times* that if Carter could not be nominated, his second choice would be U.S. Senator Hubert Humphrey (D-MN) : "I'd go with Humphrey because, for all his shortcomings, all of the others have them in spades without the benefits Humphrey brings."

A632: Tim Pawlenty

A633: Grand Rapids, MI

A634: Ted Cruz. He did this after Trump tweeted an unflattering photograph of his wife, Tiffany Cruz. Cruz also said: "It's not easy to tick me off, I don't get angry often . . . but you mess with my wife, you mess with my kids, that will do it every time."

A635: *Born to Run*. The Democratic Presidential nominee Walter Mondale questioned if that was true, and said: "Bruce Springsteen may have been born to run, but he wasn't born yesterday."

A636: Dick Cheney

A637: January 20, 2017. This was the day he was inaugurated as President.

A638: *Born Free* by Kid Rock

A639: Bob Smith of New Hampshire. Both Smith and Kerry are Vietnam Veterans. They served together in the U.S. Senate on the Senate Select Committee on POW/MIA Affairs. Kerry served as Chairman, while Smith served as Vice Chairman.

Q640: Which Republican Presidential nominee, in referencing three-ring binders his staff had made for him with resumes of females who had applied for jobs in his Gubernatorial administration, referred to these binders as: "binders full of women"?

Q641: In 1848 the son of which former President was the Vice-Presidential nominee of the newly-formed Free Soil Party?

Q642: Who did Indiana Governor Mike Pence support in the 2016 Indiana Presidential primaries?

Q643: What was the official song of the 1964 Lyndon B. Johnson Presidential Campaign?

Q644: In 1974, in the last month of his Governorship, this Darkhorse Candidate announced his candidacy for the Democratic Presidential nomination in an address to the National Press Club. Who was this ambitious Governor?

Q645: Who was the first person of ethnically Jewish heritage to garner a major party Presidential nomination?

Q646: When this Democratic Presidential candidate was caught having an affair, Republican President Ronald Reagan quipped: "Boys will be boys, but boys will not be President?"

Q647: Prior to the New York Presidential primary, which candidate said the following about his main opponent, Bill Clinton: "This guy is like Dick Nixon. He's got his own little black book and his gumshoe operation, trying to come up with little statements and dirt on anybody he can find. We're not going to let some guy from an old-style Arkansas political operation put one over on us and the people of New York"?

Q648: Who was the first person to be elected President who was born outside of the original thirteen colonies?

Q649: Who was the last Republican Presidential nominee to win New York City?

Q650: In 2000, which former Republican Presidential candidate *told The Harvard Institute of Politics*: "Just before Super Tuesday, a mysterious ad appeared in three critical states that would decide the Republican nominee. The ad was described by *The New York Times* as flawed in every claim and it savaged the environmental record of Senator John McCain. The committee called itself *Republicans for Clean Air*, which somebody said was an oxymoron had paid $2.5 million dollars for the ad."

A640: Mitt Romney

A641: John Adams. Charles Francis Adams ran with the Presidential nominee Martin Van Buren. The party was opposed to slavery in the new American territories.

A642: Ted Cruz. However, he also praised rival Donald Trump for "giving voice to the frustration of millions of Americans with the lack of progress in Washington, DC."

A643: *Hello Lyndon*, a spinoff of the medley: *Hello Dolly* by Jerry Herman

A644: Jimmy Carter of Georgia

A645: Republican Barry Goldwater in 1964. His father was Jewish.

A646: Gary Hart, in 1987

A647: Jerry Brown. Clinton retorted, by excoriating a negative advertisement Brown ran against him in the state, calling it: "the sleaziest ad I think I have ever seen run by anybody anywhere, anytime since I've been in politics." The two men later buried the hatchet, and Clinton campaigned for Brown in his successful bid to recapture the California Governorship in 2010.

Q648: Abraham Lincoln. He was born in Kentucky in 1809.

Q649: Calvin Coolidge. He won all five boroughs in the municipality in 1924.

Q650: Pat Buchanan. He bolted from the Republican Party and became the nominee of the Reform Party?

Chapter IV

Presidential Families

Presidential Families

Q1: Renowned Singer Johnny Cash was a sponsor for which Presidential brother when he was in Alcoholics Anonymous?

Q2: *C-SPAN* founder Brian Lamb was once a military and social aid to President Lyndon B. Johnson. In that capacity, he accompanied First Lady, Lady Bird Johnson down the aisle during the wedding of First Daughter Lynda Bird Johnson to which future Governor and U.S. Senator from Virginia?

Q3: Which President's father served as U.S. Secretary of War and U.S. Attorney General under President Ulysses S. Grant?

Q4: Prior to becoming President John Adams and his son John Quincy Adams both served as U.S. Ambassador to which nation?

Q5: Which daughter of a future President married future Confederate President Jefferson Davis?

Q6: Who was the only President who left office with both parents living?

Q7: Which former President, as a widower, married his late wife's niece?

Q8: Which President's daughter from his first marriage was anything but conservative. She was a non-conformist, participated in anti-nuclear protests, posed nude for *Playboy Magazine*, and wrote a candid book gossiping about her family. She had no relationship with her family for years, but later reconciled with them. Which President was her father?

Q9: Barack Obama is an eighth cousin of which former Vice President?

Presidential Families

A1: Billy Carter

A2: Chuck Robb

A3: William Howard Taft. His father was Alphonso Taft.

A4: England (The Court of St. James)

A5: Sarah Knox Taylor (the daughter of President Zachary Taylor) married Jefferson Davis; then a former Lieutenant in the United States Army and a future President of the Confederate States of America. Sarah Knox Taylor died three months into the marriage.

A6: George W. Bush

A7: Benjamin Harrison married Mary Scott Lord Dimmick, who was the niece of Harrison's first wife and 25 years Harrison's junior. Harrison's children did not approve of the marriage and boycotted the wedding.

A8: Ronald Reagan. His daughter was Patti Davis.

A9: Dick Cheney

Presidential Families

Q10: The daughter of which President married future U.S. House Speaker Nicolas Longworth (R-OH)?

Q11: Which President served as Governor of Virginia and had a father who served as Governor of Virginia?

Q12: Presidents Theodore and Franklin D. Roosevelt both served in what post?

Q13: Which first daughter was named after a song written by songwriter Joni Mitchell and sung by Judy Collins?

Q14: What three languages were President Herbert Hoover and his wife Lou fluent in?

Q15: The son of which President served as a Selectman in Tansworth, NH?

Q16: Which President's maternal grandparents were second cousins?

Q17: Which President's father, as a member of the Texas State Legislature, was the chief sponsor of a bill for that state of Texas to purchase the Alamo?

Q18: Which President's father was the youngest bank President in America?

Q19: The son of which former President was killed in WW1?

Presidential Families

A10: Theodore Roosevelt. His daughter became Alice Longworth Roosevelt.

A11: John Tyler

A12: Assistant Secretary of the Navy. Theodore served under William McKinley. Franklin served under Woodrow Wilson.

A13: Chelsea Clinton was named after the hit single "Chelsea Morning."

A14: English, Latin, and Mandarin Chinese

A15: Grover Cleveland. President Cleveland built a summer home in Tansworth, NH for his retirement. Tansworth has a population of about 2,500 people. When he was only five-years-old, Francis was staying at the summer home with his mother and siblings when he learned of his father's death. Francis lived in Tansworth until his death in 1995.

A16: John F. Kennedy's maternal grandparents were Mary Josephine "Josie" Hannon and John Fitzgerald (married in 1889).

A17: Lyndon B. Johnson

A18: John F. Kennedy's father, Joseph Kennedy Sr., became President of Columbia Trust Bank at just 25 years of age

A19: Theodore Roosevelt's son Quentin was killed while serving as a fighter pilot.

Presidential Families

Q20: Which President's first daughter married her first cousin in the White House?

Q21: The Babe Ruth Candy bar is named after the daughter of which President?

Q22: Who was elected President the same year his brother lost a bid to become Mayor of his hometown?

Q23: In 1908, the son of which President became President of Williams College in Williamstown, Massachusetts?

Q24: Actor George Hamilton once dated which first daughter?

Q25: Which President's mother was a professional wrestling aficionado? Her favorite wrestler was Mr. Wrestling II (Real name is Johnny Walker).

Q26: Which President had a mother who worked as a Nurse anesthetist, administering anesthesia for surgery?

Q27: At age 92, the mother of which newly sworn-in President made her first visit to Washington D.C. to visit her son?

Q28: Which President pardoned his half-brother on his last day in office?

Q29: Who was the roommate of David Eisenhower (the grandson of Dwight D. Eisenhower) at Phillips Exeter Academy in Exeter, NH?

Q30: The mother of which President gave him the eight-volume essay: *Great Men and Famous Women* by Charles Horn when he was just ten years old?

A20: James Monroe's daughter Maria Hester Monroe married her first cousin, Samuel L. Gouverneur, a former personal secretary to James Monroe.

A21: Grover Cleveland. His 13-year-old daughter Ruth died of diphtheria.

A22: Jimmy Carter in 1976. His brother Billy Carter lost a bid to become Mayor of Plains, GA.

A23: James Garfield. Harry Augustus Garfield was his son and served as President of Williams College. Both Harry and his father graduated from Williams College.

A24: Lynda Bird Johnson, the daughter of Lyndon B. Johnson, in 1966. Lynda invited Hamilton to a White House Dinner after seeing him play Hank Williams in "Your Cheatin' Heart." The fact that Hamilton had a deferment from serving in Vietnam became an issue. Hamilton said he had "extreme hardship to dependents." He was supporting his mother and two brothers. Some observers were outraged, as his mother's fourth husband was the heir to the Spalding Sporting Goods family. The couple broke up, and Lynda married a Marine Corps officer, Chuck Robb. Robb later became a Democratic Governor and U.S. Senator.

A25: Jimmy Carter's mother, Lillian Carter

A26: Bill Clinton's mother, Virginia Kelley Clinton

A27: Harry S. Truman. His mother was Martha Ellen Young Truman. This was also her first trip aboard an airplane. When she saw the press were there to cover it, she bemoaned: "Oh fiddlesticks! If I'd know that, I wouldn't have come."

A28: Bill Clinton. He pardoned his brother, Roger Clinton, for a cocaine possession conviction he received in 1985. Roger had served one year in prison for the crime. The U.S. Attorney who sent Roger to prison was Asa Hutchinson, who later became Governor of Arkansas.

A29: Fred Gandy, who played Burl Smith ("Gopher") on the television series Love boat. Grandy served as a Republican U.S. Representative from Iowa, and unsuccessfully sought the Republican nomination for Iowa Governor in 1994, losing to Terry Branstad.

A30: Harry S. Truman. His mother was Martha Ellen Young Truman. He called it one of his favorite books.

Chapter V

First Ladies

First Ladies

Q1: Which President coined the term "First Lady?"

Q2: Which First Lady is the first-cousin twice removed to President Franklin D. Roosevelt (through her mother)?

Q3: Which First Lady was once a teacher of her future spouse?

Q4: Who was the only First Lady to marry in the White House?

Q5: Which future First Lady served as President of the Young Republicans at Wellesley College?

Q6: Who was the first, First Lady to hold a Press Conference?

Q7: What was First Lady, Lady Bird Johnson's real first name?

Q8: Who are the only two First Ladies whose birthplaces are national historic sights?

Q9: Which former First Lady, who subsequently became an editor at Doubleday Books, edited *Moonwalk* by recording artist Michael Jackson?

First Ladies

A1: Zachary Taylor. At the funeral of Dolly Madison in 1849. Taylor eulogized her by saying: "She will never be forgotten because she was truly our First Lady for a half-century."

A2: Elizabeth Monroe

A3: Abagail Powers Fillmore. She met Millard Powers when she taught him at the New Academy in New Hope, NY. Powers was just two years his senior.

A4: Francis Folsom Cleveland. She married President Grover Cleveland. Mrs. Cleveland was the 21-year-old daughter of Grover's former law partner, Oscar Folsom. Grover Cleveland knew her since she was born. In fact, he was once her guardian.

A5: Hillary Clinton. She had been raised as a Republican. In college, she broke with the party, over their support of the U.S. War in Vietnam and their lukewarm support of Civil Rights. By 1968, Clinton was supporting Democratic Presidential candidate Eugene McCarthy.

A6: Eleanor Roosevelt. The pressers were open only to women. Consequently, many news outlets had to hire their first female reporters to cover the press conferences.

A7: Claudia. The nickname Lady Bird was coined by a nurse who said she was as pretty as a "Lady Bird."

A8: Abigail Adams (birthplace is Weymouth, Massachusetts), and Mamie Eisenhower (birthplace is Boone, Iowa).

A9: Jacqueline Kennedy Onassis. She also wrote a three-paragraph forward to the publication.

First Ladies

Q10: On the second to the last day in office, which First Lady danced on the table in the Cabinet Room?

Q11: Which First Lady played a cameo role of herself on *The Mary Tyler Moore Show*?

Q12: Who were the only two First Ladies whose birthplaces have been dedicated as historical sites?

Q13: Which President and First Lady were fifth cousins once removed?

Q14: Before the British burned down the original White House in 1812, First Lady Dolly Madison made certain that a large portrait of which President was saved?

Q15: Who was the only First Lady to give birth while in the White House?

Q16: Which First Lady taught the hearing impaired?

Q17: Who was the first, First Lady to travel outside the U.S. while in office?

Q18: Which First Lady was the daughter of a college classmate of President Benjamin Harrison at Miami University in Oxford, Ohio?

Q19: What was the birth name of First Lady Nancy Reagan?

First Ladies

A10: Betty Ford

A11: Betty Ford

A12: Abigail Adams in Weymouth, Massachusetts, and Mamie Eisenhower in Boone, IA

A13: Franklin D. Roosevelt and Eleanor Roosevelt

A14: George Washington. In fact, she refused to leave the White House until it was secured by her slave, Paul Jennings. It hangs in the White House today.

A15: Frances Folsom Cleveland, in 1891

A16: Grace Coolidge. She taught deaf children how to lip read at the Clarke School for the Hearing impaired in North Hampton, MA.

A17: Ida McKinley. She visited Mexico for a day in 1901 to participate in a dinner in her honor.

A:18. Helen Taft. Her Father was John Williamson Heron.

A19: Anne Frances Robbins. Her father, Kenneth Seymour Robbins, divorced her mother, Edith Luckett, while Nancy was an infant. Edith subsequently married Loyal Davis, who legally adopted the child and changed her name to Nancy Davis. Her last name became Reagan when she married Ronald Reagan.

Q20: After her husband's loss, which First Lady told the White House Staff her family would be back in four years? She was right.

Q21: The oldest Girl Scout House still in use is located in Palo Alto, CA. The construction was led by which future First Lady in 1922?

Q22: In 1959, which former First Lady starred in a television commercial endorsing *Good Luck Margarine*?

Q23: Which Frist lady enjoyed conversations with Americans via her CB radio, using the handle: "First Mama"?

Q24: In the 1968 battle for the Democratic Presidential nomination, future First Lady Laura Bush, at the time a Democrat, supported which Presidential candidate?

Q25: Which First Lady had the weird nickname of "Sahara Sarah" because she banned hard liquor in the White House?

Q26: Who was the first First Lady to fly in an airplane?

Q27: Which first lady persuaded her husband to disallow alcohol, profanity, and tobacco from the White House?

Q28: Which First Lady was employed by her husband as a clerk, while her husband served in the U.S. Senate?

Q29: Who was the first First Lady to go out in public wearing pants?

First Ladies

A20: Francis Cleveland. Her husband Grover lost re-election to Benjamin Harrison in 1888, then came back to beat Harrison in 1892.

A21: Lou Hoover. At the time, she was the National President of the Girl Scouts of America.

A22: Eleanor Roosevelt. She donated the revenue earned from her appearance.

A23: Betty Ford

A24: Eugene McCarthy

A25: Sarah Polk. Visitors thought that visiting the White House was like visiting the Sahara Desert, a location where no one could get a drink alcohol.

A26: Florence Harding. In 1920, after her husband won the Presidency, Mrs. Harding was a passenger in a seaplane while visiting a Naval air station in Panama.

A27: Lucretia Hayes

A28: Bess Truman

A29: Pat Nixon

Q30: Which First Lady worked in the White House as her husband's personal secretary without taking a salary?

Q31: The wife of this President died more than a year and a half before he assumed the Presidency?

Q32: Which First Lady spent her honeymoon with her husband and his two sons in a Communist nation?

Q33: Well after her husband's death, his former Chief of Staff proposed marriage to which former First Lady, who turned him down?

Q34: Which First Lady while in office wrote the book: *It Takes a Village*?

Q35: Which First Lady spent a fortune furnishing the White House and hid this cost from her husband?

Q36: Who is the only First Lady ever to appear before a Congressional Committee as the lead witness?

Q37: Which world leader did First Lady Jacqueline Kennedy send a letter to on her last night living in the White House?

Q38: After leaving office, which former First Lady had a $25,000 bounty put on her head by the Ku Klux Klan?

Q39: Which two consecutive First Ladies attended Smith College in North Hampton, MA?

Q40: Who was the only First Couple to have no children together?

First Ladies

A30: Sarah Polk

A31: Chester A. Arthur. His wife was Ellen Lewis Arthur. The President performed the daily ritual of ordering new flowers to put in front of her portrait in the White House.

A32: Jill Biden. The Biden family went to Hungary on the recommendation of Hungarian-born U.S. Representative Tom Lantos (D-CA,) a former advisor to Joe Biden.

A33: Grace Coolidge. The Chief of Staff was the widowed Everett Sanders.

A34: Hillary Clinton

A35: Mary Todd Lincoln. She sold the manure that was supposed to fertilize the White House grounds and then fired most of the White House servants to cover the cost of the furnishings.

A36: Hillary Clinton. She did this in 1993, testifying before the U.S. House Ways and Means Committee about Health Care reform.

A37: Nikita Khrushchev, the Soviet Premier. She thanked him for sending an emissary to her husband John F. Kennedy's funeral and urged "restraint" in the Cold War.

A38: Eleanor Roosevelt. She was a vociferous advocate for Civil Rights. The FBI admonished her that they couldn't guarantee her safety when she announced she would attend a Civil Rights workshop in Tennessee. She went anyway.

A39: Nancy Reagan (Class of 1943) and Barbara Bush (Class of 1947). Barbara Bush did not graduate. She dropped out after her freshman year to marry George H. W. Bush and raise a family. She did receive an honorary degree from Smith College in 1989.

A40: James and Sarah Polk

First Ladies

Q41: Which First Lady is the brother of a former Head Basketball coach at Oregon State University?

Q42: Which First Lady had the shortest tenure as an ex-First Lady?

Q43: When inventor Samuel Morse sent his first telegraph message in the U.S., which First Lady answered it?

Q44: In 1968, during a White House luncheon about juvenile delinquency, this famous singer told First Lady, Lady Bird Johnson: "Boys I know across the nation feel it doesn't pay to be a good guy. They figure with a record they don't have to go off to Vietnam. You send the best of this country off to be shot and maimed. They rebel in the street. They will take pot and they will get high. They don't want to go to school because they're going to be snatched off from their mothers to be shot in Vietnam." Who was this famous singer?

Q45: Who was the first Italian American First Lady?

Q46: Which First Lady had her daughter Abbey supplant her at social gatherings because she had an injured ankle which had not fully healed?

Q47: Jane Pierce hated politics, and spent much of her time alone in the White House writing letters to her deceased son. Varina Davis filled in for her at many social gatherings. Who was Varina Davis' husband?

Q48: Who is the only First Lady to be given an honorary seat in the U.S. Congress?

Q49: Which First Lady garnered praise from U.S. Senator Ted Cruz (R-TX) for not wearing a head scarf while in Saudi Arabia? Cruz praised her "for standing up for women & refusing to wear Sharia-mandated head-scarf in Saudi Arabia. Nicely done."

A41: Michelle Obama. Her brother is Craig Robinson.

A42: Abagail Fillmore. She developed a cold, which became a fever, then bronchitis while attending the inauguration of her husband's successor, Franklin Pierce. She died from the malady just 33 days after leaving the White House.

A43: Dolly Madison

A44: Eartha Kitt. After that remark, which stunned the assembled audience, she was blacklisted in the U.S. The CIA kept a dossier on her.

A45: Jill Biden. Her great grandmother emigrated to the U.S. from Southern Italy in 1900.

A46: Abagail Fillmore

A47: Jefferson Davis, the future President of the Confederate States of America. At the time, he was U.S. Secretary of War.

A48: Dolly Madison

A49: Michelle Obama. King Salman bin Abdulaziz Al Saud and many members of the Saudi Royal family refused to greet her.

Chapter VI

Vice Presidents

Vice Presidents

Q1: Who is the only Vice President to be honored on a U.S. Postage stamp?

Q2: Which Vice President during his second term as Vice President (from 1821-1825), became an alcoholic and would regularly preside over the U.S. Senate while drunk?

Q3: Kamala Harris was born on October 20, 1964. This was the same day that a former President died. Who was this former President?

Q4: Who was the only Vice President to marry while in office?

Q5: Who were the only two Vice Presidents who previously served as Speaker of the U.S. House of Representatives?

Q6: Who was the youngest Vice President?

Q7: Which Vice President, who served from 1837-1841, with President Martin Van Buren, believed that the U.S. Postal Service should not be allowed to deliver mail on Sundays because it was a violation of Church and State?

Q8: What number Vice President is Kamala Harris?

Q9: Who were the only three members of the U.S. Senate to vote against the confirmation of Gerald R. Ford to succeed Spiro Agnew, who resigned as Vice President in 1973?

A1: Hubert Humphrey. In 1991, the U.S. Postal Service was forced to spend $580,000 to destroy 300 million of these stamps because the stamp sheets say that he became Vice President in 1964. In actuality, Humphrey was elected in 1964, and assumed the office in 1965.

A2: Daniel D. Tompkins

A3: Herbert Hoover. He died on October 20, 1964.

A4: Alben Barkley (a widower) married Elizabeth Jane Rucker Hadley on November 18, 1949. Hadley wrote the book *Marrying the Veep*.

A5: Schuyler Colfax Jr. (1869-1873) and John Nance Gardner (1933-1941)

A6: John C. Breckinridge assumed office in 1857 at 36 years of age.

A7: Richard M. Johnson

A8: 48

A9: Thomas Eagleton (D-MO), William Hathaway (D-ME), and Gaylord Nelson (D-WI)

Vice Presidents

Q10: Which Vice President had the shortest retirement?

Q11: When Vice President Spiro Agnew resigned in 1973, who was Richard M. Nixon's first choice to succeed him?

Q12: Out of the 1,115 members of Harvard University Class of 1969, just 12 graduates served in the Vietnam War. Which future Vice President was a member of this group?

Q13: Which future Vice President wrote the 1912 song: *Melody in A Major*?

Q14: Who was the first Vice President to attend Presidential Cabinet meetings?

Q15: Which future actor and director was roommates with future Vice President Al Gore while at Harvard University?

Q16: Who is the only Vice President with Native American ancestry?

Q17: Which Vice President earned the moniker: "The Cast Iron Man" for his intransigence in defending the principle of States' Rights?

Q18: Who is the only wife of a Vice President to hold an elective office?

Q19: Who was the only President to have two Vice Presidents die during his administration?

Vice Presidents

A10: Daniel D. Tompkins, who died in 1825, just 99 days after leaving office.

A11: John Connally. He served as U.S. Treasury Secretary John Connally. Congressional leaders told Nixon that Connally would have problems being confirmed, so Nixon went with his second choice, U.S. House Minority Leader Gerald R. Ford (R-MI). A year later, Nixon was forced to resign from office, and Ford became President.

A12: Al Gore. He served as an Army journalist with *The Castle Courier*.

A13: Charles W. Dawes. In 1958, with the name changed to: *It's all in the Game*, it became a number one hit single sang by Tommy Edwards.

A14: Alben Barkley

A15: Tommy Lee Jones. Both Gore and Jones inspired, in part, the book *Love Story* by Author Erich Segal, who was on sabbatical from Harvard at the time.

A16: Charles Curtis was 1/8 Kaw native American.

A17: John C. Calhoun

A18: U.S. Senator Muriel Humphrey (D-MN). She was appointed by Governor Rudy Perpich to fill the remaining three years of her husband's U.S. Senate Term. Her husband was former Vice President Hubert Humphrey.

A19: James Madison. Both Elbridge Gerry and George Clinton died of heart failure.

Vice Presidents

Q20: Which Vice President lived the longest?

Q21: The term "Veep" stands for Vice President. The grandson of which Vice President coined the term?

Q22: This Vice President is no fan of rap music. In fact, he told *The Washington Times*: "I have trouble even following it." Who made this statement?

Q23: Who was the first Vice President to preside over a Presidential Cabinet meeting?

Q24: Which future Vice President earned the unfortunate moniker of "Headsman" because during his stint as Assistant Postmaster General, he fired 40,000 postmasters?

Q25: In 1976, this Vice President was delivering a speech in Binghamton, NY, when a spectator heckled him. In response, and in public view, this Vice President gave him the middle finger. Who was this Vice President?

Q26: Who was the first Vice President to receive an office in the West Wing of the White House?

Q27: This Vice President was awarded a $34 million retirement package when he left his job as CEO of Halliburton. Who was this Vice President?

Q28: Which Vice President served the shortest tenure in office?

Q29: In 1807, a U.S. official arrested which former Vice President on charges of Treason?

Vice Presidents

A20: John Nance Garner. He served from 1933-1941. He died in 1967, just 15 days short of turning 99 years of age.

A21: Alben Barkley

A22: Dick Cheney

A23: Richard M. Nixon. He did this while President Dwight D. Eisenhower was recovering from a heart attack.

A24: Adlai E. Stevenson

A25: Nelson Rockefeller

A26: Walter Mondale

A27: Dick Cheney

A28: John Tyler. He served for just 31 days, assuming the Presidency upon the death of President William Henry Harrison.

A29: Aaron Burr. It was alleged that Burr had organized an unauthorized military adventure to overthrow Spanish power in Mexico. However, the U.S. Court of Appeals for the Fourth Circuit acquitted Burr, despite intense pressure by President Thomas Jefferson and his Administration to convict him.

Q30: Which Vice President was sworn into office in Cuba?

Q31: Al Gore, a High School Senior at St. Albans School in Washington, D.C, applied to just one college, to which he was accepted and graduated from. In addition, all four of Gore's offspring were accepted and graduated. Which college did they all graduate from?

Q32: Why did Vice President Richard M. Johnson take a nine-month leave of office?

Q33: Which Vice President was rejected twice when he tried to join the U.S. military during WWII because he suffered from a hernia?

Q34: Who were the only two Vice Presidents to resign their office?

Q35: Who was the first Vice President to die while in office?

Q36: Which Vice President habitually got his teeth cleaned on election days when his name was on the ballot?

Q37: The Vice President earns a pension after how many years of Service?

Q38: In 1932, which Vice President opened the Olympic games in Los Angeles, CA?

Q39: In 1850, which former Vice President won a seat in the Kentucky State Legislature?

Vice Presidents

A30: William Rufus King, in 1853. He suffered from tuberculosis and was in Cuba trying to get healthy. He died just 45 days into his term.

A31: Harvard University

A32: To open up a tavern and spa in White Sulphur Spring, Kentucky. He did this because of his financial problems stemming from the Panic of 1837, which was a financial depression that spread across the country. The spa became successful. However, it proved to be a political liability for the administration of President Martin Van Buren. Johnson was spending an inordinate amount of time running the tavern and spa at the expense of his job as Vice President.

A33: Hubert Humphrey

A34: John C. Calhoun and Spiro Agnew. Calhoun resigned in 1832 in protest over President Andrew Jackson's support of the Tariff Act of 1832 and to seek a seat in the U.S. Senate representing South Carolina (He won that seat). Spiro Agnew resigned in 1973 after pleading nolo contender (no contest) to charges of not reporting income to the government.

A35: Elbridge Gerry, in 1814

A36: Dan Quayle

A37: Five years

A38: Charles Curtis. He served as Vice President under Herbert Hoover. This is the first time any member of the Executive branch preformed this feat.

A39: Richard M. Johnson

Vice Presidents

Q40: When Hubert Humphrey became Vice President, Minnesota Governor Karl Rolvaag appointed which person to fill Humphrey's U.S. Senate term?

Q41: Who was the first Vice President to have a Secret Service Guard?

Q42: Who were the only two Vice Presidents to serve under two Presidents?

Q43: During the 82 days Harry S. Truman served as Vice President, how many times did he actually speak in person with President Franklin Roosevelt?

Q44: This Texan is the only man to serve as U.S. House Speaker and Vice President on the same day. Who was this Texan?

Q45: Who is the only President or Vice President to die on his birthday?

Q46: Where does the Vice President reside?

Q47: What future Vice President defeated her former boss in her first race for public office?

Q48: Which Vice President cast the most tie-breaking votes in his capacity as the President of the U.S. Senate?

Q49: Which three Vice Presidents won Noble Peace Prizes?

A40: Walter Mondale, who coincidently also succeeded Humphrey as the next Democratic Vice President.

A41: Harry S. Truman

A42: George Clinton, who served under Thomas Jefferson and James Madison, and John C. Calhoun, who served under John Quincy Adams and Andrew Jackson

A43 Just 2 times, and Roosevelt never informed Truman about the existence of the Manhattan Project, the project to effectuate a nuclear bomb.

A44: John Nance Garner. He resigned his position as Speaker of the House and assumed the office he was elected to in 1932, the Vice Presidency.

A45: Levi Morton was born on May 16. 1824. He died on May 16. 1920.

A46: The U.S. Naval Observatory. The mansion is located at One Observatory Circle at the United States Naval Observatory in Washington D.C. The mansion was originally built to house the Superintendent of the Observatory. In 1974, the U.S. Congress declared it the official residence of the Vice President. The first Vice President to live there full-time was Walter Mondale, who took office in 1977.

A47: Kamala Harris. In 2003, she unseated District Attorney Terrence Hallinan, the man who had hired her as Chief of the Career Criminal Division. She defeated her former boss by excoriating his low felony conviction rate. Hallinan argued that the reason the conviction rate was just 29% is that his office was employing alternatives to incarceration, such as diversion. Hallinan averred: "We have 3,000 people who are in diversion. That's hell on your conviction rate." Harris made the case that Hallinan was feckless and weak on crime. She sent out flyers to prospective constituents arguing: "Enough is Enough." On the cover was a photograph of a man with a tattooed chest holding up a gang sign, while also holding a pistol. Harris won the election with 56% of the vote.

A48: John C. Calhoun. He broke 31 ties.

A49: Theodore Roosevelt (a former Vice President), for his role as President in negotiating a peace in the Russo-Japanese War in 1906, Charles W. Dawes for his role in framing "The Dawes Plan" which persuaded France to end its occupation of Germany, and Al Gore in 2007 for his efforts to combat Climate Change.

Vice Presidents

Q50: Which Vice President issued a National Performance Review titled: *The National Partnership for Reinventing Government?*

Q51: Who were the only three incumbent Vice Presidents to succeed directly to the Presidency?

Q52: Which Vice President (a former Governor) voted absentee in a mid-term election using his former address at the Governor's Mansion?

Q53: Who was the only incumbent Vice President to be elected to two consecutive terms as President?

Q54: Which Vice President dropped out of Graduate School at the University of Minnesota to help run his father's apothecary?

Q55: Who was the last Vice President not born in a U.S. State?

Q56: Which state was home to the most Vice Presidents?

Q57: Which future Vice President worked as an assistant insurance underwriter?

Q58: Who is the only Vice President who was never a President to have his portrait printed on currency?

Q59: Who are the only two Vice Presidents to have non-European ancestors?

A50: Al Gore. The report made 384 recommendations for modernizing the federal government.

A51: Thomas Jefferson in 1801, Martin Van Buren in 1841, and George H.W. Bush in 1989.

A52: Mike Pence. He was a former Governor of Indiana. His successor, Eric Holcomb, was residing in the Governor's Mansion at the time.

A53: Thomas Jefferson, in 1800

A54: Hubert Humphrey

A55: Charles Curtis. He was born in North Topeka, Kansas Territory in 1860. Kansas was admitted to the Union as a state in 1861.

A56: New York. There were nine. They were Aaron Burr, George Clinton, Martin Van Buren, Millard Fillmore, William Wheeler, Chester A. Arthur, Levi P. Morton, Theodore Roosevelt, and Nelson Rockefeller.

A57: Spiro Agnew. While attending the University of Baltimore Law School at night, he performed his underwriting duties for Maryland Casualty Company.

A58: Thomas Hendricks, who served with Grover Cleveland. His picture appears on the $10 "tombstone" silver certificate.

A59: Chares Curtis, who was 1/8 KAW Indian, and Kamala Harris who is African American and Asian American.

Vice Presidents

Q60: This Vice President disliked the original Vice Presidential seal, which had an eagle dropping its wings. Accordingly, he ordered a new one to be designed with wings pointing upwards. Who was this fussy Vice President?

Q61: Which former Vice President, who had served as Vice President under President James K. Polk, became U.S. Ambassador to England (The Court of Saint James) in 1856?

Q62: After failing out of Yale University, which future Vice President worked as a lineman before returning to school?

Q63: Who are the only two Vice Presidents to visit the American Samoan Capital of Pago Pago while in office?

Q64: Which Republican Vice President's likeness was produced on a watch, which became a very popular item?

Q65: When Vice President Hubert Humphrey resigned his U.S. Senate seat from Minnesota, which future Vice President was appointed to succeed him?

Q66: Who are the only Vice Presidents to have been appointed to office?

Q67: In 1992, Vice President Dan Quayle criticized Hollywood, telling the Commonwealth Club that a certain TV sitcom character who mothered a child out of wedlock contributor to "a poverty of values."

Q68: Which Vice President once hosted a radio talk show, calling himself: "Rush Limbaugh on decaf"?

A60: Nelson Rockefeller. He bemoaned to an advisor: "See that god damn seal? That's the most important thing I've done all year."

A61: George Dallas. He served as Ambassador to the Court of St. James (the United Kingdom) under Presidents Franklin Pierce, James Buchanan, and Abraham Lincoln.

A62: Dick Cheney. After this stint, Cheney matriculated to The University of Wyoming

A63: Dan Quayle and Joe Biden

A64: Spiro Agnew. A joke spread like wildfire that Mickey Mouse sported "a Spiro Agnew watch." Accordingly, Hale E. Dougherty, a California Democrat, effectuated a watch with a caricature of Agnew. Unbeknownst even to him, there became an elephantine demand for the product. Agnew was annoyed that he was styled a cartoon character, and tried to sue Dougherty. The case was settled out of court. In 1973, Agnew was forced to resign after pleading nolo contender to tax evasion. During the Watergate scandal, which led to the resignation of his boss, Richard M. Nixon, the following joke circulated among Nixon critics: "What sound does the Spiro Agnew watch make? Dump-Dick, Dump-Dick." Today, a 1971 model of the famous watch sells for between $50 and $100.

A65: Walter Mondale

A66: Gerald R. Ford and Nelson Rockefeller. Prior to the ratification of the 25h Amendment to the U.S. Constitution in 1967, there was no avenue to supplant a Vice President who leaves office. Once the amendment was ratified, Richard M. Nixon nominated Gerald R. Ford to supplant Spiro Agnew who resigned in disgrace. When Ford ascended to the Presidency after the resignation of Nixon, he nominated Nelson Rockefeller to become Vice President. The U.S. Senate overwhelmingly confirmed both men to office.

A67: Murphy Brown, the lead character of the television sitcom *Murphy Brown,* portrayed by Candice Bergan

A68: Mike Pence

Chapter VII

Vice Presidential Quotations

Vice Presidential Quotations

Q1: In 1812, this Vice President, a supporter of the War of 1812, averred: "We have been at peace too long. A good war will help us." Who was this Vice President?

Q2: In 1930, at the high watermark of the Great Depression, this Vice President erroneously asserted: "Good times are right around the corner." Who was this optimist?

Q3: Which Vice President labeled his office: "the most insignificant office that ever the invention of man contrived or his imagination conceived"?

Q4: This Vice President, who served under Ulysses S. Grant, observed: "I believe if we introduced the Lord's Prayer here, senators would propose a large number of amendments to it." Who was this Vice President?

Q5: Which Vice President averred: "I shouldn't toot my own horn, but he who doth not toot his own horn allowed it to remain 'untoothed'"?

Q6: Speechwriter William Safire wrote the following words, which were delivered by which Vice President: "In the United States today, we have more than our share of the nattering nabobs of negativism. They have formed their own 4-H Club – The hopeless, hysterical hypochondriacs of history"?

Q7: Which Vice President opined: "For NASA, space is still a high priority"?

Q8: This Vice President observed: "I can do only two things here. One of them is to sit up here on this rostrum and listen to you birds talk without the ability to reply. The other is to look at the newspapers every morning to see how the President's health is." Which Vice President made this statement?

Q9: This Vice President, in trying to reference Basketball legend "Michael Jordan," said: "I tell you that 'Michael Jackson' is unbelievable, isn't he? He's just unbelievable." Which Vice President confused Michael Jordan with Michael Jackson?

A1: Elbridge Gerry

A2: Charles Curtis

A3: John Adams

A4: Henry Wilson

A5: Andrew Johnson. Johnson suffered from typhoid fever, which he tried to mitigate by drinking three glasses of whisky. Consequently, he slurred his address, which was quite obvious to the audience.

A6: Spiro Agnew

A7: Dan Quayle

A8: Charles G. Dawes

A9: Al Gore

Q10: When told by Lester Holt on the *NBC* show *Today* why she had not been to the U.S.-Mexican border, Vice President Kamala Harris oddly responded that she had not visited which continent ether?

Q11: Which Vice President penned a letter to his friend Elbridge Gerry (who would later become Vice President himself), writing: "The Second Office of the government is honorable and easy, the first, but a splendid misery"?

Q12: Which Vice President joked that he "used to be the next President of the United States"?

Q13: As a Vice Presidential candidate, he observed: "Perhaps the place to start looking for a credibility gap is not in the offices of the Government in Washington but in the studios of the networks in New York!" Who made this interesting statement?

Q14: This man, who served as U.S. House Speaker, became apoplectic that he left that job to assume the Vice Presidency. He averred: "Worst damn fool mistake I ever made was letting myself be elected Vice President of the United States. Should have stuck with my old chores as Speaker of the House. I gave up the second most important job in the government for one that didn't amount to a hill of beans. I spent eight long years as Mr. [Franklin] Roosevelt's spare tire. I might still be Speaker if I didn't let them elect me Vice-President." Which Vice President made this statement?

Q15: Vice President Dick Cheney told which U.S. Senator to "go f_ _k yourself"?

Q16: Which Vice President in a visit to American Samoa told island residents: "You all look like happy campers to me. Happy campers you are, happy campers you have been, and, as far as I am concerned, happy campers you will always be"?

Q17: Three days before assuming office, this Vice President took a tour of Monticello, the former home of Thomas Jefferson, saw some busts of famous Americans and asked the museum's curator: "Who are these people?" The curator explained: "This is George Washington on the extreme right, with Benjamin Franklin close behind." Who was this soon-to-be Vice President?

Q18: U.S. Senator Barry Goldwater (R-AZ) once commented about this Vice President: "He talks so fast that listening to him is like trying to read *Playboy Magazine* with your wife turning the pages." Who was this Vice President?

Q19: Which Vice President observed: "A good story is like fine Kentucky bourbon. It improves with age, and if you don't use it too much, it will never hurt anyone"?

A10: Europe. Harris continued: "And I haven't been to Europe. And I mean, I don't understand the point you're making. I'm not discounting the point you're making."

A11: Thomas Jefferson

A12: Al Gore. He was alluding to his role in the disputed 2000 Presidential election.

A13: Spiro Agnew

A14: John Nance Garner

A15: Pat Leahy (D-VT). Cheney was indignant at Leahy for excoriating him in his role as ranking member of the U.S. Senate Judiciary Committee for the alleged profiteering of Halliburton (a company formerly led by Cheney) in Iraq.

A16: Dan Quayle

A17: Al Gore

A18: Hubert Humphrey

A19: Andrew Johnson

Q20: While presiding over the U.S. Senate, which Vice President deadpanned: "What this country really needs is a good five-cent cigar"?

Q21: Which Vice President stated: "In real life, unlike in Shakespeare, the sweetness of the rose depends upon the name it bears. Things are not only what they are. They are, in very important respects, what they seem to be"?

Q22: In 1939, Freshman U.S. Representative Wilber Mills (D-AR) met this Vice President and admitted his ignorance of politics and governance. He said: "I just don't know anything." The Vice President replied: "Shake hands with me, boy. That makes you the smartest man who ever came to Washington." Who was this Vice President?

Q23: Which Vice President popularized the catch phrase: "Pleased as Punch"?

Q24: This Vice President commented on his hardscrabble upbringing in Wheel, KY by joking: "We were so poor that we had to use hoot owls for watchdogs." Who made this joke?

Q25: In 1913, which Vice President began his Inaugural Address by stating: "I believe I'm entitled to make a few remarks because I'm about to enter a four-year period of silence"?

Q26: Losing his train of thought while speaking to the United Negro College Fund (UNCF), whose slogan is "A mind is a terrible thing to waste," this Vice President made the following confused statement: "When you take the UNCF model, that, what a waste it is to lose one's mind, or not to have a mind is being very wasteful, how true that is." Which Vice President lost his train of thought?

Q27: Which Vice President observed: "Mediocrity requires aloofness to preserve its dignity"?

Q28: Which President had developed a kinship with Vice President Garrett Hobart, telling his family after his untimely death while in office: "No one outside of this home feels the loss more deeply than I do"?

Q29: Which Vice President averred: "Being Vice President is comparable to a man in a cataleptic fit. He cannot speak. He cannot move. He suffers not pain. He is perfectly conscious of all that goes on, but has no part of it"?

A20: Thomas Riley Marshall

A21: Hubert Humphrey

A22: John Nance Garner

A23: Hubert Humphrey

A24: Alben Barkley

A25: Thomas Riley Marshall

A26: Dan Quayle

A27: Charles G. Dawes

A28: William McKinley. Garrett Hobart. He died of heart disease.

A29: Thomas Riley Marshall

Q30: Which Vice President averred: "There was a mother who had two sons. One went to sea; the other became Vice President; and neither was heard from again"?

Q31: Which President told Vice President John C. Calhoun: "John Calhoun, if you secede from my nation, I will secede your head from the rest of your body"?

Q32: In the 1956 speech at Washington and Lee University, which Vice President intimated that he was now a mere backbencher? His last words in his speech were: "I am willing to be a junior. I'm prepared to sit in the back row. For I would rather be a servant in the house of the lord than to sit in the seats of the mighty." He then had a heart attack and died before ending his speech.

Q33: After leaving the Vice Presidency in 1969, which Vice President commented that the job of Vice President: "is like being naked in the middle of a blizzard with no one to even offer you a match to keep you warm."?

Q34: This Vice President had great power as Governor of New York. He felt bored in the job of Vice President. He summed up his official duties this way: "I go to funerals -- I go to earthquakes." Who made this statement about his job duties?

Q35: Which Vice President said: "I am vice president. In this, I am nothing, but I may be everything"?

Q36: Which Vice President, in reflecting on his days as a pupil at the University of Minnesota, averred: "I had no money to buy books, so between classes and work, I haunted the library. I even tutored in French with a sliding scale of payment: twenty dollars for an A, fifteen for a B, ten for a C, five for a D."

Q37: Which Vice President averred: "In the city of Denver, while I was vice-president, a big husky policeman kept following me around until I asked him what he was doing. He said he was guarding my person. I said: "Your labor is in vain. Nobody was ever crazy enough to shoot at a Vice President. If you will go away and find somebody to shoot at me, I'll go down in history as the first vice-president who ever attracted enough attention even to have a crank shoot at him?"

Q38: Which American statesman said that the Vice President should be referred to as "Your Superfluous Excellency?

Q39: Which Vice President averred: "This is the criminal left that belongs not in a dormitory, but in a penitentiary. The criminal left is not a problem to be solved by the Department of Philosophy or the Department of English—it is a problem for the Department of Justice.... Black or white, the criminal left is interested in power. It is not interested in promoting the renewal and reforms that make democracy work; it is interested in promoting those collisions and conflict that tear democracy apart"?

A30: Alben Barkley

A31: John C. Calhoun. Vice President Calhoun broke with President Andrew Jackson over the issue of nullification (The right of a State to nullify a federal law it deems unconstitutional), and even said publicly that he would support his home state of South Carolina if it deemed it necessary to leave the Union?

A32: Alben Barkley

A33: Hubert Humphrey

A34: Nelson Rockefeller

A35: John Adams

A36: Hubert Humphrey

A37: Thomas Riley Marshall

A38: Benjamin Franklin

A39: Spiro Agnew

Chapter VIII

U.S. Cabinet Secretaries

U.S. Cabinet Secretaries

Q1: What were the four original Cabinet Departments?

Q2: Which U.S. Attorney General served the longest tenure?

Q3: In 1989, which Democratic political operative became the first African-American Chairman of a major political party?

Q4: In 1826, which former U.S. Secretary of State delivered a eulogy for the late President John Adams that lasted for over two hours?

Q5: Who was the first female U.S. Attorney General?

Q6: Which Budget Director under George W. Bush served as a trustee of the Gerald R. Ford Foundation from 1988-2018?

Q7: In 1961, George W. Ball, Undersecretary of State for Economic and Agricultural Affairs, advised President John F. Kennedy that a continued commitment in Vietnam could rise to 300,000 U.S. troops. Kennedy said Ball was: "Crazier than Hell." How many troops were in the country by 1969?

Q8: Who was the first Jewish member to serve in a Presidential Cabinet?

Q9: As a way of rising prices during the Great Depression, U.S. Labor Secretary of Labor Henry A. Wallace recommended that farmers kill 6,000,000 animals? Which animal was he recommending slaughtering?

A1: The Departments of Justice, State, Treasury, and War (now called the Department of Defense).

A2: William Wirt. He served in that post from November 3, 1817 - March 4, 1829. He served under Presidents James Monroe and John Quincy Adams.

A3: Ron Brown

A4: Daniel Webster

A5: Janet Reno. She served from 1993-2001.

A6: Paul O'Neill

A7: 543,000 troops

A8: Oscar Solomon Strauss. He became U.S. Secretary of Labor under President Theodore Roosevelt in 1906.

A9: Pigs

Q10: In 1940, Democratic President Franklin D. Roosevelt nominated which man, who was the Republican nominee for President in 1936, as his Secretary of the U.S. Navy?

Q11: The granddaughter of which U.S. Secretary of State was a roommate with Hillary Clinton at Wellesley College?

Q12: Jefferson Davis, President of the Confederate States of America, was U.S. Secretary of War (Now called the Secretary of Defense) under which President?

Q13: Which two U.S. Secretaries of State are alumni of Wellesley College in Wellesley, MA?

Q14: Which U.S. Secretary of State graduated from the University of Denver at age 19?

Q15: Who is the only U.S. Attorney General to be convicted of a crime?

Q16: Angela Rice, a teacher at Fairfield Industrial High School of Fairfield, Alabama and the mother of U.S. Secretary of State Condoleezza Rice, taught which future major league baseball player nicknamed "The Say Hay Kid"?

Q17: What is the official motto for the U.S. Department of Veterans Affairs? It was It was made official by Director Sumner G. Whittier in 1959.

Q18: Josef Korbel, the Father of U.S. Secretary of State Madeline Albright, taught which future U.S. Secretary of State in International Politics at the University of Denver?

Q19: Who was the last U.S. Secretary of State to become President?

A10: Franklin Knox

A11: Dean Acheson. She was Eleanor "Eddie" Acheson.

A12: Franklin Pierce

A13: Madeline Albright and Hillary Clinton

A14: Condoleezza Rice

A15: John Mitchell. Mitchell served under President Richard M. Nixon. He was sent to prison for the role he played as the head of the Committee to re-elect the President in the cover-up of the Watergate Affair.

A16: Willie Mays

A17: "To care for him who shall have borne the battle and his widow and his orphan." This was from President Abraham Lincoln's second Inaugural Address delivered in 1865.

A18: Condoleezza Rice

A19: James Buchanan. He served under President James K. Polk from 1845-1849.

Q20: In 1914, 50-year-old U.S. Treasury Secretary William Gibbs McAdoo Jr. married the daughter of which President?

Q21: Who served in more Presidential cabinet positions than any other American?

Q22: Who was the first person to direct the CIA as a Presidential Cabinet position?

Q23: Which U.S. Secretary of Defense was prosecuting America's role in the Vietnam War while his son Craig was protesting U.S. involvement in the war?

Q24: In 1966, President Lyndon B. Johnson nominated Robert C. Weaver as the first African-American Cabinet Secretary. What Cabinet department did he run?

Q25: In 1927, the first public demonstration of long-distance television transmission used which U.S. Secretary of Commerce to demonstrate the process?

Q26: Who was both the youngest and the oldest U.S. Defense Secretary?

Q27: Which former Vice President became the Confederate Secretary of War?

Q28: Who was the first member of the President's Cabinet to be confirmed by a tie-breaking vote in the U.S. Senate?

Q29: The longest serving U.S. Cabinet Secretary in history was James Wilson. He served Presidents William McKinley, Theodore Roosevelt, and William Howard Taft from 1897-1913 in what post?

Q30: Who was the only member of Barack Obama's Cabinet to serve for his entire eight-year term in office?

A20: Woodrow Wilson. His daughter was Eleanor. The couple divorced in 1934. The next year McAdoo, then a 71-year-old U.S. Senator from California, married his 26-year-old nurse, Doris Cross. McAdoo was 16 years older than his new father-in-law.

A21: Elliot Richardson. During the administration of President Richard M. Nixon, Richardson served as U.S. Secretary of Health, Education, and Welfare (1970-1973), U.S. Secretary of Defense (January–May of 1973), U.S. Attorney General (May-October of 1973), and as U.S. Commerce Secretary under the administration of President Gerald R. Ford (1976-1977).

A22: William Casey (1981-1987)

A23: Robert McNamara

A24: The U.S. Department of Housing and Urban Development

A25: Herbert Hoover. The transmission was sent from Washington D.C. to an auditorium in Manhattan.

A26: Donald Rumsfeld. He served under President Gerald R. Ford from 1975-1977, being sworn in at age 43. He also served under President George W. Bush from 2001-2006. He left office at age 74.

A27: John G. Breckinridge. He served as Vice President under James Buchanan.

A28: Betty Devos. Vice President Mike Pence voted to confirm her as U.S. Secretary of Education in 2017.

A29: U.S. Secretary of Agriculture

A30: Tom Vilsack

Chapter IX

Cabinet Secretary Quotations

U.S. Cabinet Secretary Quotations

Q1: Which U.S. Secretary of State told the Turkish Foreign Minister Melih Esembel: "Before the Freedom of Information Act, I used to say at meetings, 'The illegal we do immediately; the unconstitutional takes a little longer.' But since the Freedom of Information Act, I'm afraid to say things like that"?

Q2: In 1968, John Gardner, who served as Secretary of Health, Education, and Welfare under this President, gave a Commencement Address at Cornell University in 1968, and stated: "Pity the leader caught between unloving critics and uncritical lovers." Which President was Gardner referring to?

Q3: In 1987, after being acquitted on charges of larceny, which former U.S. Secretary of Labor asked assembled members of the media: "Which one of these offices do I go to get my reputation back?"

Q4: At a 1961 address at the National Gridiron Dinner, John F. Kennedy joked about nominating this man, who had never even practiced law, to become U.S. Attorney General "So he might get a little experience first." Who was Kennedy referring to?

Q5: Which British Prime Minister said that U.S. Secretary of State John Foster Dulles "was a bull who always carried a China Shop around"?

Q6: Succeeding Hillary Clinton as U.S. Secretary of State, he commented: "The big question before the country and the world is: 'Can a man actually run the State Department?' I don't know … as the saying goes, I have big heels to fill." Which new U.S. Secretary of State made this unusual comment?

Q7: Which U.S. Secretary of State made it a point to be strictly non-partisan. In fact, he did not even vote. When a reporter asked him his political affiliation, he replied: "My father was a Republican, my mother was a Democrat. I am an Episcopalian?"

Q8: In a 1985 speech delivered before the U.S. Chamber of Commerce, which U.S. Agricultural Secretary said that an advisory panel on the issue of leasing coal mining was advising him. He said of the panel: "We have every kind of mixture you can have. I have a black. I have a woman, two Jews and a cripple, and we have talent?"

Q9: The wife of which U.S. Secretary of State came to accept her husband's perpetual gambling. A patrician Bostonian once asked her if the gambling distresses her. She retorted: Oh Dear No. He Always Wins."

A1: Henry Kissinger

A2: Lyndon B. Johnson. Gardner had resigned his position in protest of U.S. involvement in the Vietnam War.

A3: Raymond James Donavan

A4: Robert F. Kennedy

A5: Winston Churchill

A6: John Kerry

A7: George Marshall

A8: James Watt. He later issued an apology for that statement.

A9: Henry Clay. His wife was Lucretia.

Q10: In 2010, Australian comedian radio hosts Hanis & Andy scored an interview with this U.S. Secretary of State. The duo gave her a gift, a bag of potato chips. She responded: "I am thrilled. cannot tell you how much this means to me." Who made this funny statement?

Q11: Getting The National Energy Act of 1978 supported by President Jimmy Carter through the U.S. Congress proved a protracted and arduous process. Which U.S. Energy Secretary said: "I understand what Hell is. Hell is endless and eternal sessions of the Natural Gas Conference"?

Q12: In 2013, when Barack Obama nominated this man to be U.S. Treasury Secretary, he noted to the assembled press his loopy signature: "Jack assures me that he is going to work to make at least one letter legible in order not to debase our currency." Which Treasury Secretary was President Obama referring to?

Q13: At a luncheon for the U.S. Conference of Mayors in 1981, which President mistook his Secretary of Housing and Urban Development for one of the mayors, greeting him with the following expression: "How are you Mr. Mayor? How are things in your city?"

Q14: In 2014, this former U.S. Secretary of Defense derided Barack Obama for not receiving a status of forces agreement with Afghanistan. He said: "A trained ape can get a status of forces agreement. It does not take a genius." Who made this statement?

Q15: U.S. Secretary of the Interior Harold Ickes commented on which populist Democratic U.S. Senator from Louisiana: "He is suffering from halitosis of the intellect; that's presuming he has an intellect."?

Q16: This former U.S. Secretary of State commented late in his life: "People say, if the Congress were more representative of the people it would be better. I say the Congress is too damn representative. It's just as stupid as the people are; just as uneducated, just as dumb, just as selfish." Who made this statement?

Q17: Which first female member of a Presidential Cabinet told a reporter: "Being a woman has only bothered me in climbing trees"?

Q18: In defending the warrantless wiretapping program of George W. Bush, which U.S. Attorney General commented: "President Washington, President Lincoln, President Wilson, President Roosevelt have all authorized electronic surveillance on a far broader scale"?

Q19: In 20111, after hearing that the U.S. had killed this world leader, U.S. Secretary of State Hillary Clinton commented: "We came. We saw. He died."

A10: Hilary Clinton

A11: James Schlesinger

A12: Jack Lew

A13: Ronald Reagan

A14: Donald Rumsfeld

A15: Huey Long

A16: Dean Acheson

A17: Francis Perkins

A18: Alberto Gonzales

A19: Muammar Gaddafi a.k.a., Colonel Gaddafi. His official title was "the Brotherly Leader and Guide of the Revolution of Libya." Gaddafi was killed by rebel forces in his country.

Q20: Prior to visiting New Zealand in 1998, which U.S. Secretary of State exclaimed: "I've never been to New Zealand before. But one of my role models, Xena, the Warrior Princess, comes from there"?

Q21: After President Ronald Reagan was shot and incapacitated in 1981, which U.S. Secretary of State told reporters: "I am in control here"?

Q22: When Johanna McGreary of *Time Magazine* asked the U.S. Secretary of State about the existence of an alleged Princeton Tigers tattoo located on his posterior, he replied: "My gosh, I have been investigated by the FBI, the IRS, by the Senate Intelligence Committee. My mail is opened. I don't have any secrets left. That's the only thing I have left, what is on my rear end." Who was this Secretary of State?

Q23: In 1966, French President Charles de Gaulle announced that France was egressing from NATO and said that all American troops must leave France. Lyndon B. Johnson ordered this U.S. Secretary of State to ask De Gaulle: "Does That include all the U.S. troops buried on French soil from the liberation of France?" Who delivered this message to President de Gaulle?

Q24: This U.S. Defense Secretary made the following unusual statement: "... There are known knowns. There are things we know that we know. There are known unknowns. That is to say, there are things that we now know we don't know. But there are also unknown unknowns. There are things we do not know we don't know." Who made this profound remark?

Q25: In 1791, which U.S. Secretary of State wrote a letter to Maryland resident Charles Carol, averring: "The most economical as well as the most humane conduct towards the Indians is to bribe them into peace and to retain them in peace by eternal bribes"?

Q26: After the successful U.S. led invasion of Grenada in 1983, which former U.S. Secretary of State commented: "The Provincetown Fire Department could have done that invasion rather better than we did."?

Q27: At a 1974 World Food Conference in Rome, which U.S. Secretary of State used a fake Italian accent to mock Pope Paul VI for his steadfast opposition to human population control. He averred: "He no play the game, he no make the rules"?

Q28: This U.S. Secretary of Health, Education, and Welfare was a stanch critic of tobacco. Jimmy Carter told in audience in North Carolina that the Secretary decided not to come with him because "he discovered that not only is North Carolina the number-one tobacco-producing state, but that you produce more bricks in the nation as well." Which Secretary was Carter commenting on?

Q29: In 1929, this U.S. Secretary of State announced the shutdown of the State Department's Cryptanalytic unit, the unit that tries to break the codes of enemy communications. In closing down this intelligence unit this Secretary joked to his analysts: "Gentlemen don't read each other's mail." Which Secretary made this comment?

A20: Madeline Albright

A21: Alexander Haig. Actually, the U.S. Constitution delegates that authority to the Vice President. Haig later asserted that he wasn't talking about transition. "I was talking about the Executive branch, who is running the government. That was the question asked. It was not, 'who is in line should the President die?' Vice President George H.W. Bush was in Fort Worth, TX at the time, and thus could not immediately be available to take charge of the Executive Branch.

A22: George Schultz

A23: Dean Rusk. President de Gaulle did not respond to President Johnson's question.

A24: Donald Rumsfeld. This statement was made when responding to a question about the evidence that Al-Qaeda was tethered to Iraq and that Iraq had reconstituted its Weapons of Mass Destruction Program.

A25: Thomas Jefferson

A26: Alexander Haig

A27: Earl L. Butz

A28: Joseph Califano

A29: Henry Stimson

Chapter X

U.S. House of Representatives

U.S. House of Representatives

Q1: Which Republican was the only Republican on the U.S. House Judiciary Committee to vote for all four Articles of Impeachment leveled against President Richard M. Nixon in 1974?

Q2: In 2020, U.S. Representative Justin Amish of Michigan officially changed his party registration from Republican to Libertarian. Who was the last sitting member of the U.S. Congress to serve in a political party other than the Democrats or Republicans?

Q3: Who is the only person to win a case under the Racketeer Influenced and Corrupt Organizations Act (RICO) representing himself?

Q4: Who was the College roommate of U.S. Representative Jerold Nadler (D-NY) at Columbia University?

Q5: In 2006, Keith Ellison became the first Muslim member of the U.S. Congress. During a reenactment of his oath, he used a *Qur'an* owned by which President?

Q6: Who was the first American of Vietnamese descent to serve in the U.S. House of Representatives?

Q7: Who was the only Republican member of the U.S. House of Representatives to vote for a Congressional Resolution calling for the 25th Amendment to the U.S. Constitution removing President Donald Trump from office during his final days in office in 2021?

Q8: Who is the only Maryland House member to serve as Majority Leader of the U.S. House of Representatives?

Q9: When he was a member of the Illinois Legislature, this future U.S. Congressman made headlines for his comic speech after members were given just 20 minutes to review a proposed piece of legislation. He averred on the House floor: "These damn bills that come out here all the damn time . . . at the last second, and I've got to try to figure out how to vote for my people! Enough! I feel like somebody trying to be released from Egypt! Let my people go!" Who made this unusual statement?

A1: Lawrence Hogan Sr. (R-MD)

A2: Vito Marcantonio. He was a member of the American Labor Party, the New York affiliate of the Progressive Party. He lost re-election in 1950. His view that South Korea provoked North Korea in the Korean War contributed to his defeat by Democrat James Donavan.

A3: James Traficant, at the time serving as the Sheriff of Mahoning County, OH. The future U.S. Representative was acquitted on charges of racketeering and accepting bribes.

A4: Political Strategist Dick Morris. Morris managed Nadler's successful campaign for student government body President.

A5: Thomas Jefferson

A6: U.S. Representative Anh "Joseph" Cao (R-LA.) He served for one term, from 2009-2011, representing a Congressional District that was 64% African-American.

A7: Adam Kinzinger (R-IL)

A8: Stenny Hoyer

A9: Mike Boost (R-IL)

Q10: U.S. Representative Nancy Mace (R-SC) holds the esteemed distinction of being the first female graduate from which South Carolina University?

Q11: Which U.S. House member has authored five books on knitting?

Q12: All U.S. House members are required to submit annual financial disclosure forms. Who do they submit these forms to?

Q13: In 1968, Alabama House Speaker Rankin Fite made the first telephone call to which important telephone number? He made the call to U.S. Representative Tom Bevill (D-AL). Bevill was waiting to take the call at the Haleyville, AL Police Station.

Q14: What is the official title of the longest serving member of the U.S. House of Representatives?

Q15: Who was the first U.S. House member who also served on the House Judiciary Committee, to publicly call for the impeachment of President Richard M. Nixon?

Q16: In 1985, Joe DioGuardi (R-CT) assumed office in the U.S. House of Representatives. He became the first member of which profession to serve in the House?

Q17: Who are the only 2 members of the U.S. House of Representatives to vote against both the impeachment of President Bill Clinton in 1998 and the first impeachment of Donald Trump in 2019.

Q18: Who was the only member of the Congressional Black Caucus to vote against the Patient Protection and Affordability Act, a.k.a. the Democrats Health Care Plan, in 2009?

Q19: Who were the only three U.S. House members to serve for at least 50 years?

A10 The Citadel, a military college located in South Carolina

A11: Chellie Pingree (D-ME)

A12: The U.S. House Clerk

A13: 9-1-1

A14: The Dean. The Dean is charged with the duty of swearing in the House Speaker. The Speaker then swears in all other members.

A15: Jerome Waldle (D-CA)

A16: A Certified Public Accountant. Joe DioGuardi was also the first Albanian-American to serve in the U.S. House.

A17: Collin Peterson (D-MN) and Peter King (R-NY)

A18: U.S. Representative Artur Davis (D-AL)

A19: James L. Whitten, (D-MS) 1941-1995, Carl Vinson (D-GA) 1914-1965, and John Dingell Jr. (D-MI) 1955-2015.

Q20: Who was the first Jewish American to serve in the U.S. House Of Representatives?

Q21: Who was the first Chinese American woman to serve in the U.S. House of Representatives?

Q22: Who was the first female to Chair a Congressional Committee?

Q23: Who was the first Socialist to be elected to the U.S. House of Representatives?

Q24: Who were the only two Republicans to sign the Southern Manifesto, which opposed the U.S. Supreme Court's decision requiring desegregation in public schools?

Q25: Who was the first U.S. Representative to use Second Life, a computerized virtual world?

Q26: What U.S. Representative popularized the term: "Waiving the Bloody Shirt"?

Q27: Who is the only Congressional Republican to vote against both the use of force in the Persian Gulf War in 1991 and the Iraq War in 2002?

Q28: Who was the only member of the U.S. Congress to vote against the Authorization of the Use of Force in Afghanistan in the wake of the September 11th hijackings?

Q29: Who was the first Iranian American to serve in the U.S. House of Representatives?

A20: U.S. Representative Lewis Charles Levi, a member of the Nativist American Party (a.k.a. Know Nothing Party). He was elected to represent Pennsylvania's First Congressional District in 1850.

A21: U.S. Representative Judy Chew (D-CA). She assumed office in 2009.

A22: U.S. Representative Ella Nolan (D-CA 1923-1925). She chaired the House Committee on Expenditures in the Post Office Department. She represented the same Congressional District later represented by Nancy Pelosi, the first female House Speaker.

A23: Victor L. Berger of Wisconsin. He was elected in 1910 as a member of the Socialist Party of America.

A24: Jim Broyhill and Richard Poff of Virginia

A25: Ed Markey (D-MA)

A26: U.S Representative Benjamin Franklin Butler (R-MA 1867-1875 and 1877-1879). Butler was an ardent opponent of the Ku Klux Klan. He waved a shirt worn by A.P. Huggins (a Mississippi Superintendent of Schools who was beaten by members of the Klan), on the House Floor while excoriating the actions of the Klan.

A27: U.S. Representative Connie Morella (R-MD)

A28: U.S. Representative Barbara Lee (D-CA)

A29: Stephanie Brice (R-OK.) She assumed office in 2021.

Q30: Who was the first Korean-born American elected to the U.S. House of Representatives?

Q31: Which U.S. House member was the first recipient of the John F. Kennedy Profile in Courage Award?

Q32: Which U.S. House member coined the term: "smoking gun?"

Q33: Who was the first Puerto Rican elected to the U.S. House of Representatives?

Q34: Who was the first female elected to the U.S. House of Representatives?

Q35: Who were the only five Democrats in the U.S. Congress to vote for the impeachment of Bill Clinton in 1998?

Q36: Who was the first geologist to serve in the U.S. Congress?

Q37: Which actor from the television series *Dukes of Hazard* served in the U.S. Congress from 1989 - 1993?

Q38: Who were the only two Catholic Priests to serve in the U.S. Congress?

Q39: U.S. Representative Bob Goodlate (R-VA) and his successor, Ben Cline (R-VA), both attended which college in Maine?

A30: U.S. Representative Chang-jun Kin (R-CA, 1993-1999)

A31: U.S. Representative Carl Elliot (D-AL, 1949-1965) for his opposition to racial segregation and for his support for public schools.

A32: U.S. Representative Barber Conable Jr. (R-NY). The phrase was used to describe a tape he heard in which President Richard M. Nixon told his Chief of Staff, H.R. Haldeman, to tell the FBI not to investigate the Watergate Burglary any further.

A33: U.S. Representative Herman Badillo (D-NY). Later in life, Badillo abandoned the Democratic Party and ran for Mayor of New York in the Republican Primary, losing to Media Mogul Michael Bloomberg in 2001.

A34: Democrat Mary Norton of New Jersey. She served from 1925-1951.

A35: U.S. Representatives Virgil Goode of Virginia, Ralph Hall of Texas, Paul McHale of Pennsylvania, Charlie Stenholm of Texas, and Gene Taylor of Mississippi. Goode, Hall, and Taylor later switched their political affiliation to the Republican Party.

A36: U.S. Representative John S. Wold (R-WY). He was elected in 1968 and served for just one term.

A37: U.S. Representative Ben Jones (D-GA)

A38: They were U.S. Representative Robert Drinan (D-MA, 1973-1981), and Robert Cornell (D-WA, 1975-1981). In 1980, Pope John Paul II decreed that priests not serve in elective office.

A39: Bates College, in Lewiston, Maine

Q40: Who was the only member of the U.S. Congress to endorse a third-party candidate for President in the 2008 General Election campaign?

Q41: What was the name of the houseboat that U.S. Representative Gary Ackerman (D-NY) lived on while in Washington, D.C.?

Q42: The 2021 COVID-19 relief package passed both houses of the U.S. Congress on a party-line vote, with all but one Democrat voting in favor, and all Republicans voting against. Who was the one maverick Democrat?

Q43: How did future U.S. Representative Emilio Daddario (D-CT) pay for his honeymoon?

Q44: Who was the first female to serve in the U.S. House of Representatives?

Q45: If half of the U.S. House Members sign this petition, a stalled bill gets out of committee and goes to the full house for an up or down vote. What is the name of this petition?

Q46: When a U.S. House member introduces proposed legislation, where does it go?

Q47: Who was the only member of the U.S. House of Representative to march with Civil Rights Leader Martin Luther King Jr. from Selma to Montgomery, AL?

Q48: Who is the first openly bi-sexual person to serve in the U.S. House and in the U.S. Senate?

Q49: Who was the first member of the U.S. House of Representatives to take Paternity Leave?

A40: U.S. Representative Ron Paul (R-TX). He supported the candidacy of Constitution Party nominee Chuck Baldwin.

A41: *Unsinkable II.* His first houseboat, named *Unsinkable*, sank in the harbor.

A42: Jared Golden of Maine. He issued a statement reading: "I know there are people who will continue to need assistance getting through the final stages of this pandemic, which is why I have argued that Congress should have addressed their needs with a targeted bill that extends unemployment benefits, funds vaccine distribution, and increases investments in our public health infrastructure."

A43: Daddario was a semipro football player and played a game on his wedding day. He used the paycheck to pay for his honeymoon.   His honeymoon was in 1940.

A44: U.S. Representative Jeannette Rankin (R-MT). Rankin, who assumed office in 1917, was a devout pacifist. She voted against U.S. involvement in WWI. Rankin did not run for re-election, choosing instead to run for the U.S. Senate. She lost. After a two-decade congressional hiatus, Rankin won back her House seat in 1940. In 1941, she was the only member of the U.S. Congress to vote against a declaration of War on Japan following the Pearl Harbor invasion. Rankin questioned if President Franklin D. Roosevelt had provoked the attack.

A45: A Discharge Petition

A46: To the Hopper

A47: Ken Hechler (D-WV)

A48: Kyrsten Sinema (D-AZ)

A49: Colin Allred (R-TX). He did this in 2021.

Q50: What is the only committee in the U.S. House of Representatives which always has the same number of Democrats and Republicans?

Q51: Who certifies that legislation is passed in the U.S. House of Representatives?

Q52: Who is the only member of the U.S. House of Representatives to have voted for the impeachment of two Presidents?

Q53: As Chairman of the Republican National Committee, which U.S. Representative excoriated the moral lasciviousness of the administration of Democratic President John F. Kennedy, after guests were spotted doing the new dance known as "the twist" at a White House dinner?

Q54: This U.S. Representative engaged in a fistfight with a waiter in a Washington D.C. restaurant because he alleged that the waiter was not showing proper deference for a sitting member of Congress. Who was this political brawler?

Q55: In 1964, a coterie of young Republican members of the House of Representatives called "the young Turks" successfully persuaded which veteran Republican to challenge U.S. House Minority Leader Charles Halleck (R-IN) ?

Q56: Who was the first member of the U.S. House of Representatives to file proposed legislation to repeal the Patient Protection and Affordability Act of 2010 (a.k.a. Obamacare)?

Q57: Who was the first Indian-American elected to the U.S. House of Representatives?

Q58: What is the oldest continuously serving Standing Committee in the U.S. House of Representatives?

Q59: How did former U.S. Representative Jeremiah Haralson (R-AL) die?

A50: The House Committee on Official Standards and Conduct, more commonly known as "The House Ethics Committee."

A51: The U.S. House Clerk

A52: Fred Upton (R-MI). He voted for the impeachment of Bill Clinton in 1998, and voted for the second impeachment of Donald Trump in 2021.

A53: William Miller (R-NY). In 1964, likely Republican Presidential nominee Barry Goldwater selected the obscure Miller to be his Vice-Presidential running mate, in his bid to unseat Democratic President Lyndon B. Johnson and his Vice-Presidential running mate Hubert Humphrey. Many Americans had never heard of Miller. Goldwater said that he selected him because "he drives Johnson nuts." A song was composed about the selection: "Here's a riddle, it's a killer/Who the hell is William Miller?"

A54: Mike Myers (D-PA)

A55: Gerald R. Ford (R-MI). Ford did in fact defeat Halleck.

A56: U.S. Representative Michelle Bachmann (D-MN)

A57: U.S. Representative Dalip Singh Saund (D-CA). He served from 1957-1963.

A58: The U.S. House Committee on Ways and Means. It began as a Select (not permanent) Committee in 1789, and became a Standing Committee (permanent) in 1797.

A59: It is presumed that he was killed by wild animals while on a hunting expedition in Colorado in 1916.

U.S. House of Representatives

Q60: In 1865, which future President was sworn in to represent the Second Congressional District in Ohio without having campaigned for the office?

Q61: Who was the first U.S. House member to call for a complete withdrawal of U.S. troops in Vietnam?

Q62: Who served the longest tenure as U.S. House Whip?

Q63: While defending Vice Presidential nominee Dan Quayle's lack of military service during the Vietnam War, this Republican U.S. Representative from Texas told the Houston media: "So many minority youths had volunteered for the well-paying military positions to escape poverty and the ghetto that there was literally no room for patriotic folks like himself." Who made such an odd statement?

Q64: Which three future Presidents served as Chairman of the potent U.S. House Ways and Means Committee?

Q65: The U.S. House includes five non-voting delegates. Who do they represent?

Q66: During a 2005 Congressional debate, U.S. Representative Marian Berry (D-AR) referred to this 30-year-old Congressman as a "Howdy Doody looking nimrod." Who was Berry referring to?

Q67: Since what year has a member of the Dingell family represented the Fifteenth Congressional District of Michigan?

Q68: Howard Buffett, the father of Warren Buffet (CEO of Berkshire Hathaway Inc.), represented which state in the U.S. House of Representatives from 1943-1949?

Q69: Who was the first Hispanic American to serve in the U.S. House of Representatives?

A60: Rutherford B. Hayes. In 1864, he refused to leave the U.S. Army to campaign, after the Republicans nominated him. Instead, he wrote letters to voters explaining his position on issues. Hayes defeated Democratic incumbent Alexander Long.

A61: U.S. Representative Tim Lee Carter (D-KY)

A62: Leslie C. Arends (R-IL). He served as the Republican Whip from 1943-1974. He was both the Minority and the Majority Whip, depending on which party held the majority in the House.

A63: Tom Delay

A64: James K. Polk, Millard Fillmore, and William McKinley

A65: American Samoa, Guam, the District of Columbia, the Northern Mariana Islands, and the U.S. Virgin Islands. (Puerto Rico elects a Resident Commissioner rather than a delegate.)

A66: U.S. Representative Adam Putnam (R-FL). Representative Putnam does in fact have an eerie resemblance to Howdy Doody. The word "Nimrod" means dimwitted. It originated in the cartoon series Looney Tunes where Bugs Bunny and Daffy Duck hurled insults at Elmer Fudd, including calling him a nimrod.

A67: Since 1935. John Dingell Sr. served from 1935 until his death in 1955. His son, John Dingell Jr. succeeded him and represented the District until 2017. His wife, Debbie Dingle succeeded him.

A68: Nebraska

A69: Joseph Marion Hernandez (Whig-Florida). He was first elected in 1822.

Q70: As a District Attorney from the Southern District of New York, future New York City Mayor Rudolph Giuliani led a criminal investigation of which U.S. Representative from Texas for alleged cocaine use in 1980?

Q71: In 1889, U.S. Representative William Duncan Vandiver (D-MO) coined what term, which is now the nickname of Missouri?

Q72: In 1981, which member of the U.S. House of Representatives resigned his seat and ran for re-election in a Special Election as a member of another political party?

Q73: Who was the first openly gay person to be elected to the U.S. Congress as a freshman?

Q74: In 1982, which ultra-conservative Democrat became the second President of the ultra-conservative John Birch Society, succeeding the organization's founder Robert Welsh?

Q75: U.S. Representative Gary Condit (D-CA 1989-2003) and U.S. Representative John Kasich (R-OH 1983-2001) shared an affinity for rock-and-roll concerts, and once jumped into a mosh pit at a performance of which band?

Q76: Who was the first presenter when *C-SPAN* began live televising proceedings in the U.S. House of Representatives in 1979?

Q77: U.S. Representative Ben Chandler (D-KY 2004-2013) is the grandson of which Major League Baseball Commissioner?

Q78: Which Republican U.S. Representative from Wisconsin won the lottery three times?

Q79: Which Republican U.S. Representative from Ohio developed his own proof to the Pythagorean Theorem ($a^2 + b^2 = c^2$)?

A70: Charlie Wilson. Wilson was also the featured character in a 2007 movie about his efforts to provide military aid to the Arab-Afghan Mujahideen. The movie was titled *Charlie Wilson's War*. The cocaine case never went to trial because of a lack of evidence.

A71: "Show Me." In an 1899 speech at the Five O'clock Club in Pennsylvania, Vandiver remarked: "I come from a state that raises corn and cotton, and cockleburs, and Democrats, and frothy eloquence neither convinces nor satisfies me. I am from Missouri. You have got to show me." The phrase "show me" had become synonymous with Missouri, and the Vandiver address solidified it. Consequently, the state's unofficial nickname became: "The Show Me State."

A72: Phil Gramm of Texas. House Speaker Tip O'Neill (D-MA) dislodged Gramm, a conservative Democrat, from his membership in the coveted House Budget Committee for his role in being the lead Democrat sponsor of the Gramm-Latta Omnibus Reconciliation Bill, which effectuated Ronald Reagan's economic program. Subsequently, Gramm resigned his seat and ran "as a Republican" for an open seat in a Special Election and won.

A73: U.S. Representative Jared Polis (D-CT). He was first elected in 2008.

A74: Larry McDonald

A75: Pearl Jam

A76: U.S. Representative Al Gore (D-TN)

A77: Albert Benjamin "Happy" Chandler (1945-1951)

A78: James Sensenbrenner. He won $250,000 in the District of Columbia lottery in 1997. In 2007, he twice won $1,000 in the Wisconsin Lottery. Sensenbrenner comes from a patrician background, and is an heir to the Kimberly-Clark Corporation paper products fortune.

A79: James Garfield. The Proof was published in *The Journal of Education* in 1876.

U.S. House of Representatives

Q80: In 2001, this U.S. House member was sworn in to a fifth term after defeating challenger Barrack Obama in the Democratic Primary. This is the only individual to defeat Obama in an election.

Q81: U.S. Representative Mike Ross (D-AR) began his political career as a travel aid to which politician running to regain the Arkansas Governorship in 1980?

Q82: U.S. Representative David Scott (D-GA) is the brother-in-law of which Atlanta Braves great?

Q83: Which cast member of the 1997 hit reality series *The Real World Boston* served in the U.S. House of Representatives?

Q84: What Character from the TV Series *Love Boat* became a member of the U.S. House of Representatives?

Q85: Who was the first African-American to serve in the U.S. House of Representatives?

Q86: In 2020, who was the only U.S. House Democrat to vote against Washington DC statehood?

Q87: U.S. Representative Aaron Shock (R-IL) re-decorated his Congressional office to look like the set of which British television show?

Q88: Which U.S Representative did British Prime Minister Winston Churchill give credit for mentoring him?

Q89: Which former U.S. Representative is the nephew of Jack Haley, the actor who played The Tin Man in the original version of the movie *The Wizard of OZ*?

Q90: Which U.S. Representative was known by the moniker: "Battling Bella?"

A80: U.S. Representative Bobby Rush (D-IL). Rush trounced Obama by 31 percentage points in 2000 when Obama challenged the incumbent for the House seat in the First Congressional District of Illinois in the Democratic Primary.

A81: Bill Clinton. Clinton returned the favor when campaigning for Ross in his first Congressional run in 2000 two days before the election. Ross eked out a narrow victory, and Clinton's appearance may have made the difference.

A82: Hank Aaron

A83: Sean Duffy (R-WI)

A84: Fred Grandy (R-IA). He played "Burl "Gopher" Smith" in the series. He served from 1987-1995. He told People Magazine: "If there were not Gopher, there would be no Fred Grandy in Congress." He did not seek re-election in 1994, instead running unsuccessfully for the Republican Gubernatorial nomination, losing to Terry Branstad

A85: Joseph Rainey (R-SC). He was elected in 1870. Though he stayed in South Carolina, he moved his family to Windsor, CT once violence in the South became unbearable. He lost re-election in 1878.

A86: Colin Peterson of Minnesota

A87: *Downton Abbey.* He was forced to reimburse the federal government for $40,000.

A88: William Bourke Cockran (D-NY). He was a family friend and believed to have been involved romantically with Churchill's mother, Lady Randolph.

A89: Bob Dornan (R-CA)

A90: Bella Abzug (D-NY). She was referred to as "Battling" because of her quick propensity for confrontation within the Chamber.

Chapter XI

U.S. House of Representatives Quotations

U.S. House of Representatives Quotations

Q1:   This Arizonian lost a bid for Chairman of the U.S. House Democratic Caucus on a secret ballot. A majority of the caucus had told him they would vote for him. He mused: "I have learned the difference between a cactus and a caucus. On a cactus, the pricks are on the outside." Who was this Representative?

Q2:   Which U.S. House Minority Leader from Missouri was approached by two ladies in an airport who were debating if he was [Former Vice President] "Dan Quayle or the Weatherman on *CNN*"?

Q3:   After losing his reelection bid in 1834, this U.S. Representative exclaimed: "I told the people of my district that I would serve them as faithfully as I had done; but if not ... you may all go to hell, and I will go to Texas." He did go to Texas and died at the Battle of the Alamo on March 6, 1836. Who was this Congressman?

Q4:   Which U.S. House member urged people to get: "in good trouble"?

Q5:   This U.S. House Majority Leader commented: "I am not a federal employee. I am a Constitutional Officer. My job is the Constitution of the United States; I am not a government employee. I am in the Constitution." Who made this statement?

Q6:   During a 2009 interview with *Pajamas TV*, which U.S. Representative observed: "I find it interesting that it was back in the 1970s that the swine flu broke out then under another Democrat president, Jimmy Carter. And I'm not blaming this on President Obama, I just think it's an interesting coincidence"?

Q7:   Shortly after being elected to the U.S. House of Representatives in 1988, this California Republican was asked if he ever smoked pot. His answer was: "Everything but the bong water (The fluid used in a water pipe)." Who was this Californian?

Q8:   In 1995, this U.S. Representative observed: "Asking an incumbent member of Congress to vote for term limits is a bit like asking a chicken to vote for Colonel Sanders." Who made this statement?

Q9:   This Chairman of the U.S. House International Relations Committee advised in 2002: "There are things in the Constitution that have been overtaken by events, by time. Declaration of war is one of them. There are things no longer relevant to a modern society. Why declare war if you don't have to?" Who was this House Chairman?

A1:   Mo Udall

A2:   Richard Gephardt

A3:   David "Davy" Crocket

A4:   John Lewis (D-GA). "Good Trouble" is trouble that helps advance a worthy cause.

A5:   Tom Delay (R-TX)

A6:   Michele Bachmann (R-MN). Actually, the last swine flu break occurred in 1976, when Republican Gerald R. Ford was President.

A7:   Dana Rohrabacher

A8:   Bob Ingles (R-SC)

A9:   Henry Hyde (R-IL)

U.S. House of Representatives Quotations

Q10: In 1977, when President Jimmy Carter cancelled the B1 Bomber, which U.S. Representative opined: "They're breaking out the Vodka bottles in Moscow"?

Q11: One of the most liberal members of the U.S. House of Representatives, and a constant thorn in the side of Republican Presidents Richard M. Nixon and Gerald R. Ford, stated: "Richard Nixon impeached himself. He gave us Gerald Ford as his revenge." Who made this statement?

Q12: During the 1967 Republican Response to Democratic President Lyndon B. Johnson's State of the Union Address, which U.S. House Minority Leader stated: "The years have slipped by and now Americans in 1967 see the decade that dawned in hope fading into frustration and failure, bafflement and boredom"?

Q13: In 1998, the Chairman of the U.S. House Government and Oversight Committee (which was investing alleged campaign finance violations by President Bill Clinton) told *The Indianapolis Star* Editorial Board: "If I could prove 10 percent of what I believe happened, he'd [Clinton] be gone. This guy's a 'scumbag.' That's why I'm after him." Who made this statement?

Q14: In 1998, during the Monica Lewinsky episode, this U.S. House Majority Leader was asked what he would do if he ever found himself in a similar situation. The majority Leader replied: "If I were, I would be looking up from a pool of blood and hearing [my wife ask] 'How do I reload this thing?'" Who made this reply?

Q15: In 1994, which incoming Chairman of the U.S. House Natural Resources Committee labeled the environmental movement: "environmentalist – the self-centered bunch, the waffle-stomping, Harvard-graduating intellectual idiot that don't understand that they're leading this country into environmental disaster"?

Q16: In 2006, the U.S. House Majority Leader was told to put out a cigar he was smoking at the Ruth Chris Steak House in Washington, D.C. He was informed that a Federal government regulation disallows individuals from smoking in public restaurants. The Majority Leader replied: "I am the Federal Government." Who was this Majority Leader?

Q17: When this Vice President was contemplating being tried by the U.S. Congress rather than having to be tried in a court of law for accepting bribes and falsifying tax returns, U.S. Representative Charles Vanik (D-OH) deadpanned: "He's trying to take the decision out of the hands of twelve honest men and give it to 435 Congressmen." Who was this Vice President?

Q18: After which U.S. Representative released a statement excoriating a U.S. Supreme Court decision ruling that the Defense of Marriage Act is unconstitutional, Nancy Pelosi (D-CA) responded: "Who cares"?

Q19: In 1997, this former musician was sworn into the U.S. House of Representatives. Immediately after being sworn in, he looked around and observed: "I feel like the black sheep, but here I am." Who was this newly-minted Congressman?

A10: Bob Dornan

A11: Bella Abzug (D-NY)

A12: Gerald R. Ford (R-MI)

A13: Dan Burton (R-IN)

A14: Dick Armey (R-TX)

A15: Don Young (R-AK)

A16: Tom Delay (R-TX)

A17: Spiro Agnew. Agnew eventually pleaded *nolo-contendere* to the lesser charge of falsifying tax returns in Federal Court and did not face a trial on the condition that he resign his office. The legal phrase *nolo*-contendere (no contest) is a plea wherein a defendant accepts conviction although he/she does not accept guilt.

A18: Michele Bachman (R-MN)

A19: Sonny Bono (R-CA). Bono once sang with Cher in the duo "Sonny and Cher."

U.S. House of Representatives Quotations

Q20: In 2009, when Barack Obama was addressing a Joint Session of the U.S. Congress regarding Healthcare Reform, the President said: "The reforms I'm proposing would not apply to those who are here illegally." This U.S. Representative then shouted: "You Lie." Who offered this impulsive comment?

Q21: Which U.S. House member coined the term: "Too big to fail"?

Q22: In her 1970 book, *Unbought and Unbossed*, this U.S. Representative and future Presidential candidate observed: "Congress seems drugged and inert most of the time. The idea of meeting a problem is to hold hearings or, in the extreme case, to appointing a commission." Who made this comment?

Q23: During a 2000 address on the US. House Floor, which U.S. Representative observed: "Fool me once, shame on you. Fool me twice, shame on you"?

Q24: In 1993, which U.S. Representative and future felon told the *Blade-Citizen* of Oceanside, California that Democrats who were stifling Republican legislation "ought to be lined up and shot. I'm talking about the liberal leadership"?

Q25: After Arkansas Governor Jim Guy Tucker and two of President Bill Clinton's former business partners (James and Susan McDougal) were convicted on Whitewater-related charges, which U.S. House Minority Leader deadpanned: "Say what you want about the President, but we know his friends have convictions"?

Q26: Which member of the U.S. Congress (who was the oldest person ever to serve in the U.S. House of Representatives), who left office at age 91 after losing a renomination to his seat in 2015, said the following about his long life: "I have always taken care of my body; I'm not a drinker, I've never smoked. And I've always exercised. That's all you have to do"?

Q27: In 1995, which U.S. House Majority Whip maintained: "The EPA, the Gestapo of government, pure and simple, has been one of the major claw-hooks that the government maintains on the backs of our constituents"?

Q28: In 2006, which U.S. Representative said: "Mississippi gets more than their fair share back in federal money, but who the hell wants to live in Mississippi?"

Q29: Which U.S. Representative told the U.S. House Chamber in 1999: "Government regulations on the sale of cabbage are 27,000 words. Mr. Speaker, now if that is not enough to stuff your cabbage roll, regulations cost taxpayers $400 billion a year, $4,000 per every family each and every year, year in and year out. Unbelievable. It is so bad, if a dog urinates in a parking lot, the EPA declares it a wetland"?

Q30: Which U.S. House member admonished Americans that terrorists are sending their pregnant black widows to the U.S. so that "[their children] could be raised and coddled as future terrorists [and] twenty, thirty years down the road, they can be sent in to help destroy our way of life"?

A20: Joe Wilson. Wilson later apologized to the President for his obvious "lack of civility."

A21: Stewart B. McKinney (R-CT). In 1984, after the Federal Government bailed out the Continental Illinois Bank just before it went into default, McKinney stated: "We have a new kind of bank. It is called 'Too Big to Fail:' TBTF, and it is a wonderful bank." The term gained notoriety during the Bank bailout of 2009 when the federal government bailed out the nation's banks.

A22: Shirley Chisholm (D-NY)

A23: Virginia Fox (R-NC)

A24: Randy "Duke" Cunningham (R-CA)

A25: Dick Armey (R-TX)

A26: Ralph Hall (R-TX)

A27: Tom Delay (R-TX)

A28: Charlie Rangel (D-NY). Rangel later clarified: "I certainly don't mean to offend anyone, I just love New York so much, and can't understand why everyone else wouldn't want to live here." His Democratic colleague Gene Taylor from Mississippi retorted that, having been stationed in New York while in the Coast Guard, he knows some New Yorkers "are stuck up about their home. You can tell him I want to live in Mississippi and wild elephants and tigers and bears couldn't keep me from living in Mississippi. Hurricane Katrina couldn't keep me from building back here." Taylor lost his home during the hurricane.

A29: James Traficant (D-OH)

A30: Louis Gohmert (R-TX)

Chapter XII

U.S. House Campaigns

U.S. House Campaigns

Q1:   Who was the first Hindu elected to the U.S. House of Representatives?

Q2:   In a 1937 Special election, after the death of U.S. Representative James P. Buchanan (D-TX), this Texas political upstart was elected, aided by $10,000 his wife inherited from her mother's estate?

Q3:   In 1946, this Massachusetts Democratic Congressional candidate was asked about his heroics as a Commander of a Patrol boat (PT-109) that was cut in half by a Japanese destroyer while out on patrol. He responded: "It was easy. They cut my boat in half." Who was this Congressional candidate?

Q4:   When this former conservative Democratic U.S. Representative announced that he would run to try to gain his old Seat as a Republican, he exclaimed: "I was never a good Democrat. So, I could be just as bad a Republican." Who was this U.S. Representative?

Q5:   In 1942, this former Massachusetts Governor won a U.S. House seat by telling the crowd about his Democratic Primary opponent, Thomas H. Elliot: "My young opponent is a Unitarian. Do you know what a Unitarian is? A Unitarian is a person who believes that our Lord and Savior is a funny little man with a beard who runs around in his underclothes." Who was this former Governor?

Q6:   In 1788, which two future Presidents faced each other in a U.S. House race?

Q7:   In 1992, which U.S. House Minority Whip was under fire in an unexpectedly formidable challenge for renomination to the U.S. Congress?

Q8:   In 1953, Democrat James Bowler (D-IL) was elected to the U.S. House of Representatives in a Special Election campaign, making him the oldest freshman ever elected. How old was he?

Q9:   Which former NFL Quarterback defeated U.S. Representative Charles Taylor (R-NC) in 2006 by supporting "mountain values."

Q10:   In the 2020 U.S. House elections, every Democrat who lost re-election was a freshman; except which member, who had been in office since 1991?

Q11:   What Late Night Talk Show Host interned for then Massachusetts State Representative Barney Frank on his successful 1980 campaign for Congress while a high school student?

A1: Tulsi Gabbard (D-HI). She was elected to represent the Second Congressional District in 2012.

A2: Lyndon B. Johnson. His wife was Lady Bird Johnson.

A3: John F. Kennedy

A4: Gene Taylor

A5: James Michael Curley

A6: James Madison and James Monroe were political opponents in a race to represent the First Congressional District of Virginia. Madison won the election in a landslide victory. The two men then became allies. Monroe served as Secretary of War and as Secretary of Defense in Madison's Presidential administration.

A7: Newt Gingrich (R-GA). His opponent, Herman Clark, a former state legislator, argued that Gingrich was ignoring his constituents while effectuating a national profile. Clark excoriated Gingrich for writing 22 check overdrafts at the U.S. House Bank, including a bad check to the IRS. In fact, Gingrich was banned from his use of a chauffeured limousine paid for by taxpayers. The race was so close that a recount was done. Gingrich won by just 980 votes. Interestingly, in 1990, Gingrich was re-elected by just 974 votes.

A8: He was 78 years old. He served until his death in 1957 at the age of 82.

A9: Heath Shuler

A10: Colin Peterson (D-MN). He represented a district that Donald Trump won twice by 30 percentage points.

A11: Conan O'Brien. He was a student at Brookline High School in Brookline, Massachusetts at the time.

Chapter XIII

Speakers of the U.S. House of Representatives

Speakers of the U.S. House of Representatives

Q1:   Who was the first Speaker of the U.S. House of Representatives?

Q2:   Who were the four House Speakers from Massachusetts to serve in the Twentieth Century?

Q3:   When is the U.S. House Speaker required to vote?

Q4:   Who was the only Republican U.S. House Speaker to serve between 1931 and 1995?

Q5:   Who is the only U.S. House Speaker to visit Hiroshima, Japan?

Q6:   When does a U.S. House Speaker not preside over a Joint Session of the House and Senate?

Q7:   Future U.S. House Speaker Newt Gingrich (R-GA) lost his first two attempts to win a seat in Georgia, losing to which conservative Democrat?

Q8:   In 1997, Newt Gingrich became the first Republican U.S. House Speaker to be elected to two consecutive terms since which other House Speaker?

Q9:   In 1961, which future U.S. House Speaker visited the White House to watch the official swearing in of her father to the Federal Renegotiation Board? The now defunct agency was a watchdog against excessive profits awarded in Defense and space contracts.

Speakers of the U.S. House of Representatives

A1:   Frederick Muhlenberg (Democratic-Republican-Pennsylvania.). He assumed the Speakership in 1789.

A2:   Frederick Gillette, Joe Martin, John McCormick, and Thomas P. Tip O'Neill Jr. Republican Frederick Gillette was Speaker from 1919-1925; Republican Joe Martin was Speaker from 1947-1949 and from 1953-1955; Democrat John McCormick was Speaker from 1962-1971; and Democrat Thomas P. Tip O'Neil Jr. was Speaker from 1977-1987?

A3:   When there is a tied vote in the House Chamber.

A4:   Joe Martin of Massachusetts served for the only four years the Republicans were in control of the chamber, 1947-1949 and 1953-1955.

A5:   Nancy Pelosi (D-CA). She placed a bouquet of flowers at the memorial to the victims of the Atomic Bomb, which ended WWII. She is the highest-ranking U.S. official to do so.

A6:   When the Electoral College votes are officially counted. In that case, the Vice President (The Senate President) resides.

A7: Jack Flynt. Flynt decided not to seek re-election in 1978, and Gingrich won the open seat against Democratic State Senator Virginia Sheppard.

A8: Nicolas Longworth of Ohio in 1927

A9: Nancy Pelosi (D-CA). President John F. Kennedy was at the event.

Speakers of the U.S. House of Representatives

Q10: Which actress is a descendant of U.S. House Speaker (from 1799-1801) Theodore Sedgwick (Federalist-Massachusetts)?

Q11: Which former U.S. House Speaker was featured on the cover of the first edition of *Time Magazine*, which debuted on March 3, 1923?

Q12: Which U.S. Representative served as either Minority Leader or House Speaker every year from 1939-1959?

Q13: Who is the only Italian-American to serve as U.S. House Speaker?

Q14: In 1889, this U.S. House Speaker resigned the Speakership and his House seat in the middle of his term. He did this in protest of the activist-interventionist policy his party was supporting under the stewardship of President William McKinley. Who was this House Speaker?

Q15: Who was the first U.S. House Speaker to represent a Congressional District west of the Rocky Mountains?

Q16: Who was the first U.S. House Speaker to publish a blog?

Q17: Which state has had the most Speakers of the U.S. House of Representatives?

Q18: In 1994, U.S. House Speaker Tom Foley (D-WA) allowed this long-time Minority Leader (who dreamed of becoming Speaker himself), wield the gavel before retiring. Who was this Minority Leader?

Q19: Which U.S. House Speaker was a vociferous proponent of the Superconducting Super Collider, a particle accelerator complex being constructed underneath Waxahachie, TX, which benefited his constituents greatly?

Q20: How many freshman members were elected as U.S. House Speaker?

A10: Kyra Sedgwick. She starred in the hit TNT crime series *The Closer*.

A11: Joe Cannon (R-IL)

A12: Joe Martin (R-MA)

A13: Nancy Pelosi (D-CA)

A14: Thomas Brackett Reed (R-ME)

A15: Tom Foley (D-WA 1989-1995)

A16: J. Dennis Hastert (R-IL). He did this in 2005.

A17: Massachusetts has had eight Speakers
Theodore Sedgwick,1799-1801, (Federalist)
Joseph Bradley Varnum, 1807-1811, (Democratic-Republican)
Robert Charles Winthrop, 1849-1851, (Whig)
Nathaniel Prentice Banks, 1856-1857, (R)
Frederick Gillett, 1919-1925, (R)
Joseph Martin, 1947-1949 and 1953-1955), (R)
John McCormack, 1962-1971, (D)
Tip O'Neill, 1977-1987, (D)

A18: Bob Michael (R-IL)

A19: Jim Wright (D-TX). The program was halted after he left office, when President Bill Clinton signed legislation to cancel it.

A20: Three. They were Frederick Muhlenberg (Democratic-Republican) in 1789, Henry Clay (Democratic-Republican- KY) in 1811, and William Pennington (R-NJ) in 1860.

Chapter XIV

U.S. House Speaker Quotations

U.S. House Speaker Quotations

Q1: In 1966, this future U.S. House Speaker addressed a rally at the Massachusetts State House in support of the U.S. role in Vietnam: He took direct aim at his Cambridge, MA constituents, many in academia: "I believe in Academic Freedom, but not as it is expounded by kooks, commies, and egghead professors." Who was this future Speaker of the House?

Q2: Which U.S. House Speaker said of his colleagues: "They never open their mouths without subtracting from the sum of human knowledge"?

Q3: Which future U.S. House Speaker and Presidential candidate described his Missouri District as "The rich Mesopotamian Country of the Western World"?

Q4: Which U.S. House Speaker is credited with coining the phrase "All Politics is Local?"

Q5: Which future U.S. House Speaker said of Ronald Reagan during the Iran-Contra scandal, "He will never again be the same Ronald Reagan he was before he blew it. He is not going to regain our trust or faith easily"?

Q6: When this U.S. House Speaker was asked by members of his party to campaign against his longtime counterpart, U.S. House Minority Leader Joe Martin (R-MA), he countered: "Speak against Joe? Hell, if I lived up there, I'd vote for him." Who was this House Speaker?

Q7: In 1985, after it was announced that President Ronald Reagan would meet with Soviet General Secretary Mikhail Gorbachev, which future U.S. House Speaker warned that the meeting would be "The most dangerous summit for the West since Adolf Hitler met with Chamberlain [Former British PM] in 1938 in Munich"?

Q8: Which Republican U.S. House Speaker gave new Congressmen the following advice: "A closed mouth gathers no feet"?

Q9: In 1977, when U.S. Representative Tip O'Neill (D-MA) was sworn in as U.S. Speaker of the House, he was introduced by which U.S. House Minority Leader as "The greatest one-term Speaker in the History of the House." O'Neill retorted: "I understand you have your eye on the Speaker's seat. I'm sure that's all you'll have on it." Which House Leader made this statement when introducing O'Neill?

Q10: This U.S. House Speaker said of President William Howard Taft: "The trouble with Taft is that if he were Pope, he would find it necessary to appoint a few Protestant Cardinals." Who was this House Speaker?

Q11: This U.S. House Speaker famously reminded his colleagues: "No one has a finer command of language than the person who keeps his mouth shut." Who is responsible for this quote?

Q12: Which U.S. House Speaker explained his relationship with this Democratic President as: "like a cobra and a mongoose"?

A1: Tip O'Neill (D-MA). He came out against the war a year later.

A2: Thomas Bracket Reed (R-ME)

A3: Champ Clarke (D-MO)

A4: "Tip" O'Neill Jr. (D-MA). Tip had lost a campaign for City Council in Cambridge, Massachusetts. His father told him he should have campaigned more in his own neighborhood, where surprisingly he had underperformed. O'Neill finished ninth out of sixty candidates in a race where the top eight finishers were elected. The senior O'Neill told Tip to remember that, "All Politics is Local."

A5: Newt Gingrich (R-GA)

A6: Sam Rayburn (D-TX)

A7: Newt Gingrich (R-GA)

A8: Joe Martin (R-MA)

A9: John Rhodes (R-AZ)

A10: Joseph Cannon (R-IL). Taft chose to get opinions from all sides of the political aisle.

A11: Sam Rayburn (D-TX)

A12: Joe Martin (R-MA). The President he was referring to was Democrat Harry S. Truman.

Chapter XV

U.S. Senators

U.S. Senators

Q1: In the 1986 World Series, actor Michael Sergio parachuted into Shea Stadium during Game 6 of the World Series. On the parachute was the following message: "Let's go Mets." Play was stopped as Sergio was escorted off of the field. He was arrested for not naming the pilot who flew the aircraft. However, he was released from jail when which U.S. Senator intervened on his behalf?

Q2: In 2018, she became the first U.S. Senator to give birth while in office. Who was this new mother Senator?

Q3: Who was the last U.S. Senator to be elected by a state Legislature?

Q4: Which Massachusetts U.S. Senator was the first since the Civil War to resign his seat to serve in the U.S. Army?

Q5: U.S. Representative Preston Brooks (D-SC) attacked which U.S. Senator after the Senator delivered a speech on the Senate floor excoriating slaveholders, one of whom was a relative of Representative Brooks?

Q6: Who was the first female U.S. Senator?

Q7: Who was the first African-American U.S. Senator?

Q8: In 2001, the year when this U.S. Senator left the Republican Party to become an Independent, he broke what was the longest-held Republican seat in history. Who was this Senator?

Q9: Who was the first U.S. Senator to be elected and to serve whose husband had not been a U.S. Senator?

U.S. Senators

A1: Alfonse D'Amato (R-NY)

A2: Tammy Duckworth (D-IL)

A3: Joseph T. Robinson. He was elected by the Arkansas Legislature to fill the term of Democrat Jefferson Davis, who had died before assuming office. Robinson was elected by the Legislature on January 27,1913 and took office on March 4, 1913. The Seventeenth Amendment to the U.S. Constitution mandates the direct election of U.S. Senators. It was ratified on April 8, 1913

A4: Henry Cabot Lodge Jr. Lodge did this during WWII.

A5: U.S. Senator Charles Sumner (R-MA). His speech criticized the Kansas-Nebraska Act which mandated a policy of "popular sovereignty," meaning that settlers in new American territories could decide whether or not to allow for the institution of slavery. One of the authors of the legislation was U.S. Senator Andrew Butler (D-SC) a cousin, of Brooks. The legislation was signed into law by President Franklin Peirce in 1856. Brooks attacked Sumner two days later with a cane, after telling him: "Mr. Sumner, I have read your speech twice over carefully. It is a libel on South Carolina and Mr. Butler, who is a relative of mine." There was a woman in the Chamber and as a courtesy, Brooks waited for her to leave before embarking in the caning.

A6: Democrat Rebecca Ann Felton (1922). Peach State Governor Thomas Hardwick appointed her to replace Senator Thomas E. Watson, who died in office. Senator Felton was 87 years of age and was a veteran of the Woman's Suffrage Movement. Unfortunately, her tenure in the U.S. Senate was short, only lasting one day. A day later the newly elected U.S. Senator, Walter George, was sworn into office.

A7: Hiram Revels (R-MS). He was appointed to fill the seat vacated by U.S. Senator Albert G. Brown. Brown resigned when the South seceded from the Union at the beginning of the U.S. Civil War in 1861.

A8: Jim Jeffords

A9: Nancy Kassebaum. She was elected in Kansas in 1978. All others female Senators prior to 1978 succeeded their late husbands.

Q10: The longest tenure for a state having the same two U.S. Senators is South Carolina. This occurred from November 8, 1966 to January 3, 2005. Who were these two Senators?

Q11: Who was the youngest U. S. Senator to be sworn into a sixth term?

Q12: Which two future U.S. Senators recovered from their wounds suffered during WWII at Percy Jones Army Hospital in Battle Creek, MI?

Q13: Who was presiding over the U.S. Senate when John F. Kennedy was shot in 1963?

Q14: Who is the only Democrat in Vermont history to serve in the U.S. Senate?

Q15: Illinois has a record three African Americans who served in the U.S. Senate. Who were they?

Q16: This former Democratic U.S. Senator has owned the Milwaukee Bucks since 1985. Who is this former Senator?

Q17: Who is the only member of the U.S. Senate to walk on the Moon?

Q18: In what state, when a U.S. Senate vacancy occurs, does the Central Committee of the party of the retired or deceased Senator select three possible successors from their party?

Q19: In 1965, which U.S. Senator with a sweet tooth put candy in his desk for his colleagues to take at their leisure?

A10: Strom Thurmond and Ernest "Fritz" Hollings

A11: Joe Biden. He was sworn in at 66 years old in 2009. He was first elected in 1972 at age 29.

A12 Bob Dole (R-KS) and Daniel Inouye (D-HI)

A13: Ted Kennedy (D-MA)

A14: Pat Leahy. He was first elected in 1974. Bernie Sanders is an Independent, though he caucuses with the Democratic Party.

A15: Carol Moseley Braun (1993-1999), Barack Obama (2005-2008), and Roland Burris (2009-2011). All three are Democrats.

A16: Herbert Kohl (D-WI)

A17: Harrison Schmitt (R-NM 1977-1983). He was a NASA astronaut aboard Apollo 17 when the spacecraft landed on the Moon in 1972.

A18: Wyoming. They then submit the list to the Governor who selects the new Senator.

A19: George Murphy (R-CA). The tradition continues, in what is called: "the candy desk."

Q20: Who was the youngest U.S. Senator in history?

Q21: Wisconsin has a Jewish population of less than 1%, yet between 1991 and 2011, the state had two Jewish U.S. Senators. Who were they?

Q22: In 1963, U.S. Senate President pro tempore Carl Hayden (D-AZ) was ill and unable to discharge his duties. Accordingly, which U.S. Senator was designated as Permanent Acting President pro tempore of the U.S. Senate, a position he would continue to hold until he died in office in 1978?

Q23: How many boarding schools did US. Senator Ted Kennedy (D-MA) attend in 13 years?

Q24: In 1969, this U.S. Senator suffered a stroke, but served out the remainder of his term, which expired in 1973. Who was this Senator?

Q25: U.S. Senator Robert C. Byrd and Real Estate Mogul Leona Helmsley both had dogs with the same name. What was the name?

Q26: U.S. Senator David Boren (D-OK 1971-1994) is a cousin of this musician and actor who starred in the movie *Gremlins* and wrote the song The Pusher, later recorded by the hard rock band Steppenwolf for the popular 1969 movie Easy Rider. Who was this musician and actor?

Q27: In a 2004 U.S. Senate primary race in Illinois, businessman Blair Hull outspent this opponent 6-1, yet finished in third place, garnering just 12% of the vote. Who won this race?

Q28: Who was the first U.S. Senator to fly in space?

Q29: From 1955-1961, Massachusetts had two statewide officials with the same first and last name. What was the name?

A20: John Henry Eaton. Although under the U.S. Constitution a Senator must be at least 30 years old, Eaton supposedly did not know his age and the issue was never challenged. However, based on the birth date on his tombstone, Eaton would have been only 28 years old when he was sworn into the U.S. Senate in 1818.

A21: Democrats Russ Feingold and Herb Kohl.

A22: Lee Metcalf (D-MT). He remains the only person in history to hold this rather unusual title.

A23: 10

A24: U.S. Senator Karl Mundt (R-SC). He was not able to cast a single vote. He was stripped of all his Committee assignments because he could not participate in the hearings.

A25: Trouble

A26: Hoyt Axton

A27: Barack Obama

A28: Jack Garn (R-UT). He served as a Payload Specialist aboard the Space Shuttle "Discovery."

A29: John F. Kennedy. John Fitzgerald Kennedy served in the U.S. Senate. Concomitantly, John Francis Kennedy served as Massachusetts State Treasurer.

Q30: In 1953, U.S. Senator Frank Carlson (R-KS) organized which important religious function held each year in Washington, D.C?

Q31: What was U.S. Senator John Edwards' (D-NC 1998-2005) birth name?

Q32: Who was the youngest U.S. Senator ever elected to the post of U.S. Senate Majority Leader?

Q33: Which future U.S. Senator failed the third, seventh and ninth grades, yet later in life was awarded a Ph.D. in Economics from The University of Georgia?

Q34: In 1957, this U.S. Senator filibustered a record 24 hours and 18 minutes against the Civil Rights Act of 1957. Who was this loquacious Senator?

Q35: In 1954, U.S. Senator Leverett Saltonstall (R-MA), in his capacity as U.S. Senate Majority Whip, was the only member of the U.S. Senate Republican leadership to vote for a Senate Resolution which passed 67-22 to censure which Republican colleague?

Q36: Which U.S. Senator acquired a 24-acre property from a widowed aunt who could no longer take care of it. In return, the Senator gave the aunt his boyhood home and a $100 stipend each month.

Q37: Who were the only three southern U.S. Senators who did not sign the Southern Manifesto of 1956 (which opposed desegregation efforts)?

Q38: Who was the first married woman U.S. Senator in U.S. History?

Q39: U.S. Senator John V. Tunney (D-CA) was a roommate at the University of Virginia Law School with which future colleague from Massachusetts?

A30: The National Prayer Breakfast

A31: Johnny

A32: William Knowland (D-CA). In 1953, the 45-year-old assumed the role of Senator.
\

A33: Phil Gramm (R-TX)

A34: Strom Thurmond. He was a Democrat at the time, but later switched to the Republican Party.

A35: U.S. Senator Joe McCarthy (R-WI). He was censored for his overzealous role investigating domestic communism. McCarthy's Massachusetts colleague, John F. Kennedy (D-MA), was the only member of the body not to vote on the resolution. He was in the hospital after back surgery. Kennedy, a staunch ally of McCarthy, never indicated how he would have voted.

A36: Lyndon B. Johnson (D-TX). The deal was consummated in 1951, and the property became the LBJ Ranch, a functioning second White House when Johnson assumed the Presidency.

A37: Albert Gore Sr., Estes Kefauver of Tennessee, and U.S. Senate Majority Leader Lyndon B. Johnson of Texas. All three were Democrats.

A38: Dixie Bibb Graves (D-AL). All other female Senators had been widows. U.S. Senator Hugo Black (D-AL) resigned his seat in 1937 to assume a seat on the U.S. Supreme Court. Alabama Governor Bibb Graves appointed his wife, Democrat Dixie Bibb Graves, to the vacant Senate seat. She served for almost six months as an interim Senator until a special election could be held to fill the remainder of the term.

A39: Ted Kennedy (D-MA)

U.S. Senators

Q40: Who are the only two U.S. Senators in history with Native American-lineage?

Q41: In 1970, which Democrat won a U.S. Senate seat from Florida, in part by embarking on a 1,033 mile walk through the state, from Pensacola to Key West?

Q42: In 1832, U.S. Senator William Marcy (D-NY) defended President Andrew Jackson's nomination of former Secretary of State Martin Van Buren (a Jackson political supporter) as the Ambassador to the Court of St. James (England) by declaring what?

Q43: Who is the only member of the U.S. Senate to serve as Sergeant-at-Arms after leaving the Senate?

Q44: President Lyndon B. Johnson declared September 30, 1968 a day to honor this retiring U.S. Senator, who achieved his final legislative goal in getting the Central Arizona Project authorized?

Q45: This Democratic U.S. Senator, a steadfast supporter of the United Nations Convention on the Prevention and Punishment of the Crime of Genocide Treaty, delivered a speech every day the Senate was in session for almost twenty years. He did this until the U.S. Senate ratified the Convention in 1986. He gave a total of 3,211 speeches on the subject. Who was this perennial speaker?

Q46: During the 103rd U.S. Congress, the Chairman of the Democratic and Republican Senatorial Campaign Committees shared the same last name. What was their last name?

Q47: Who was the only person to serve as Whip in both Chambers of the U.S. Congress?

Q48: Which state holds the all-time record for one party controlling both seats in the U.S. Senate?

Q49: U.S. Senator Ted Kennedy (D-MA) was born on February 22, 1932. This was the 200th birthday of which President?

A40: Charles Curtis (R-KS 1907-1913 and 1915-1929). The second was Ben Nighthorse Campbell (D-CO and R-CO 1993-2005).

A41: Lawton Chiles. The 91-day journey earned him the moniker of "Walking Lawton."

A42: "To the victor goes the Spoils." This is the origin of the term "spoils system."

A43: Wall Doxey (D-AL)

A44: Carl Hayden (D-AZ.). The project was an aqueduct which diverts water from the Colorado River to the Bill Williams Wildlife refuge.

A45: William Proxmire of Wisconsin.

A46: Bob Graham (D-FL) and Phil Gramm (R-TX)

A47: Trent Lott (R-MS)

A48: Louisiana. The streak was broken in 2005 when Republican David Vitter was sworn into office.

A49: George Washington

Q50: This future U.S. Attorney General worked for six months on the staff of U.S. Senator Joseph McCarthy (R-WI), and also worked on the staff of the Senate Committee on Investigations chaired by McCarthy during the Army-McCarthy Hearings. Who was this Attorney General?

Q51: In 1974, the liberal publication *New Times Magazine* named this U.S. Senator "The Dumbest Congressman." He responded by calling a press conference to deny the charges. Who was this Senator?

Q52: U.S. Senator Joe Lieberman (I-CT 1989-2013) said this Frank Sinatra song is his favorite. What is the name of the song?

Q53: Who holds the record for appearing the most times on NBC's *Meet The Press*?

Q54: U.S. Senator Lindsey Graham (R-SC) lives in the same town that former U.S. Senator and Vice Presidential candidate John Edwards (D-NC) was born in. What is that town?

Q55: On the day he was elected to serve in the U.S. Senate from New York in 1964, he did not meet the requirement to vote in the state of New York. Who was this Senator?

Q56: This U.S. Senator from North Dakota earned the moniker: "Gerald The Giant Killer" for his role in unearthing corruption in the administration of Republican President Warren G. Harding after his death. Who was this Senator?

Q57: Which future Democratic Presidential nominee saved the life of a Republican Senator in 1988?

Q58: In a 1996 U.S. Senate race in Virginia, the Democratic and Republican nominees shared which last name?

Q59: Who is the only Democratic U.S. Senator to be reelected from Idaho?

A50: Robert F. Kennedy

A51: William Lloyd Scott (R-VA)

A52: *My Way*

A53: Bob Dole. He appeared on the program 64 times.

A54: Seneca, South Carolina

A55: Robert F. Kennedy. Although he was not qualified to vote in the state of New York, he was in fact qualified to run for office.

A56: Gerald Nye

A57: John Kerry. As U.S. Senator Chic Hech (R-NV) left a Republican Senate luncheon, he almost choked to death on an apple. Kerry spotted Hecht in the hallway and noticed that he was in distress. Kerry proceeded to perform the Heimlich maneuver four times. The apple was safely dislodged, saving Hecht's life. Ironically, Senator Kerry was Chairman of the Democratic Senatorial Campaign Committee that year and was targeting Hecht for defeat in Nevada.

A58: Warner. The Democrats nominated Mark Warner to challenge Republican U.S. Senator John Warner. Mark Warner's slogan was "Mark not John." John Warner won the election.

A59: Frank Church. First elected in 1956, Church was re-elected in1962, 1968 and again in 1974. He lost his bid for a fifth term in 1980 to Republican Steve Symms. Idaho is one of the most Republican states in the country, having not voted for a Democrat at the Presidential level since Lyndon B. Johnson won the state in 1964.

Q60: During his 30-year tenure in the U.S. Senate (from 1967-1997), this Republican voted against every single military appropriations bill. Who was this Senator?

Q61: How many votes are required for a treaty to be ratified by the U.S. Senate?

Q62: This future U.S. Senator once dated Janet Auchincloss, the half-sister of First Lady Jacqueline Kennedy, and once joined the Kennedy family to watch an America's Cup Race. Who was this Senator?

Q63: Which former University of Cincinnati head football coach assumed a U.S. Senate seat in 2021?

Q64: In 1963, this U.S. Senator was awarded a Law Degree by President John F. Kennedy at the American University's College of Law in Washington D.C. He attended as a night school student. Who was his Senator?

Q65: In 1973, which South Dakotan became the first Arab America to serve in the U. S. Senate?

Q66: While a student at Yale Law School in 1970, Bill Clinton was a volunteer for this State Senate candidate in Connecticut in his successful battle to dislodge State Senate Majority Leader Edward Marcus. The man later became a U.S. Senator. Who was this politician?

Q67: This future U.S. Senator was recruited by Green Bay Packers coach Lisle Blackburn for a tryout. The Harvard Crimson football player turned down the offer, telling Blackburn that he "intended to go into another contact sport, politics." Who was this candidate for a position on the Green Bay Packers?

Q68: While a student at Georgetown University, Bill Clinton secured a position as a clerk for the U.S. Senate Foreign Relations Committee under the tutelage of which committee Chairman?

Q69: Who coined the term: "McCarthyism," referring to the escapades of U.S. Senator Joe McCarthy (R-WI) searching for domestic Communists?

A60: Mark Hatfield of Oregon

A61: Two-thirds of all members present in the body.

A62: John Kerry (D-MA)

A63: Tommy Tuberville (R-AL)

A64: Robert C. Byrd (D-WV)

A65: James G. Abourezk

A66: Joe Lieberman

A67: Ted Kennedy. Kennedy was a star wide receiver at Harvard, and a letter winner as well.

A68: J. William Fulbright (D-AR). Fulbright became a mentor to Clinton. While President, Clinton awarded Fulbright a Presidential Medal of Freedom. In 1995, Clinton gave a eulogy at his funeral.

A69: Herbert Block, a *Washington Post* Political cartoonist.

Q70: At age 66, which Republican U.S. Senator married Nancy Moore, the 22-year-old Miss South Carolina?

Q71: Who were the only two U.S. Senators to vote against Hillary Clinton's 2009 confirmation to the U.S. Senate?

Q72: Who were the only two U.S. Senators to vote against The Gulf of Tonkin Resolution, which would provide President Lyndon B. Johnson carte blanche to use force in Southeast Asia?

Q73: Which U.S. Senator was nicknamed "Tom-Tom" because he had a habit of beating his chest like a drum while speaking?

Q74: In 1996, U.S. Senator Nancy Kassebaum (R-KS) married which former U.S. Senate Majority Leader?

Q75: At 22 years old, which future U.S Senator was named *Cosmopolitan's* Sexiest man?

Q76: Who was the only U.S. Senator to vote against the U.S.A. Patriot Act in 2001?

Q77: Who was the only Southern U.S. Senator to not leave the Union to join the Confederacy during the Civil War?

Q78: Who was the only Democratic U.S. Senator to vote against the confirmation of Elena Kagan to the U.S. Supreme Court in 2010?

Q79: Who were the only two Republican U.S Senators to vote against the ten-year $1.35 trillion tax cut package presented by President George W. Bush in 2001?

A70: Strom Thurmond

A71: Jim DeMint (R-SC) and David Vitter (R-LA)

A72: Ernest Groening (D-AK) and Wayne Morse (D-OR)

A73: Thomas Heflin (D-AL 1920-1931)

A74: Howard Baker (R-KS)

A75: Scott Brown (R-MA)

A76: Russell Feingold (D-WI)

A77: Andrew Johnson (R-TN). He was awarded for his actions, by becoming the Vice Presidential nominee with Abraham Lincoln in 1865.

A78: Ben Nelson of Nebraska

A79: Lincoln Chaffe of Rhode Island and John McCain of Arizona

Q80: In 1999, Bethel, Maine dedicated a record 122-foot-tall snowwoman named for which Republican U.S. Senator?

Q81: Which U.S. Senator was a Republican (1945-1952), an Independent, (1952-1955) and a Democrat (1955-1969)?

Q82: What is the largest committee in the U.S. Senate?

Q83: Between 1997 and 2010, there were no Republican members of the Massachusetts Congressional Delegation. This all changed when which person won an open U.S. Senate seat?

Q84: In 1959, U.S. Senator John F. Kennedy (D-MA) co-sponsored legislation offered by U.S. Senator Leverett Saltonstall (R-MA) to designate land in Massachusetts as a national park? Which land was this?

Q85: Which future U.S. Senate Majority Leader had no record of voting until he was 36?

Q86: After Gerald R. Ford pardoned his predecessor, Richard M. Nixon, which former Nixon opponent stunned the political world by supporting the decision, averring: "The pardon is right. It's the only decision the President could have made"?

Q87: What is it called when the U.S. Senate issues an official opinion, which is non-binding, and does not require a Presidential signature?

Q88: Who is the only U.S. Senator to reach 100 years of age while in the U.S. Senate?

Q89: What is the name of the privilege that allows all members of the U.S. Congress to send official correspondence to their constituents without paying postage?

A80: Olympia Snow. Snow commented about the edifice, known as: "Mount Olympia:" "just my luck I'd have a world record-breaking monument named after me — and it will be gone by summer."

A81: Wayne Morse of Oregon

A82: The Committee on Appropriations. It consists of 29 members.

A83: Scott Brown

A84: Cape Cod. In 1961, then President John F. Kennedy signed the legislation establishing Cape Cod National Sea Shore, which he had co-sponsored as a U.S. Senator. It is the first time the federal government created a national park out of land that was once privately owned.

A85: Bill Frist. He was elected to represent Tennessee in 1994 at 42 years old.

A86: Hubert Humphrey, who, as the Democratic Presidential nominee in 1968, had lost to Nixon.

A87: A Sense of Congress Resolution

A88: Strom Thurmond. The Republican was 100 years old when he left office in 2003.

A89: The Franking privilege

Q90: U.S. Representative Joseph P. Kennedy III (D-MA) met his wife while a student in Harvard Law School in a class taught by this future U.S. Senator. Who was his future Senator?

Q91: Who was the first Republican member of the U.S. Senate to call for President Richard M. Nixon to resign because of his role in the Watergate affair?

Q92: Who was the longest-serving female member of the U.S. Senate?

Q93: Who was the first retired admiral to serve in the U.S. Senate?

Q94: In 1967, President Lyndon B. Johnson called which U.S. Senator to tell him he was going to appoint him to the National Commission on Civil Disorders, a.k.a., the Kerner Commission (Johnson had a contentious relationship with the Senator because of the Senator's opposition to his policy on Vietnam)?

Q95: Which U.S. Senator made it a ritual to walk 127 miles of beaches in his home state of New Jersey every Labor Day (four-day weekend) to meet with constituents and to check on the state of the beaches?

Q96 Which steadfast supporter of the Chinese island of Formosa (referred to today as Taiwan) was given the nickname "The Senator from Formosa" because of his staunch support of Chaiang Kai-Shek's takeover of the island?

Q97: Who was the first Truman scholar to serve in the U.S. Senate?

Q98: Who is the only U.S. Senator with a star on the Hollywood Walk of Fame?

Q99: Which two U.S Senators were Prisoners of War in Vietnam?

Q100: President Lyndon B. Johnson and his Republican opponent in the 1964 Presidential run, Barry Goldwater, spoke at the funeral for which former U.S. Senator who died in 1972. He was President Pro Tempore from 1957-1967?

A90: Elizabeth Warren

A91: Edward Brooke of Massachusetts

A92: Margaret Chase Smith (R-ME) She served in that body from 1949-1973.

A93: Jeramiah Denton (R-AL). He served from 1981-1987.

A94: Fred Harris (D-OK). At the outset of the colloquy for Harris, Johnson would not take "no" for an answer. He explained to Harris: "I want you to remember that you're a 'Johnson man.' If you don't, Fred, I'll take out my pocketknife and cut your peter off. You're from Oklahoma; you understand that kind of talk, don't you?" Harris agreed.

A95: Bill Bradley

A96: William Knowland (R-CA)

A97: Chris Coons (D-DE). The scholarship gives $30,000 to students who demonstrate a commitment to public service.

A98: George Murphy (R-CA). Before entering politics in 1952, he was an esteemed song-and-dance man and the President of the Screen Actors Guild.

A99: Jeremiah Denton (R-AL) and John McCain (R-AZ)

A100: Carl Hayden (D-AZ)

Chapter XVI

U.S. Senate Campaigns

U.S. Senate Campaigns

Q1: Campaigning for Democrat Doug Jones over Republican Roy Moore in a 2017 U.S. Senate election in Alabama, which Alabama native and former NBA star told a crowd in Birmingham: "At some point, we've got to stop looking like idiots to the Nation"?

Q2: After Republican U.S. Senate nominee Harry McMaster challenged his opponent to take a drug test, his opponent responded: "I'll take a drug test if you take an IQ test." Who was this opponent?

Q3: In 1952, at the high watermark of his political popularity, anti-Communist U.S. Senator Joseph McCarthy (R-WI) barnstormed the country supporting Republican U.S. Senate candidates. Who was the only Republican Senator who asked for McCarthy to campaign for him, but McCarthy refused?

Q4: During an 1858 debate for the U.S. Senate, Stephen A. Douglas (D-IL), mentioned that he first met his Republican opponent as a customer at his bar. This opponent deadpanned: "I have left my side of the counter but Mr. Douglas still sticks as tenaciously as ever, to his." Who was this opponent?

Q5: During his successful 1976 campaign for a U.S. Senate Seat in California, which Republican exclaimed: "We should Keep the Panama Canal. After all we stole it fair and square"?

Q6: This U.S. Senator, who represented the liberal bloodline of the Texas Democratic Party, when running against more conservative candidates in the primary, tried to buttress his populist appeal with the inimical campaign slogan: "Let's put the jam on the lower shelf so the little people can reach." Which Senator said this?

Q7: After losing to Democrat Barack Obama in a race for an open U.S. Senate Seat in Illinois in 2004, this Republican nominee refused to call Obama and concede the election, claiming it would be a "false gesture." He said that Obama stands for "a culture evil enough to destroy the very soul and heart of my country." Which Republican Senate candidate made this statement?

Q8: In what year was it the first time that the nominees of both major parties in a U.S. Senate election were females?

Q9: In 1964, the Democrats nominated Robert F. Kennedy for U.S. Senate in New York. Kennedy moved to New York to run for the seat and was labeled a "carpetbagger" (Kennedy did spend part of his earlier years living in Riverdale and Bronxville, NY). His Republican opponent began a press conference by joking: "Well, ladies and gentlemen, we all know what we're here for. And I want to announce at the outset that I will not be a candidate for the United States Senate from Massachusetts." Massachusetts was the state Kennedy formerly had lived in. Who made this statement?

U.S. Senate Campaigns

A1: Charles Barkley

A2: Ernest "Fritz" Hollings (D-SC)

A3: Henry Cabot Lodge Jr. (R-MA). McCarthy had a close personal relationship with Lodge's Democratic opponent, U.S. Representative John F. Kennedy (D-MA) and the Kennedy family. In fact, in support of McCarthy, John F. Kennedy stormed out of a Harvard Reunion Dinner when a speaker extolled the fact that alleged American Communist Alger Hiss and Joseph McCarthy had never graduated from Harvard. Kennedy bellowed: "How dare you couple the name of a great American patriot with that of a traitor!"

A4: Abraham Lincoln

A5: Samuel Ichlye Hayakaw

A6: Ralph Yarborough

A7: Allan Keyes

A8: 1960. U.S. Senator Margaret Chase Smith (R-ME) defeated Lucia Cormier, the Minority Leader of the Maine House of Representatives.

A9: Kenneth Keating

Q10: In 1918, this President endorsed Pat Harrison in the Democratic U.S. Senate Primary against the incumbent Democrat James K. Vardaman (D-MS). The President was inflamed that Vardaman had voted against the Congressional Declaration of War with Germany. Vardaman did not take Wilson's endorsement of Harrison in stride. He called the President "the coldest blooded, most selfish ruler beneath the stars today." Who was this President?

Q11: In 1972, Democratic upstart Joe Biden upset long-time Republican U.S. Senator Caleb Boggs. How old was Biden at this time?

Q12: After losing his bid for renomination for the Democratic U.S. Senate nomination in 2006, Joe Lieberman won as the nomination of which political party?

Q13: In 2010, it was revealed that this U.S. Senate Republican candidate from Delaware, had "dabbled in witchcraft" when she was younger. In response to this criticism, she appeared in a TV advertisement declaring: "I am not a witch." Who was this candidate?

Q14: After starting her career castrating pigs, she won the 2014 Republican nomination for an open U.S. Senate seat in Iowa. In a campaign advertisement, she exclaimed: "I grew up castrating pigs on an Iowa farm. So, when I get to Washington, I'll know how to cut pork. Let's make 'em squeal." Who made this unusual statement?

Q15: In 2004, this Chicago Bulls legend wrote a check to U.S. Senate Candidate Barack Obama. Upon seeing the check, Obama mused: "I wasn't sure whether I should cash it or frame it." Who was this Chicago Bulls legend?

Q16: In a 2010 interview with Dan Rae of *WBZ* radio, this Massachusetts Democratic U.S. Senate nominee was asked about former Red Sox World Series hero Curt Schilling's endorsement of her Republican opponent, Scott Brown. She replied: "Curt Schilling is a Yankee fan." Who was this U.S. Senate nominee?

Q17: During a 2012 U.S. Senate Campaign, this Senate candidate was criticized by her opponent, U.S. Representative Rick Berg (R-MT), for being too much like President Obama. In a debate with Berg, she stated: "Congressman Berg will repeatedly talk about . . . Barack Obama, and I find it interesting because this morning when I woke up and brushed my teeth, I looked in the mirror and I did not see a tall, African-American, skinny man." Who was this Obama non-lookalike?

Q18: In his 1996 concession speech, after losing a hotly-contested U.S. Senate race to incumbent John Kerry, this Republican Massachusetts Governor announced: "I'm not stupid. I got the message. The message is I'm a real good Governor, and I should stick to that." Who was this Massachusetts Governor?

Q19: In his 2004 successful re-election bid, which U.S. Senator faced a firestorm of criticism for saying that his Democratic opponent, Daniel Monglaro, "looks like one of [Iraqi President] Saddam Hussein's sons . . . I mean before they were dead, of course . . . .. I really mean that he looks like one of Saddam's sons, and he even dresses like them, too"?

A10: Woodrow Wilson

A11: The Constitutionally permissible age to serve in the U.S. Senate is 30. Biden turned 30 after being elected, but before assuming office.

A12: The Connecticut for Lieberman Party

A13: Christine O'Donnell

A14: Joni Ernst

A15: Michael Jordan

A16: Martha Coakley. Coakley, the Massachusetts Attorney General, was running for a U.S. Senate seat. Curt Shilling was a star pitcher for the Boston Red Sox and in the news a lot. The fact that Coakley did not know who Curt Shilling was proved embarrassing for her campaign, which the news media latched onto.

A17: Heidi Heitkamp (D-ND)

A18: Bill Weld

A19: Jim Bunning (R-KY)

Q20: Memphis, TN political boss Ed Crump was a vociferous opponent of this Democratic U.S. Senate candidate in his home state. Crump wrote an editorial lampooning him by comparing him to a pet coon. The candidate then sported a coonskin hat, telling supporters: "I may be a coon, but I ain't Mr. Crump's pet coon." From that point forward, he wore a coonskin cap when addressing a crowd. Who wore this coonskin cap?

Q21: In 2008, while U.S. Senator Joe Biden (D-DE) was the Democratic Vice Presidential nominee, he was also up for a sixth term as a U.S. Senator. Which conservative activist, who was the Republican nominee, tried to shame Biden into debating her, but to no avail?

Q22: This Catholic Priest left the Priesthood to run against U.S. Senator John O. Pastore (D-RI) in 1970. He lost the race, and subsequently became an advisor to President Richard M. Nixon. Later in life, he hosted a public affairs television program. Who was this Priest?

Q23: In 2014, as this U.S. Senator was running for re-election, he told a crowd about how as a kid he visited his father's family farm in Richton, Mississippi. He mused that he did "all kinds of indecent things to animals." Who was this Senator?

Q24: During a 2014 campaign stop at the Red Arrow Diner in Manchester, New Hampshire, this U.S. Senate candidate responded to *The Associated Press*: "Do I have the best credentials? Probably not, cause, you know, 'whatever.' But I have long and strong ties to this state." Who made this statement?

Q25: During a U.S Senate debate on *NBC*'s *Meet the Press* in 2006, this Democratic U.S. Senate nominee was asked by moderator Tim Russert: "Bill Clinton raised money for you. Do you think Bill Clinton was a great President?" She responded: "I think he's been a great leader but I don't want my daughter near him."

Q26: Speaking at a campaign rally for California's 2010 Republican Senate nominee Carly Fiorina, this U.S. Senator chastised her opponent, U.S Senator Barbara Boxer (D-CA). He said: "Barbara Boxer is the most bitterly partisan, most anti-defense Senator in the United States Senate today. I know that because I've had the unpleasant experience of having to serve with her." Who made this statement?

Q27: Who was the first female to defeat an incumbent U.S. Senator?

Q28: In 1998, a campaign staffer, who worked for the Democratic U.S. Senate nominee in North Carolina, secretly recorded a speech delivered by Jonathan Hill, the Chief of Staff of his Republican opponent U.S. Senator Lauch Faircloth (R-NC). In the recorded speech, Hill appears to belittle the average voter. Who was this campaign staffer working for?

Q29: In 2020, which former Democratic Vice Presidential nominee appeared in an advertisement for Republican U.S. Senator Susan Collins in her re-election bid?

A20: Estes Kefauver

A21: Christine O'Donnell. Biden spent $7 million on his reelection effort in the blue state, while O'Donnell spent just $115,000. Biden won the race with 64.7% of the vote. After being elected, and sworn into a third term, Biden resigned the seat. Democratic Governor Ruth Ann Miner appointed Biden's longtime advisor Ted Kaufman to succeed him in the Senate.

A22: John McLaughlin. He hosted *The McLaughlin Group*

A23: Thad Cochran (R-MS)

A24: Scott Brown (R-MA)

A25: Claire McCaskill (D-MO). She later apologized to Clinton for the comments.

A26: John McCain (R-AZ)

A27: Carol Moseley Braun defeated Democrat Allan Dixon of Illinois in the Democratic Primary in 1992. Moseley Braun served for just one term, losing her re-election bid in 1998 to Republican Peter Fitzgerald.

A28: John Edwards. In the speech, Hill told a crowd in Greensboro, NC: "The average person watching television, who does not have your intellect, the average person doesn't know what is going on in the real world. They are sitting there watching Oprah and what they see on television - - they believe." Faircloth said after the tape was released that he: "took Hill to the woodshed." The Faircloth campaign responded: "John Edwards is Linda Tripp (who tape recorded Monica Lewinsky) with a better haircut going around secretly taping people." Edwards won the race, and six years later was the unsuccessful Democratic Vice-Presidential nominee.

A29: Joe Lieberman

Q30: In 2000, which Massachusetts Republican U.S. Senate candidate held a press conference where he released a report highlighting a number of issues from his personal life? In the report, he denied allegations by a female that he forced himself on her. He alleged that the woman harassed him because he wanted to break off the relationship with her. He then defended himself against charges of violating an author's copyright while attempting to publish a book about Pan American Airlines. He also addressed why he failed the bar three times, and a drunken driving and dangerous weapons charge. Who is this Senate candidate?

Q31: In 1994, U.S. Senator Chuck Robb (D-VA) said that his Republican opponent: "is a document-shredding, Constitution-trashing, Commander in Chief-bashing, Congress-thrashing, uniform-shaming, Ayatollah-loving, arms-dealing, criminal-protecting, résumé-enhancing, Noriega-coddling, Social Security-threatening, public school-denigrating, Swiss-banking-law-breaking, letter-faking, self-serving, election-losing, snake-oil salesman who can't tell the difference between the truth and a lie." The next day, Robb won the Senate election. Who was the opponent that he was criticizing?

Q32: During the 2020 U.S. Senate Debate in Georgia, how many times did Republican Kelly Loffler refer to her opponent as: "Radical liberal Raphael Warnock?"

Q33: In 1948, future Republican President Ronald Reagan ventured to Minnesota to campaign for the election of which Democrat to the U.S. Senate?

Q34: In 1988, which liberal Republican U.S. Senator became the first person in Connecticut to secure the endorsement of the Connecticut A.F.L.-C.I.O?

Q35: In 2020, which Democratic U.S. Senate candidate raised a record $57 million from across the country, the record for any Senate candidate?

Q36: In 1995, which Republican, running for a seventh term, said he supported term limits. He averred: "It might be just as well for people to have a change in their Congressman?"

Q37: In 2020, Willie Wilson ran for the U.S Senate in Illinois as the nominee of which political party?

Q38: In 1984, as Ronald Reagan was winning a 49-state landslide nationally, who was the only Republican to defeat an incumbent Democratic U.S. Senator?

Q39: In 2020, which former Republican U.S. Senator from Kansas bucked her party and endorsed Democrat Barbara Boiler in her U.S. Senate race against Republican Roger Marshall?

A30: Jack E. Robinson

A31: Oliver North

A32: 13

A33: Hubert Humphrey

A34: Lowell Wiecker. He lost the race to Democrat Joe Lieberman.

A35: Jamie Harrison in South Carolina. He lost to Republican incumbent Lindsey Graham by over eight percentage points.

A36: Storm Thurmond

A37: Willie Wilson Party

A38: Mitch McConnell. He upended incumbent Democrat Dee Huddleston. McConnell had trouble garnering electoral traction with rural voters. Many saw him as a cosmopolitan politician from Louisville, awkward in rural Kentucky. McConnell was not helped when President Ronald Reagan, knowing little about him, referred to him as "Mitch O'Donnell." The blockbuster advertisement featured a pack of bloodhounds searching for Huddleston. The voiceover averred: "My job was to find Dee Huddleston and get him back to work. Huddleston was skipping votes but making an extra fifty thousand dollars giving speeches. Let's go, boys!" McConnell eked out a victory by less than 0.5% of the vote. He was the only Republican to dislodge an incumbent Democratic U.S. Senator that year, despite the landslide by Ronald Reagan nationally.

A39: Nancy Kassebaum Baker

Q40: In a 2020 debate, this U.S. Senator did not know the break-even price for a bushel of soybeans?

Q41: In 1938, U.S. Senate Majority Leader Alben Barkley (D-KY) was enveloped in a battle royal trying to keep his Senate Seat against which incumbent Kentucky Governor who maintained that the Barkley campaign had tried to poison him?

Q42: In 2005, President George W. Bush kissed which U.S. Senator? His Democratic primary opponent used it against him the following year.

Q43: In 2020, Democrat Ben Lajan won the seat of which U.S. Senator, who was the only Democrat to retire that year?

Q44: In 1858, which two Illinois U.S. Senate candidates had seven debates about the issue of slavery?

Q45: Which U.S Senator lost his re-election bid, in part by seeming to focus too much on national issues and ignoring campaigning for re-election?

Q46: During his 1958 re-election campaign to the U.S. Senate, who coined the term "missile gap?"

Q47: Republican Richard M. Nixon was elected to the U.S. Senate in 1950 by characterizing which Democratic opponent, as "the pink lady" and "pink right down to her underwear," alleging she had "communist sympathies."?

Q48: In 2014, who challenged U.S. Senate Minority Leader Mitch McConnell (R-KY) for the Republican U.S. Senate nomination and had typed Massachusetts Institute of Technology on his LinkedIn Page, even though he only attended an executive education program there, which the school did not recognize?

Q49: In 1994, which former Democratic Governor, who was running for a U.S. Senate seat in Virginia, dropped out of the race and eventually endorsed Democratic nominee Chuck Robb?

A40: Joni Ernst (R-IA). She still won the race.

A41: Happy Chandler. Chandler suffered from a high fever coupled with chest pains. His doctor, Dan Talbott alleged that he drank ice water that had been "doctored with poison" which he was provided at a hotel, where he was delivering a radio address. The doctor contended that someone from the Barkley campaign had "tried to kill him [Chandler]" to get Barkley re-elected.

A42: U.S Senator Joe Lieberman (D-CT). The footage was soon disseminated by progressives around the state of Connecticut in an attempt to tether Lieberman to Bush. Lieberman's Democratic opponent, Ned Lamont, categorized the kiss as the tethering of Lieberman to Bush. Lamont won the primary, but Lieberman ran against him again in the General Election as the nominee of The Connecticut for Lieberman Party, and upended Lamont.

A43: Tom Udall (D-NM)

A44: Abraham Lincoln and Stephan Douglas. Lincoln opposed slavery. Douglas supported the concept of popular sovereignty which meant that each state should decide for themselves the question of slavery. Douglas won the election.

A45: Jeramiah Denton (R-AL). He led a quixotic charge to separate charges of spousal rape from non-spousal rape, deadpanning:" when you get married, you kind of expect you're going to get a little sex."

A46: John F. Kennedy (D-MA). Kennedy contended that the Russians were hegemonic in terms of ballistic missile technology. It was later revealed that Kennedy knew this was a fallacy, yet he continued to make the charge during his successful 1960 Presidential campaign.

A47: Helen Gahagan Douglas. In addition, the Nixon campaign employed dirty tricks against Douglas, including sending flyers out to voters telling them to answer their telephones when they would ring at a certain time, to win "prizes galore." When the voters picked up, there were no prizes, just a voice averring: "Did you know Helen Gahagan Douglas was a Communist?" After Nixon won the race, his campaign strategist said: "The purpose of an election is not to defeat your opponent, but to destroy them." Ronald Reagan campaigned for Douglas.

A48: Matt Bevin. McConnell called him out on the claim, because Bevin was not a graduate of the school, but attended an executive education program, which the school does not recognize. Bevin soon erased the school from his resume, supplanting it with: "School of life."

A49: Doug Wilder. He attributed his dropping out of the race to his failure to garner traction in the polls. He averred: "Though I don't attach great significance to polls, they are influential, and the influence on financing capabilities is great."

Chapter XVII

U.S. Senate Quotations

Q1: After this U.S. Senator announced her support of the use of nuclear weapons against the Soviet Union, Soviet President Nikita Khrushchev labeled her: "the devil in disguise as a woman." Who was this Senator?

Q2: When told that the Imperial Wizard of the Ku Klux Klan was going to come to Louisiana, this Democratic U.S. Senator said: "You tell that Imperial bastard in Mississippi to keep out of Louisiana. Tell that son of a bitch that I am not just using an expression; I am referring to the circumstances of his birth." Who made this statement?

Q3: After the Persian Gulf War had concluded, which U.S. Senator told *The Independent of London:* "The Gulf War was like teenage sex. We got in too soon and out too soon"?

Q4: In 1927, this U.S. Senate Majority Leader appeared in a magazine advertisement for Lucky Strike Cigarettes. In the advertisement, it states: "Lucky Strikes do not affect the voice. I notice that most of my colleagues in the Senate now use them. They do so, not only because they know that they are kind to the throat, but also they give the greatest enjoyment." Which Senator made this advertisement?

Q5: After being elected to the U.S. Senate in 1994, this Tennessee Republican quipped: "I've still got a lot to learn about Washington. Thursday, I accidentally spent some of my own money." Who was his new Senator?

Q6: In 1990, while blasting President George H.W. Bush's environmental speech at the Grand Canyon, this U.S. Senator exclaimed: "Anyone who sees George Bush as the environmental President at the Grand Canyon ought to look closely for Elvis, alive and well, rafting by on the Colorado River. A zebra cannot change its stripes by standing on a busy street corner in a city." Which Senator blasted President Bush?

Q7: Speaking to the National Rifle Association Convention in 1994, this U.S. Senator garnered applause by saying: "I own more shotguns than I need, but not as many as I want." Who made this statement?

Q8: A Maine constituent asked her U.S. Senator: "What would you do if you woke up one morning and found yourself in the White House?" She deadpanned: "I would go to the President's wife and apologize, and then leave at once." Which Maine Senator gave this funny response?

Q9: This Chairman of the U.S. Senate Select Committee on Intelligence joked: "I have the privilege of being Chairman of the Senate Intelligence Committee. It is not an oxymoron I assure you." Who made this joke?

A1: Margaret Chase Smith (R-ME)

A2: Huey Long

A3: Tom Harkin (D-IA)

A4: Charles Curtis (R-KS)

A5: Fred Thompson

A6: Al Gore (D-TN)

A7: Phil Gramm (R-TX)

A8: Margaret Chase Smith

A9: Pat Roberts (R-KS)

U.S. Senate Quotations

Q10: In 1984, which U.S. Senator announced he would not seek re-election after being diagnosed with non-Hodgkin Lymphoma? He said: "No one on his deathbed ever said, I wish I had spent more time on my business."

Q11: In 1990, noting the ideological diversity of the Democratic Party, which U.S. Senator said: "You get fifteen Democrats in a room, and you get twenty opinions"?

Q12: In 2009, which U.S. Senator observed: "The Senate is a graveyard for good ideas. Gridlock, hyper-partisanship, delay, obstruction – it adds up to one thing: broken"?

Q13: 1989, when asked about the powers he would employ upon assuming the office of U.S. Senate Majority Leader, which Senator replied: "You have to kiss 99 asses"?

Q14: During the closing arguments on the impeachment of President Bill Clinton before the U.S. Senate, which former U.S. Senator, arguing for the defense, told his former Senate colleagues: "H. L. Mencken [Essayist] said one time, 'When you hear somebody say: This is not about money' – it's about money.' And when you hear somebody say: 'This is not about sex' – it's about sex"?

Q15: In 1953, this U.S. Senator from Oregon left the Republican Party believing that the party had moved too far to the right. He was now an Independent and the Republican Party no longer afforded him a seat on the Senate Floor. Accordingly, he brought his own chair to the Senate Floor from home. He said: "Since I haven't been given any seat in the Senate, I've decided to bring my own." Two years later, this Senator became a Democrat and received a chair on the Democratic side of the aisle. Who was this Senator?

Q16: This U.S. Senator, a vociferous critic of President Bill Clinton, told *The Raleigh News and Observer* in 1995: "Mr. Clinton better watch out if he comes down here. He'd better have a bodyguard." He was referring to Clinton's unpopularity throughout military bases in North Carolina. This Senator later said it was "an offhand remark." Who was the Senator who made this controversial remark?

Q17: At a dinner, this U.S. Senator inadvertently picked up a press release rather than a speech written for him by aides, and then said to the crowd: "Ladies and Gentlemen, it is a great pleasure to be with you today. For immediate release today." Who made this gaffe?

Q18: This U.S. Senator was a member of the Gang of Six, who negotiated Health Care Reform. He opposed the Democrats' Healthcare Plan. Speaking to his constituents at a Wyoming town hall meeting, he insisted that he was trying to negotiate concessions, and defended his negotiations with the Democrats by saying: "If you're not at the table, you're on the menu." Who said this?

Q19: Which U.S. Senator said of Admiral Lewis Strauss (a rejected nominee to serve on the Atomic Energy Commission): "He is the only guy I know that could strut sitting down"?

A10: Paul Tsongas (D-MA)

A11: Patrick Leahy (D-VT)

A12: Tom Udall (D-NM)

A13: George Mitchell (D-ME)

A14: Dale Bumpers (D-AR)

A15: Wayne Morse

A16: Jesse Helms (R-NC)

A17: Joseph Montoya (D-NM)

A18: Mike Enzi (R-WY)

A19: Warren Magnuson (D-WA)

Q20: During his address to the Republican National Convention in 2012, this U.S. Senate Majority Leader received laughter when he joked that: "For years, Barack Obama has been running from the nation's problems. He hasn't been working to earn re-election. He's been working to earn a spot on the PGA [Professional Golf Association] Tour." Which Senator made this statement about Barack Obama?

Q21: As Bill Clinton's job approval rating increased in 1997, which U.S. Senator quipped: "If they reach 60 percent, then he can start dating again"?

Q22: At a 2005 event at Del Sol High School in Las Vegas, this U.S. Senate Minority Leader said of President George W. Bush: "This man's father was a wonderful human being. I think this guy is a loser." Reed later apologized to Deputy Chief of Staff Karl Rove for making this remark. Who made the remark?

Q23: During a debate on legislation to combat Aids in 1991, which U.S. Senator said: "I'm so old-fashioned, I believe in horse-whipping"? (Horsewhipping is the act of whipping a horse to control it)

Q24: In 1961, this Western conservative U.S. Senator joked at a press conference: "Sometimes I think this country would be better off if we could just saw off the Eastern Seaboard and let it float out to sea." Who was this Senator?

Q25: In 1995, this U.S. Senator told ABC News, "What these peckerwoods call pork is infrastructure." Which Senator made this statement?

Q26: Upon seeing Presidents Jimmy Carter, Gerald R. Ford and Richard M. Nixon standing together at the 1978 funeral of Vice President Hubert Humphrey, which U.S. Senator exclaimed: "See no evil, hear no evil — and evil."?

Q27: A stalwart supporter of President Lyndon B. Johnson on most issues this progressive Democrat broke from the President on his handling of the Vietnam War. He told the President he was persuaded by nationally syndicated columnist Walter Lippmann that the U.S. should negotiate with the North Vietnamese Government. Johnson responded: "The next time you want a dam in Idaho, go talk to Walter Lippmann." Who was President Johnson responding to?

Q28: When this Alaska Governor was elected to the U.S. Senate in 2002, he appointed his daughter, Lisa to fill out the remaining two years of his senate seat. In response to charges of nepotism, Mrs. Murkowski responded: "I have never once asked Alaskans to like how I got this job." Who was this Alaskan Governor?

Q29: This former actor was elected to the U.S. Senate in 1994. Two years into his first term, he observed: "After two years in Washington, I often long for the realism and sincerity of Hollywood." Who was this Senator?

A20: Mitch McConnell (R-KY)

A21: Ernest "Fritz" Hollings (D-SC)

A22: Harry Reid (D-NV)

A23: Jesse Helms (R-NC)

A24: Barry Goldwater (R-AZ)

A25: Robert C. Byrd (D-WV)

A26: Bob Dole (R-KS)

A27: Frank Church (D-ID)

A28: Frank Murkowski (R-AK)

A29: Fred Thompson (R-TN)

Q30: In a conference call with Iowa reporters, this U.S. Senator, the Chairman of the Senate Agricultural Committee, said: "The farm bill is like giving birth to a porcupine. It's very painful." Which Senator made this porcupine analogy?

Q31: During a 1978 debate on the U.S. Senate Floor about restructuring the Committee System, which U.S. Senator observed: "The Senate is a little like [George] Orwell's *Animal Farm*. All pigs are equal, but some are more equal than others"?

Q32: This U.S. Senator knew his colleagues were no angels. Accordingly, he often told his friends that some were "liars, trimmers, and pussy-footers." Who said this?

Q33: Lyndon B. Johnson said that this U.S. Senator: "could be standing right in the middle of the worst Mississippi flood ever known, and blame it on the negroes helped by the communists." Who was Johnson referring to?

Q34: Which U.S. Senator said: "If there was any other race other than the human race, I'd go join it"?

Q35: Observing the actions of this Freshman U.S. Senator, veteran U.S. Senator Alben Barkley (D-KY) said to him: "You are the smartest lunatic I have ever seen in my whole life." Who was Barkley referring to?

Q36: On the U.S. Senate Floor, this Senator performed a rendition of the popular Children's song E-I-E-I-O in opposition to the proposed crime bill supported by Bill Clinton. While standing next to a drawing of a pink pig, this Senator sang: "President Clinton had a bill, E-I-E-I-O. And in that bill was lots of pork, E-I-E-I-O. New pork here, old pork there, here pork, there pork, everywhere pork, pork." Who was this singing Senator?

Q37: Which U.S. Senator claimed that anything goes at U.S. Congressional luncheons with Lobbyists. Regarding what was allowed, he said: "Anything you can eat, drink, or fornicate in one afternoon"?

Q38: In 2013, this U.S. Senator filibustered for 13-hours to get the administration of Barack Obama to say they would not kill non-combatants in America. Though he has become identified as a critic of drones, when he found out that drones are being used for beer delivery at an outdoor music festival in South Africa, he tweeted: "Perhaps I am not against all drones." Who was this Senator?

Q39: In 2012, this U.S. Senator told *GQ Magazine* that the rapper Pit Bull's songs are "all party songs. There's no message for him, compared to like an Eminem. But look, there's always been a role for that in American music. There's always been a party person, but he's a young guy. You know, maybe as he gets older, he'll reflect in his music more as time goes on. I mean he's not Tupac. He's not gonna be writing poetry." Who was this Senator?

A30: Tom Harkin (D-IA)

A31: Lawton Chiles (D-FL)

A32: Harry S. Truman (D-MO)

A33: James Eastland (D-MS)

A34: Thomas Gore (D-OK)

A35: Huey Long (D-LA)

A36: Alfonse D'Amato (R-NY)

A37: Paul Douglas (D-IL)

A38: Rand Paul (R-KY)

A39: Marco Rubio (R-FL)

Q40: In 2014, the U.S. emplaced sanctions on Russia and certain Russian officials for Russia's invasion and annexation of the Crimean Peninsula. In retaliation, Russia imposed sanctions on some U.S. government officials, including this U.S. Senator. In response, this Senator tweeted: "I guess this means my Spring Break in Siberia is off, my Gazprom stock is lost, and my secret bank account in Moscow is frozen." Who was this Senator?

Q41: In an appearance on *Larry King Live*, this former U.S. Senate Majority Leader said that he is a test subject for Viagra. He joked: "I wish I had bought stock in it. Only a Republican would think the best part of Viagra is the fact that you could make money off of it." Which Senator made this statement?

Q42: This former Republican Senator explains the difference between the Democrats and Republicans this way; "We have two political parties, the Stupid Party and the Evil Party. I belong to the Stupid Party." Who was this former Senator?

Q43: In 2001, this 79-year-old U.S. Senator became friends with U2 Front Man Bono. He even attended a U2 Concert. The conservative Senator told *The Charlotte News & Observer*: "It was the noisiest thing I ever heard. I turned my hearing aids all the way down and kept my hands over my ears much of the time." Who was this "rock and roll" Senator?

Q44: At his 2002 100th birthday celebration, this U.S. Senator said to the crowd: "I love all of you men, but you women even more." This Senator was known as a ladies' man. When he was 66 years old, he married Nancy Moore, the 22-year-old Miss South Carolina. Who was this ladies' man?

Q45: When this U.S. Senator was confronted with a photograph taken through a telephoto lens of his colleague U.S. Senator Ted Kennedy (D-MA) in compromising photographs with a female companion aboard his yacht, he averred: "I see Senator Kennedy has changed his position on offshore drilling." Which Senator made this statement?

Q46: This U.S. Senator would often say: "The first 9 pages of the Internal Revenue Code define income; the remaining 1,100 pages spin the web of exceptions and preferences." Who made this statement?

Q47: On matters of foreign policy, this U.S. Senator was considered by many as a hawk during the Cold War. However, he rejected that characterization, saying: "I'm not a hawk nor a dove, I just don't want my country to be a pigeon." Which Senator made this statement?

Q48: This U.S. Senator was known for his ability to compromise. He said: "I am a man of fixed and unbending principles, the first of which is to be flexible at all times." Who was this compromiser?

Q49: This U.S. Senator was a lead sponsor of a Deficit Reduction Act with Warren Rudman (R-NH) and Phil Gramm (R-TX). He remarked on Gramm's tendency to enjoy the limelight: "If you want a lesson in political anonymity, sponsor a bill with Phil Gramm." Who was this sponsoring Senator?

A40: John McCain (R-AZ)

A41: Bob Dole (R-KS)

A42: Allan Simpson (R-WY)

A43: Jesse Helms (R-NC)

A44: Strom Thurmond (R-SC)

A45: Howell Heflin (D-AL)

A46: Warren Magnuson (D-WA)

A47: Henry "Scoop" Jackson (D-WA)

A48: Everett Dirksen (R-IL)

A49: Ernest "Fritz" Hollings (D-SC)

Q50: Conservative columnist George Will said that this U.S. Senator wrote 18 books, and added that this Senator "wrote more books than most Senators read." Who was George Will referring to?

Q51: Which U.S. Senator, the Chairman of the U.S. Senate Agricultural Committee, led the fight against proposed cuts by President Ronald Reagan to the Tobacco Support Program? Speaking before The Tobacco Associates, he asked the crowd to repeat after him: "There is no tobacco subsidy."

Q52: U.S. Senator Sherrod Brown (D-OH) asked U.S. Senator Dan Sullivan (R-TX), who was presiding over the Chamber, to wear a mask. Another Republican Senator tweeted that Brown "is being a complete ass? He wears a mask to speak when nobody is remotely near him as an ostentatious sign of a fake virtue." Who made this statement against Senator Brown?

Q53: Which U.S. Senator, who later became Vice President, averred: "The Senate is a place filled with goodwill and good intentions, and if the road to hell is paved with them, then it's a pretty good detour.

Q54: In 2002, this U.S. Senate Minority Leader was forced to step down from his position after praising U.S. Senator Strom Thurmond (R-SC). Thurmond had run as a Segregationist for President. He was the nominee of the State's' Rights Democrats Party, a.k.a. The Dixiecrat Party?

Q55: In 1966, which Republican U.S. Senator from California, known for his moderate proclivities, said of the burgeoning conservative bloodline spearheaded by Gubernatorial nominee Ronald Reagan: "A fanatical neo-fascist political cult of right-wingers in the GOP driven by a strange mixture of corrosive hatred and sickening fear that is recklessly determined to control our party to destroy it"?

Q56: Which U.S. Senate opponent of the U.S. role in the Vietnam War averred: "After you have been bombing villagers with napalm, it's going to be very difficult to persuade people that you are their friend."

Q57: Which U.S. Senator deadpanned: "If God had wanted us to use the metric system, Jesus would have had 10 apostles"?

Q58: U.S. Senator Milton Young (R-ND) once said to which Southern Senator: "You people in the South are more military-minded than in the North." The Southern Senator responded; "Milton, you'd be militarily minded too if (Civil War General John) Sherman had crossed into North Dakota. Which Senator made this response?

Q59: According to *The New York Times*, which U.S. Senator, in referring to the Senate, told his colleagues: "This place sucks"?

A50: Daniel Patrick Moynihan (D-NY)

A51: Jesse Helms (R-NC). He was a fiscal conservative and wanted to differentiate that the federal loans made to tobacco farmers were actually "market regulators." Helms also averred: "I was with some Vietnamese recently, and some of them were smoking two cigarettes at the same time. That's the kind of customers we need."

A52: Ted Cruz (R-TX). Senator Sullivan did not take off his mask, bellowing to Senator Brown: "I don't wear a mask when I'm speaking. I don't need your instructions."

A53: Hubert Humphrey

A54: Trent Lott (R-MS). He was speaking at Thurmond's 100th birthday party. He averred: "When Strom Thurmond ran for President, we voted for him. And if the rest of the country had followed our lead, we wouldn't have had all those problems over the years, either?"

A55: Thomas Kuchel

A56: Ernest Gruening (D-AK)

A57: Jesse Helms (R-NC)

A58: Richard Russell (D-GA)

A59: Joe Manchin (D-WV)

Chapter XVIII

U.S. Judiciary

U.S. Judiciary

Q1:   In what legal case did the U.S. Supreme Court establish itself as the arbiter of the U.S, Constitution, deciding their cases based upon Constitutional permissibility?

Q2:   In 1994, conservative Talk Show Host Rush Limbaugh married aerobics instructor Marla Fitzgerald. Which U.S. Supreme Court Justice officiated the event?

Q3:   The oldest person to join the U.S. Supreme Court was Horace Lurton. He was nominated by President William Howard Taft and confirmed by the U.S. Senate in 1909. How old was he at that time?

Q4:   On two occasions Dwight D. Eisenhower offered to nominate this former New York Governor to become Chief Justice of the United States. However, he turned down the offer both times. Who was this individual?

Q5:   Which U.S. Supreme Court Justice was the runner-up for the Heisman Trophy while a halfback for the University of Colorado Buffaloes?

Q6:   Which former U.S. Supreme Court Justice was the first female to lie in state in the nation's capital?

Q7:   Which U.S. Supreme Court Justice attended the World Series game at Wrigley Field in Chicago where New York Yankees slugger Babe Ruth allegedly pointed to Centerfield before hitting a home run in that area of the outfield?

Q8:   What is the official title of John Roberts?

Q9:   In 2020, the U.S. House of Representatives voted to replace a statue of which Chief Justice of the United States with a statue of Thurgood Marshall, the first African American Supreme Court Justice?

A1: *Marbury v. Madison* (1803)

A2: Clarence Thomas

A3: 65 years old. He served on the Court until his death in 1914 at age 70.

A4: Thomas E. Dewey

A5: Byron "Whizzer" White. He lost to Yale Quarterback Clint Frank who was awarded the Heisman Trophy that year. White was the fourth overall selection in the 1938 NFL draft, picked by the Pittsburg Steelers.

A6: Ruth Bader Ginsberg

A7: John Paul Stevens

A8: Chief Justice of the United States (Not Chief Justice of the United States Supreme Court)

A9: Roger Taney. He authored the *Dread Scott v. U.S.* decision, which ruled that African Americans were not U.S. citizens?

Q10: In 1989, by swearing Dan Quayle into office, she became the first female to swear in a Vice President. Who was she?

Q11: Who was the youngest person ever to serve on the U.S. Supreme Court?

Q12: Who is the only U.S. Supreme Court Justice to be impeached?

Q13: Who was the first female to petition before the U.S. Supreme Court?

Q14: U.S. Supreme Court Justice Melville Fuller instituted which formal greeting among Court members, which is still used today?

Q15: In Puerto Rico, what age are Supreme Court Justices required to leave the bench?

Q16: Under what 3 circumstances do Supreme Court Justices exit from office?

Q17: The front of the U.S. Supreme Court displays what following inscription?

Q18: In 2000, which U.S. Supreme Court Justice scored a hole-in-one at the Paradise Valley Country Club in Scottsdale, Arizona?

Q19: When the U.S. Supreme Court deliberates in private, who holds the solemn responsibility of opening the door when someone knocks on it?

A10: Sandra Day O'Conner

A11: Joseph Story. He was just 32 years old when the U.S. Senate confirmed him in 1811. He served on the High Court until his death in 1845.

A12: Samuel Chase. In 1804, the Democratic-Republican controlled House charged Chase with allowing his partisan Federalist philosophy to influence his rulings. The U.S. Senate acquitted him.

A13: Ann Bennett Lockwood. The suffragist preformed this task in 1879.

A14: The Conference Handshake. Each Justice shakes the hands of every other justice before deliberating to discuss a case.

A15: 70

A16: 1) Death, 2) Impeachment and Conviction by the U. S. Congress, and 3) Retirement

A17: "Equal Justice Under the Law"

A18: Sandra Day O'Connor

A19: The most junior justice

Q20: The U.S. Supreme Court was established in 1790. In what year did it hear its first case?

Q21: Which Chief Justice of the United States wore gold stripes on his robe?

Q22: How many justices were on the original U.S. Supreme Court?

Q23: Chief Justice of the United States William Rehnquist was born on October 1, 1924. Which President was born on that same day?

Q24: Which U.S. Supreme Court Justice resigned his position and became the Assistant Secretary of War for the Confederate States of America?

Q25: How many Federal District Courts are there in the U.S?

Q26: Who was the longest serving U.S. Supreme Court Justice in history?

Q27: Which future U.S. Supreme Court Justice ordered Major League Baseball to restore free agency?

Q28: How many U.S. Supreme Court Justices must agree to hear a case?

Q29: In 1982, federal legislation was passed authorizing the U.S. Supreme Court Police to carry what item?

A20: 1792. It spent the first two years defining its role and establishing authority.

A21: William Rehnquist. He did this as a tribute to Lord Chancellor, a character in the Gilbert and Sullivan Opera *Lolanthe.*

A22: 6

A23: Jimmy Carter

A24: John Archibald Campbell

A25: 94

A26: William O' Douglas. He served from 1939-1973.

A27: Sonia Sotomayor. As a District Court Judge, she drafted a preliminary injunction against Major League Baseball, ordering the League to restore free agency. This ended the Baseball Strike of 1994-1995. She took just fifteen minutes to issue her injunction. The Second Circuit Court of Appeals upheld the decision.

A28: 4

A29: Firearms

Chapter XIX

U.S. Supreme Court Quotations

U.S. Supreme Court Quotations

Q1:   When asked about his days as a campus radical while a student at the College of the Holy Cross in Worcester, Massachusetts, this U.S. Supreme Court Justice responded: "Yeah, but I was no dope head. The sixties were different"?

Q2:   In the U.S. Supreme Court ruling: *Jacobellis v. Ohio* 378 U.S. 184 (1964), regarding possible obscenity in the movie *The Lovers*, this Justice remarked: "I shall not today attempt further to define the kinds of material I understand to be embraced within that shorthand description [pornography]; and perhaps I could never succeed in intelligibly doing so. But I know it when I see it, and the motion picture involved in this case is not that." Who was U.S. the Supreme Court Justice who made this remark?

Q3:   In 1927, the U.S. Supreme Court ruled in *Buck v. Bell* that states are permitted to pass laws to forbid: "feebleminded and socially inadequate" individuals from procreating using compulsory sterilization. Which Justice, in writing for the Majority, declared: "Three Generations of imbeciles is enough"?

Q4:   Which U.S. Supreme Court Justice, in discussing a case which rejected a Nevada challenge to restrictions on worship services, remarked: "Take a look at the Constitution. You will see the free-exercise clause of the first amendment, which protects religious liberty. You will not find a craps clause, or a blackjack clause, or a slot machine clause"?

Q5:   Melville Fuller, Chief Justice of the United States, was a near doppelganger with which famed nineteenth century author? In fact, a man once came up to Melville Fuller thinking he was the author, and asked him for an autograph. He obliged and wrote: "It is delicious to be full. But it is heavenly to be Fuller. I am cordially yours, Melville W. Fuller." Who was this lookalike author?

Q6:   In a 2004 address at Harvard University, this U.S. Supreme Court Justice was asked about sexual morality. The Justice stunned the crowd by telling them: "I even accept for the sake of argument that sexual orgies eliminate social tensions and ought to be encouraged." Who was this U.S. Supreme Court Justice?

Q7:   When he was nominated by President Lyndon B. Johnson to serve on the U.S. Supreme Court, this Justice remarked: "I have a lifetime appointment and I intend to serve it. I expect to die at 110, shot by a jealous husband." In fact, the Justice died in 1993 at the age of 84, and did not die at the hands of a jealous husband --- he died from heart failure. Who was this Justice?

Q8:   Which U.S. Supreme Court Justice averred: "President's come and go, but the Supreme Court goes on forever"?

Q9:   Which U.S. Supreme Court Justice stated about his job: "When you put on a robe, at that point, the politics is over"?

U.S. Supreme Court Quotations

A1:   Clarence Thomas

A2:   Porter Stewart

A3:   Oliver Wendell Holmes Jr. This ruling remains on the books today.

A4:   Samuel Alito

A5:   Mark Twain

A6:   Antonin Scalia

A7:   Thurgood Marshall

A8:   William Howard Taft. Taft is the only person to serve as both President and as a member of the U.S. Supreme Court. He was President from 1909 to 1913 and Chief Justice of the United States from 1921 to 1930.

A9:   Stephen Breyer

Chapter XX

Founding Documents

Founding Documents

Q1: Who was the only person to sign all four founding documents; the Continental Association, The Declaration of Independence, The Articles of Confederation and Perpetual Union, and The U.S. Constitution?

Q2: Who wrote the Articles of Confederation and Perpetual Union, the precursor to the U.S. Constitution?

Q3: Which word is misspelled in the original U.S. Constitution?

Q4: What were the Declaration of Independence and the U.S. Constitution written with?

Q5: Though some people believe the Declaration of Independence was written on hemp paper, it was actually written on which substance?

Q6: Who was the youngest person to sign the U.S. Constitution?

Q7: The U.S. Constitution required 9 of the 13 states to be ratified. What state was the ninth to ratify?

Q8: Under the Articles of Confederation and Perpetual Union, who appointed Colonels and lower ranking military officers?

Q9: Who was the oldest person to sign the U.S. Constitution?

Founding Documents

A1: Roger Sherman

A2: John Dickinson

A3: The word Pennsylvania is misspelled as "Pensylvania" (sic) directly above the signers of the documents.

A4: Quill pens

A5: Parchment paper, which is derived from animal skin

A6: Jonathan Dayton, a former army captain who was just 26 years old. Dayton, a member of the Federalist Party, later became Speaker of the U.S. House of Representatives and a U.S. Senator representing New Jersey.

A7: New Hampshire

A8: The State Legislatures

A9: Benjamin Franklin. He was 81 years old.

Q10: How many words are in the U.S Constitution?

Q11: How many words are in the Declaration of Independence?

Q12: Who were the only future Presidents to sign the Declaration of Independence?

Q13: On what day did the U.S. officially declare independence from Great Brittan?

Q14: What is written on the back of the original Declaration of Independence?

Q15: Under the U.S. Constitution, what are the requirements for one to serve in the U.S. House of Representatives?

Q16: On what system is the U.S. Constitution based upon?

Q17: How many delegates to the Constitutional Convention signed the U.S. Constitution?

Q18: What was the nation's first governing document?

Q19: How many articles are there in the U.S. Constitution?

Founding Documents

A10: 4,400 words

A11: 1,337 words

A12: John Adams and Thomas Jefferson

A13: July 2nd, 1776. However, the language of the Declaration of Independence was not formalized until July 4, 1776. The delegates of the Constitutional Convention did not sign the document until August 2, 1776. The July 2nd motion to declare independence was made by Delegate Richard Henry Lee of Virginia.

A14: Original Declaration of Independence dated July 4th July 1776.

A15: A person must be 25 years of age, a United States Citizen for at least 7 years, and an inhabitant of the state represented. (There is no requirement to be a resident of the Congressional District).

A16: The Roman Republic, which lasted from 509 B.C.E. to 20 B.C.E.

A17: 39

A18: The Mayflower Compact. This document created a governing structure for the newly formed Plymouth Colony. The compact set up a Direct Democracy. In 1620, the forty-one surviving passengers of the Mayflower signed the document, agreeing to be public citizens and agreeing to abide by the opinion of the majority of the new colonists.

A19: 6

Q20: How many times are political parties mentioned in the U.S. Constitution?

Q21: Only two Founding Fathers signed the Declaration of Independence, the Articles of Confederation and Perpetual Union, and the United States Constitution? Who were these two gentlemen?

Q22: Under the Articles of Confederation and Perpetual Union, how were federal taxes collected?

Q23: Where are the original Declaration of Independence, the U.S. Constitution, and the Bill of Rights located?

Q24: What is the oldest written Constitution still in use?

Q25: Under the U.S. Constitution, what are the requirements for a person to serve in the U.S. Senate?

Q26: How many amendments are there to the U.S. Constitution?

Q27: Which state was the first to ratify the U.S. Constitution?

Q28: Who were the only three delegates at the Constitutional Convention who refused to sign the U.S. Constitution?

Q29: Who was the only Catholic to sign the Declaration of Independence?

A20: 0

A21: Robert Martin and Roger Sherman

A22: From state governments

A23: At the National Archives in Washington, D.C.

A24: The U.S. Constitution. It was ratified in 1787.

A25: A person must be at least thirty years of age, must be a U.S. citizen for at least nine years, and must be a resident of the state on Election Day.

A26: 27

A27: Delaware, on December 7, 1787

A28: Elbridge Gerry, George Mason, and Edmund Randolph

A29: Charles Carroll

Chapter XXI

Governors

Governors

Q1: In what two states are governors chosen every two years?

Q2: In which state can a Governor be recalled by a petition signed by voters equal to 12% of the last Gubernatorial vote, with signatures from each of the state's five counties commensurate to 1% of the last Gubernatorial vote?

Q3: In what six states are there no official residences (Governor's mansions)?

Q4: How many states have term limits for Governors?

Q5: How many State Governors have the Line-Item-Veto authority?

Q6: In 2011, while on a jog with his dog, which Texas Governor encountered a coyote, and fearing the coyote would attack him or his dog, shot the coyote with his pistol?

Q7: Former Massachusetts Governor Willard Romney's middle name is Mitt. How did he come by this unusual middle name?

Q8: Which California Governor dated singer Linda Ronstadt during his first term in office?

Q9: In 1955, which West Virginia Governor-elect was the first guest on the popular television game show, *To Tell the Truth*?

A1: New Hampshire and Vermont

A2: California

A3: Arizona, California, Idaho, Massachusetts, Rhode Island, and Vermont

A4:   36

A5: 43. The states which don't have it are: Indiana, Maryland, Nevada, New Hampshire, North Carolina, Rhode Island, and Vermont.

A6: Rick Perry

A7: Milton Romney, a cousin of his father, George Romney, played Quarterback for the Chicago Beard from 1925-1929.

A8: Jerry Brown

A9 Cecil Underwood

Q10: What is the only state where a Governor is only allowed to serve one non-consecutive term as Governor?

Q11: Which Texas Governor regularly sat in the front row behind the bench at Texas Longhorns Basketball games with her good friend, U.S. Representative Barbara Jordan (D-TX)?

Q12: Former New York Governor Thomas E. Dewey suffered from a heart attack and died after playing golf with which future Boston Red Sox Hall-of-Famer in Miami?

Q13: In 2006, the Virginia State Capital in Richmond was undergoing renovations. Accordingly, Tim Kaine was inaugurated as Governor in Williamsburg, instead. Who was the last Virginia Governor prior to that to be inaugurated in that municipality?

Q14: Which Alabama Governor appeared before the state Board of Education in 1995, and danced like a monkey, while exhibiting his vociferous opposition to textbooks which teach evolution?

Q15: In 2013, which African American Governor appointed an African American to the U.S. Senate?

Q16: Before becoming Governor of New York, he obtained 72 convictions of 73 prosecutions for organized crime as a District Attorney. Who was this successful D.A?

Q17: Which future Virginia Governor guaranteed the $1.35 million mortgage to Bill and Hillary Clinton to purchase a home in Chappaqua, NY?

Q18: Which former Governor served as the Second Commissioner of Major League Baseball?

Q19: Which Mississippi Governor, known as a staunch segregationist, said he was "fed up with these fence-riding, pussy-footing, snow-digging Yankee Republicans" meaning transplants from the North?

Governors

A10:   Virginia. The Lieutenant Governor can run for a consecutive term.

A11:   Ann Richards

A12:   Carl Yastrzemski

A13:   Thomas Jefferson, in 1789

A14:   Fob James. He wanted the state to place a sticker on each textbook, reading: "No one was present when life first appeared on earth. Therefore, any statement about life's origins should be considered as theory, not fact." His 1998 Republican opponent for re-election, Winton Blount, lamented that Fob James' action was embarrassing for the state. James retorted by excoriating Blount's weight: "If I dance like a monkey, then he must dance like a fat monkey." James also averred: "I'm a monkey that's in good shape. I'm not a fat monkey." James then attacked Blount, whose father had helped fund his campaign. "I'm not a monkey whose daddy has put $2.5 million in my campaign either . . . . If he says I'm a monkey, I must say. 'Well, I'm a pretty slim monkey. I'm not a fat monkey." James' wife also got in on the action, calling Bobbie Blount, the wife of Winston Blount, "a big, fat sissy." James upended Blount for the nomination, then lost in the General Election to Democrat Don Siegelman.

A15:   Deval Patrick. He appointed Mo Cowans as an interim replacement for John Kerry, who became U.S. Secretary of State. Cowans served until Democrat Ed Markey won a Special Election.

A16:   Thomas E. Dewey

A17:   Terry McAuliffe

A18:   Benjamin Happy Chandler

A19:   Ross Barnett

Q20: This Governor had a contentious relationship with the media. He ordered his press secretary to hand out press passes with the words "official jackal" (wild dog) printed next to their names? He told them: "By the way, I noticed that only a few people are wearing their credentials today. Congratulations for having a sense of humor . . . and to those that don't, go stick your head in the mud." Who was this Governor?

Q21: In 1939, Georgia Governor Eurith D. Rivers proclaimed a state holiday for the premier of which historic movie?

Q22: In 1976, Governor George Busbee gave President-elect Jimmy Carter full usage of the First floor of the Governor's mansion to use as a transition headquarters. Which state was George Busbee Governor of?

Q23: Which future New York Governor was offered a $150,000 per year partnership with the prestigious law firm Sullivan and Cromwell by future U.S. Secretary of State John Foster Dulles?

Q24: After Atlanta Braves slugger Hank Aaron belted his record-breaking 715th homerun, which Governor presented him with a license plate with the number 715?

Q25: How many Idaho Governors were born in Iowa?

Q26: Which Maryland Governor signed a Fair Housing Act? In addition, he signed legislation repealing an anti-miscegenation law, and was the first Old Line State Governor to appoint an African-American to his senior staff. Who was this Governor?

Q27: Which Alaska Governor was nicknamed: "Sarah Barracuda' in High School, for her aggressive Basketball playing style?

Q28: Arkansas Governors Bill Clinton and Mike Huckabee were both born in which small town?

Q29: Which future Utah Governor dropped out of High School to play keyboard in the rock-and-roll band Wizard?

A20: Jesse Ventura. The badges also featured a photograph of Ventura pointing to the camera. Ventura had recently authored the book: *Do I Stand Alone? Going to the Mat Against Political Pawns and Media Jackals.* Media outlets expressed outrage at this. David Pyle, the Minnesota Bureau chief for *The Associated Press*, averred: "While this may have been intended as a joke, we take this matter seriously and will not subject AP staffers to wearing something that may be intended to demean them and their profession," After criticism, Ventura rescinded the order to have the journalists sport the badges. However, some wore them as a lark when Ventura spoke to the National Press Club.

A21: *Gone with the Wind*

A22: Georgia. Busbee succeeded Carter as Governor of the state in 1975.

A23: Thomas D. Dewey. However, while he initially accepted the partnership, he then backtracked when Republicans beseeched him to run for District Attorney, a job, which paid just $20,000.

A24: Jimmy Carter of Georgia

A25: 5

A26: Spiro Agnew

A27: Sarah Palin. She played for the Wasilla (Alaska) High School basketball team.

A28: Hope, Arkansas

A29: John Huntsman Jr. Once his rock-and roll dream died, Huntsman earned a GED and eventually graduated from the University of Pennsylvania.

Q30:   Which Governor's birth name was James George Janos?

Q31:   Which Acting Governor of Massachusetts commuted 110 miles to work at the State House?

Q32:   Which former Arkansas Governor tried to re-assume the Governorship in 1986, losing badly to incumbent Bill Clinton in the Primary? He was the longest serving Governor in the state's history.

Q33:   Who was the youngest Governor in American history?

Q34:   Which Democratic Governor holds the moniker of "The Singing Governor?"

Q35:   In 1967, which California Governor signed the Mulford Act, which prohibited "the carrying of firearms on one's person or in a vehicle, in any public place or on any public street"?

Q36:   In 2007 and in 2011, Massachusetts Governor Deval Patrick was inaugurated on the Mendi Bible. The Mendi Bible was given to which former President who represented freed slaves in the 1841 U.S. Supreme Court case: *United States v. The Amistad?*

Q37:   Which Georgia Governor designated one day per month as "People's Day," allowing Georgia residents to meet with him personally to tell him about their concerns?

Q38:   While the Arkansas Governor's Mansion was being renovated, which Governor lived in a "triple-wide" (a large mobile home on the grounds of the mansion)?

Q39:   The oldest Governor in American history was Walter Samuel Goodland of Wisconsin. How old was he when he died in office in 1947?

A30: Jesse Ventura of Minnesota

A31: Jane Swift. She lived in Williamstown, MA on the New York border, and was driven to Boston.

A32: Orval Faubus. Clinton won the race, mustering $60.58% of the vote. Fabus garnered just 27.08% of the vote. Fabus had been Governor from 1955-1967.

A33: Stevens T. Mason. In 1835, Mason, a former territorial Governor of the Michigan Territory, was elected as Governor of the newly-established state of Michigan at just 24 years old.

A34: Jimmie Davis. He served two non-consecutive terms, from 1944-1948 and 1960-1964. His genre was country music and gospel. He popularized the hit single: *You Are My Sunshine* in 1949, with songwriter Charles Mitchell. Today, it is Louisiana's official state song.

A35: Ronald Reagan

A36: John Quincy Adams. He was a Massachusetts native. The Mende people are an ethnic group from Sierra Leone.

A37: Lester Maddox

A38: Mike Huckabee, in 1998

A39: 84-years-old

Q40: Who was the first African-American Governor in the U.S.?

Q41: Which former Arkansas Governor became a bank teller in Huntsville, AR, earning just $5,000 per year?

Q42: Who was the first Governor to give birth while in office?

Q43: After endorsing Democrat Barack Obama for President and Independence Party nominee Tom Horner for Governor, which former Republican Governor was banned from all state party events for two years?

Q44: In 1973, which Georgia Governor alleged to have seen a UFO?

Q45: Who were the first two Americans of Greek decent to become Governors?

Q46: How are the Governors seated at the National Governors Conferences?

Q47: Who was the first female Governor to die in office?

Q48: Who was the first female to be elected Governor of a U.S. state?

Q49: How much money did Bill Clinton make each year as Governor of Arkansas?

A40: Pinckney Benton Stewart Pinchback of Louisiana. Pinchback was the state's Lieutenant Governor and was promoted to Governor when Governor Henry Clay Warmouth was forced to resign for his role in election fraud. Governor Pinchback served the last thirty-five days of Warmouth's unexpired term.

A41: Orval Faubus

A42: Jane Swift. The acting Massachusetts Governor gave birth to twins in 2001.

A43: Arnie Carlson of Minnesota

A44: Jimmy Carter. He filed a report with the Center for UFO Studies in Evanston, Illinois, claiming to have seen an unidentified flying object (UFO). Carter says he witnessed the sighting in the sky over Leary, Georgia in 1969 as he was leaving a Lions Club meeting.

A45: Republican Spiro Agnew became Governor of Maryland in 1967. Democrat Michael Dukakis became Governor of Massachusetts in 1975. Agnew became Vice President in 1969 under Richard M. Nixon. Dukakis was the failed Democratic Presidential nominee in 1988.

A46: By the year their state was admitted into the Union.

A47: Lurlene Brigham Wallace (D-AL). She died of cancer on May 7, 1968.

A48: Nellie Ross of Wyoming in 1924

A49: $35,000

Q50: After leaving office, New Mexico Governor Gary Johnson climbed which mountain?

Q51: In 1973, this Democrat became the first Governor to call publicly for Richard M. Nixon to resign for his role in the Watergate Affair?

Q52: Who was the first Governor to sign legislation requiring competency testing for all public school teachers?

Q53: Which future New York Governor played in the Pittsburg Pirates Minor League system, but had to quit because he was hit in the head by a pitch?

Q54: Who was both the youngest and oldest Governor in West Virginia history?

Q55: In 2006, Massachusetts Governor Mitt Romney spent much of his time out of the state, mostly campaigning for Republican candidates. How many days did he spend outside of Massachusetts?

Q56: Who was the first African-American Governor in U.S. History?

Q57: Which future Republican Governor of Arizona saved the life of Bill Clinton when Clinton was in college?

Q58: In 1992, which Texas Governor purchased the first Texas lottery ticket at a convenience store in Oak Hill, TX?

Q59: Who is the first Governor in U.S. history to survive a recall attempt?

A50:   Mount Everest, the world's highest mountain. It is located in Nepal, and is 26,029 feet above sea level.

A51:   Jimmy Carter of Georgia

A52:   Bill Clinton of Arkansas in 1983. He signed a bill requiring all public school teachers in the state to submit to take an academic skill examination. The statute inflamed unions against Clinton. Clinton defended the plan by averring: "'The American people are saying they are willing to take the shirts right off their backs if it will help improve education, 'But they demand accountability. They want us to get rid of the teachers who are really bad." The Arkansas Education Association failed in an attempt to sue to overturn the law. In 1985, the Democratic state House of Representatives pressured by the Arkansas Education Association voted to repeal the law. Clinton then appeared in radio advertisements asking constituents to call their State Senators and demand they vote against repeal. The gambit worked, and the Senate voted against the repeal effort.

A53:   Mario Cuomo. The $2,000 bonus he secured for signing with the organization was used to pay for an engagement ring for his fiancé, Matilda.

A54:   Cecil Underwood. In 1957, the 35-year-old became the youngest Governor in West Virginia history. He could not run for re-election in 1960 because at the time there were term-limits for Governor. In 1997, after a 37-year hiatus, Underwood again assumed the office. This time he became the oldest governor in West Virginia history.

A55:   212 days

A56:   Pinckney Benton Stewart Pinchback. He was serving as Lieutenant Governor and was promoted to Governor when Governor Henry Clay Warmouth was forced to resign for his role in election fraud. Governor Pinchback served the last thirty-five days of Warmouth's unexpired term.

A57:   Fife Symington of Arizona. Symington and Clinton were at a mutual friend's birthday party in Hyannis Port, Massachusetts when Clinton went for a swim but got caught in riptide. Symington swam out and saved Clinton. Clinton returned the favor in his last day in office as President by pardoning Symington who had gotten in trouble for bank and wire fraud. The mutual friend who was the subject of the birthday party was future novelist Tommy Kaplan.

A58:   Ann Richards. The lottery was inaugurated during her Gubernatorial term.

A59:   Scott Walker (R-WI). In 2011, he introduced and signed a Budget Repair Bill, which would eliminate collective bargaining privileges for most state employees. This led to a recall effort. Walker survived the recall with 53.1% of Wisconsin voters voting against the recall effort.

Chapter XXII

Gubernatorial Quotations

Gubernatorial Quotations

Q1: In 1996, this Republican Massachusetts Governor lost a bid to serve in the U.S. Senate, losing to incumbent John F. Kerry. In an interview with *The New York Times*, this losing candidate poked fun at both his loss and his patrician pedigree. He told reporter Sara Rimer: "It was not my first defeat. There was the Rhodes scholarship. The Marshall scholarship. *Harvard Law Review*. My life is a tangled wreck of failures." Who was this losing candidate?

Q2: On June 15, 1991, after the U.S. Senate voted to authorize President George H.W. Bush to use military force to repel Iraqi forces from Kuwait, this Governor told members of the media: "I guess I would have voted with the majority if it was a close vote. But I agree with the arguments the Minority made." Who made this statement?

Q3: When this Governor of California ran for re-election in 1970, he promised voters his feet were "in concrete" against establishing a withholding system for state income tax. However, as Governor he reversed course, signing a tax increase to obliterate the state's $200 million deficit. Using humor as opposed to an excuse, he commented: "I can hear the concrete cracking around my feet." Who was this California Governor?

Q4: When U.S. Senate Minority Leader Harry Reid (D-NV) called this Montana Governor to ask him who he would appoint to the U.S. Senate seat vacated by Democrat Max Baucus (who became U.S. Ambassador to China), he responded: "None of your damn business. You know what? Stay out of my decision-making. This is a decision I make and no one else. This is one of those decisions that voters entrusted me with." He ultimately appointed Lieutenant Governor John Walsh to the seat. Who was this Governor?

Q5: Upon becoming Governor of Arkansas in 1971, Dale Bumpers observed: "It's not enough anymore to say 'Thank God for Mississippi.'" Why did the Governor say this?

Q6: When a coterie of German editors visited his office in Providence, Rhode Island, this Governor, who stood at just 5-foot-4 inches tall, stated: "Rhode Island is the smallest state in the Union, and I am the smallest Governor in the United States." Who was this short Governor?

Q7: During an appearance on *Morning Joe on MSNBC*, this former Democratic Governor was asked to cite "a single thing Democratic President Barack Obama has done that you consider a positive achievement? The former Governor answered: "My mother, God rest her soul, told me if you can't think of something nice to say about something change the subject?" Who was this former Democratic Governor?

Q8: The day before his 2008 arrest for allegedly soliciting bribes in return for an appointment to the U.S. Senator seat being vacated by President-Elect Barack Obama, this Illinois Governor told a press conference: "I don't believe there's any cloud that hangs over me. I think there's nothing but sunshine hanging over me." Who said this?

Q9: In 1996, this former California Governor averred: "Oh, I know what to do.' You don't. I didn't have a plan for California. Clinton doesn't have a plan. Bush doesn't have a plan.... You say you're going to lower taxes; you're going to put people to work, you're gonna improve the schools, you're going to stop crime … crime is up, schools are worse, taxes are higher. I mean, be real!" Which former Governor made this outlandish statement?

Gubernatorial Quotations

A1: Bill Weld

A2: Bill Clinton (D-AR)

A3: Ronald Reagan

A4: Steve Bullock

A5: In many economic rankings Arkansas was 49th, while Mississippi was ranked 50th.

A6: John O. Pastore

A7: Brian Schweitzer of Montana

A8: Rob Blagojevich

A9: Jerry Brown

Gubernatorial Quotations

Q10: In a 1999 interview with *Playboy Magazine*, which Minnesota Governor said: "Every fat person says it's not their fault, that they have gland trouble. You know which gland? The saliva gland. They can't push away from the table"?

Q11: In 2006, which Governor pardoned lead guitarist Keith Richards of the rock band The Rolling Stones? Richards was pulled over for reckless driving in 1975 and was assessed a $162.50 fine for the offense. When the Governor was accused of pardoning Richards because of his celebrity status, he replied: "Hey, if you can play guitar like Keith Richards, I'll consider pardoning you too." The pardon was a "goodwill gesture" initiated by the Governor, not Keith Richards.

Q12: When Democratic Texas Agricultural Commissioner Jim Hightower was informed that a particular Republican Governor was studying Spanish, he deadpanned: "Oh Good. Now he'll be bi-ignorant." Who was this bi-ignorant Governor?

Q13: In a 2011 press conference prior to Hurricane Irene reaching the New Jersey shore, the Governor announced to the public: "Get the hell off the Beach in Asbury Park and get out. You're done. It's 4:30 PM. you've maximized your tan. Get off the beach. Get in your cars and get out of those areas." Who was the New Jersey Governor who scolded his beach people?

Q14: In 2005, in his role as the Chairman of the Republican Governors Association, which Massachusetts Governor made fun of his home state to Republican audiences? He would say: "Being a conservative in Massachusetts is a bit like being a cattle rancher at a vegetarian convention."

Q15: Which Maine Governor became inflamed after State Senator Troy Jackson suggested that the Governor's veto threat of the State Budget was a "stunt"? The Governor responded: "Jackson claims to be for the people, but he's the first one to give it to the people without providing Vaseline."

Q16: State Representative Barney Frank (D-MA) was a vociferous critic of this Massachusetts Governor during his first term in office. Frank excoriated him for budget cuts he believed hurt the poor. A reporter asked Frank if he had a problem with the Governor riding the subway from his Brooklyn home to his office in the State House. Frank replied: "No, I don't object that he rides the subway. I merely object that he gets off at the State House." Who was this Governor?

Q17: In 1987, Arizona Governor Evan Mecham was under investigation for misuse of campaign funds and was taking heat for canceling the state's paid Martin Luther King Holiday. His predecessor as Governor told *Newsweek Magazine*: "Evan Mecham proves that [Charles] Darwin was wrong." Who was this Governor?

Q18: Discussing his willingness to work with Democrats in the State Legislature, this Republican California Governor said on *The Charlie Rose Show* on *PBS*: "I have no trouble understanding Democrats. I sleep with one every night." He was referring to his wife, Maria Shriver. Who was this Republican Governor?

Gubernatorial Quotations

A10: Jesse Ventura

A11: Mike Huckabee (R-AR)

A12: Bill Clements

A13: Chris Christie (R-NJ)

A14: Mitt Romney

A15: Paul LePage

A16: Michael Dukakis

A17: Bruce Babbitt

A18: Arnold Schwarzenegger. He was married to Maria Shriver at the time.

Chapter XXIII

Gubernatorial Elections

Q1:   In 1970, Jimmy Carter defeated former Georgia Governor Carl Sanders in the Democratic Gubernatorial Primary. Carter's campaign team referred to him as "Cufflinks Carl." Why did they call him Cufflinks Carl?

Q2:   During a 2010 New York Gubernatorial debate, which candidate responded to a question about his views on Gay marriage this way: "The Rent Is Too Damn High Party believes that if you want to marry a shoe, I'll marry you"?

Q3:   During a tough 1980 re-election bid, which Governor was cited for driving 80mph on a freeway where the speed limit was just 55mph enroot to a library dedication? This Governor was from a state that was promoting a safe-driving campaign at the same time.

Q4:   In 1966, the California Governor Pat Brown lost re-election to Republican Ronald Reagan. The Democratic Party was split asunder between Brown and this California House Speaker, who Brown labeled "the architect of my defeat." Who was this bitter brown rival?

Q5:   Which California Governor won re-election by defeating a future President in 1962, then was defeated by a different future President in 1966?

Q6:   Which game show host moderated a 2018 Pennsylvania Gubernatorial debate between Democrat Tom Wolf and Republican Scott Wagner?

Q7:   In 1991, this Louisiana Democratic Gubernatorial candidate was asked about the similarities between himself and his Republican Gubernatorial opponent, David Duke, a former Grand Wizard of the Ku Klux Klan. His response was: "We're both wizards in the sheets. Who made this remark?

Q8:   During a 1990 Massachusetts Gubernatorial debate, Republican nominee Bill Weld exploited a claim made by this Democratic nominee that beavers created so much wetland that preserving wetlands should not be of concern. Weld quipped: "Would you tell us doctor, what plans, if any, you have for the preservation of open spaces in Massachusetts, other than leave it to beavers?" Who was this Gubernatorial candidate who spoke so eloquently about the beavers?

Q9:   When First Lady Hillary Clinton spoke at a rally for Texas Gubernatorial nominee Gary Mauro in Austin, a heckler bellowed: "We don't want your phony war, Hillary" referring to threats from the Clinton administration to bomb Iraq. This former Texas Governor upstaged the heckler by yelling; "Somebody help this man. He's going to have a heart attack. Medic! Medic! Medic!"? The crowd roared with laughter. Who was the former Governor who went after the heckler?

A1:   They called him Cufflinks Carl to portray him as an urbane, wealthy, elitist Liberal. Sanders was a rare Southern Progressive who did not distance himself from the more liberal national party. He supported racial integration. Carter slammed Sanders for selling out "to the ultraliberal wing of the Democratic Party . . . exchanging the favor of Hubert Humphrey [The liberal former Vice President] for the goodwill of Georgians."

A2:   Jimmy McMillian, the nominee of the Rent is Too Damn High Party.

A3:   Bill Clinton. Clinton was running for re-election as Governor in culturally conservative Arkansas, and was taking heat for the fact that his wife went by the name "Hillary Rodham" rather than "Hillary Rodham Clinton." Concomitantly, he was caught driving 80 mph on a freeway, where the speed limit was 55mph. Clinton tried to conflate the two issues, jocularly suggesting that he should name his first child: "Hot Rodham."

A4:   Jesse Unruh. Unruh was the Democratic nominee against Reagan in his re-election bid in 1970.

A5:   Edmund Gerald "Pat" Brown Sr. He defeated Richard M. Nixon in 1962, then lost to Ronald Reagan in 1966.

A6:   Alex Trebeck, the host of *Jeopardy*. Wolf won the election.

A7:   Edwin Edwards

A8.   John Silber

A9:   Ann Richards

Q10: Which Republican won the Michigan Governorship in 2018, calling himself: "One tough nerd"?

Q11: In 2016, West Virginia voters elected which Democrat for Governor? Just one year later, he became a Republican.

Q12: This Illinois Gubernatorial candidate said: "I think the most important thing is to restore a sense of idealism and end the cynicism in state government. Bring to the job a desire to really make things happen and help people and give confidence back to the public." Who uttered these remarks?

Q13: Which Jimmy Carter loyalist lost a bid to succeed him as Governor of Georgia in 1974?

Q14: In 1966, while running for a third term as California Governor, which candidate compared his opponent, Ronald Reagan, to former actor John Wilkes Booth, who assassinated Abraham Lincoln?

Q15: Republican Gubernatorial nominee Sheffield Nelson lost to two Democratic Governors; one in 1990 and the other in 1994 in Arkansas Who were these two Arkansas Governors?

Q16: The day before the 2006 Illinois Gubernatorial election, Republican Gubernatorial nominee Judy Baar Topinka was gladhanding voters at Union Station in Chicago. The previous day she said of this Democratic Governor who she was running against: "Maybe he ought to run for manager of the Cubs. They're a bunch of losers too and need some help." Who was this Governor?

Q17: In 1994, Republican New York City Mayor Rudy Giuliani stunned his Republican Party by endorsing which Democratic Governor in his bid for a fourth term over Republican nominee George Pataki?

Q18: In 1990, which former Georgia Governor, known nationally for his support of segregation, made a quixotic bid to re-capture the Governorship after a 14-year hiatus, said of his opponent, Zell Miller: "There's' not a position Zell Miller hasn't stood for at one time or another. He wanted to ride a bicycle in a parade, but they wouldn't allow him because he was declared a danger with all his zig zagging all over the place?"

Q19: In 2003, opponents of this California Governor gathered the requisite number of signatures to effectuate a recall election against him. The Governor said: "It's like the Oakland Raiders saying to Tampa Bay: 'We know you beat us, but we want to play the Super Bowl again.'" The Governor was recalled, and lost the recall election to actor Arnold Schwarzenegger. Who was this Governor who was recalled?

A10:   Rick Snyder

A11:   Jim Justice

A12:   Rob Blagojevich. As Governor, he was impeached and convicted for allegedly trying to sell the U.S. Senate seat being vacated by Barack Obama.

A13:   Bert Lance. Lance lost to State Senator George Busbee.   Lance later served as President Carter's Budget Director.

A14:   Pat Brown. This gaffe contributed to Brown's loss. Brown was asked by a high school student who Brown's opponent was. Brown responded: "I'm glad you asked. I'm running against an actor. And did you know it was an actor who shot Abraham Lincoln." The Gaffe precipitated Brown's downfall in the polls. Reagan won the election in a landslide, garnering 55.5% of the vote.

A15:   Bill Clinton in 1990 and Jim Guy Tucker in 1994

A16:   Rob Blagojevich. A commuter at Union Station bellowed at Topinka: "Go Cubs." She garnered boos from passersby. Blagojevich was in the enviable position of defending the hometown team, averring: "If she wants to say I'm a loser and call me names . . . God bless her, but leave the Cubs alone. She ought to retract the attack on the Cubs."   The next day, Blagojevich was re-elected by an 11-point landslide.

A17:   Mario Cuomo. Giuliani averred: "George Pataki's only essential characteristic is that he offers an alternative. Strangely, however, after lengthy analysis and a lot of soul-searching, I've come to the conclusion that it is George Pataki who best personifies the status quo of New York politics -- a candidate taking as few positions as possible, all of them as general as possible, taking no risks and being guided and scripted by others. He has simply not made the case that he is the agent of change." Giuliani also asserted that Pataki was spouting slogans "out of a political consultant's playbook."

A18:   Lester Maddox. Maddox attacked Miller for using his office to get perks: Miller gave Maddox a blank deadly stare after the comment. Miller won the race. Maddox garnered just 3% of the vote.

A19:   Gray Davis

Q20: During the 1970 Florida Gubernatorial race, incumbent Republican Claude Kirk Jr. said of his Democratic opponent: "a nice, sweet-looking fellow, but being Governor is a tough job and being a mamma's boy won't get the job done." The opponent responded simply: "I love my Mamma." Who won the election?

Q21: In 1961, which U.S. Navy Secretary resigned his post to run for the Democratic Gubernatorial nomination in Texas?

Q22: In 1966, which Democratic Gubernatorial nominee tattooed his Republican opponent Howard Hollis Bo Calloway as "a baby in his crib reaching for his rattler"?

Q23: In 2006, this humorist and musician ran for Governor of Texas as an Independent. His campaign slogan was: "How hard could it be?" He lost the race to Republican Governor Rick Perry. He garnered just 12.4% of the vote. Who was this humorist and musician?

Q24: In his successful 2018 campaign for Governor of Ohio, which Republican nominee promised that if he were elected, he would be "the adult in the room" for the Republican Party?

Q25: In 1999, U.S. Representative Asa Hutchinson (R-AR) was an Impeachment Manager during the U.S. Senate trial of Bill Clinton. Clinton was acquitted of Perjury and Obstruction of Justice. One of the jurors was Hutchinson's brother, U.S. Senator Tim Hutchinson (R-AR). In 2014, this Democratic Gubernatorial candidate used the issue against Asa Hutchinson, who was now his Republican opponent for Arkansas Governor. He told *The Associated Press*: "He may be the only lawyer in American who has conducted a trial with his brother on the jury and lost." Which candidate made this statement?

Q26: In 2014, this former Republican Governor ran for Governor of Florida as a Democrat. He had branded himself "a pro-life, pro-gun, anti-tax Republican" before becoming a Democrat. Republican political strategist Rick Wilson commented on the party's willingness to support someone like this. Wilson said: "Democrats are so desperate to win the Governor's race, if he had a dead hooker in the trunk of his car, they'd still be fine. We're good. He's the guy." Who was his politician who changed parties?

Q27: In 1989, who became the first African-American elected Governor of a state.

Q28: At the end of the final 2002 Massachusetts Gubernatorial debate between this Republican and Democrat Shannon O'Brien, host Tim Russert said: "Enjoy the Buffalo Bills-New England Patriots game on Sunday." The Republican replied: "And may the best team win." Who was the Massachusetts Gubernatorial candidate who chose: "the best team" over the New England Patriots?

Q29: In 1978, Massachusetts Republican Ed King lost his bid for the Republican Gubernatorial nomination to Frank Hatch. Had Ed King won, he would have faced the Democratic nominee. Who was the Democratic nominee?

A20:   Reubin Askew

A21:   John Connally. He won the nomination and the runoff. In the General Election, Connally defeated Republican John Cox. Connally blasted Cox for switching from the Democratic to the Republican Party just one year earlier. Interestingly, Connally himself became a Republican in 1973.

A22:   Lester Maddox

A23:   Kinky Friedman

A24:   Mike DeWine. This was seen by many political observers as a way for DeWine to distance himself from the often vituperative Republican President Donald Trump.

A25:   Mike Ross

A26:   Charlie Crist

A27:   Doug Wilder of Virginia

A28:   Mitt Romney

A29:   Ed King (no relation). It would have been Ed King vs. Ed King.

Q30: James Meredith, the first African-American to attend the University of Mississippi, supported the Louisiana Gubernatorial campaign of which controversial figure in 1991?

Q31: In 1946, which California Governor won the endorsements of both the Democratic and Republican Parties in his bid for re-election?

Q32: In 1998, which Democratic Lieutenant Governor endorsed Texas Republican Governor George W. Bush for re-election over Democrat Gary Mauro, even though he was the God Father of Mauro's two children?

Q33: In 2007, Louisiana voters made which Republican the first Indian-American Governor in U.S. history?

Q34: In 2010, New Mexico voters made her the first Latina to be elected Governor of a state?

Q35: In 1952, which man garnered the nominations of both the Democrat and the Republican Parties for the Governorship of Texas?

Q36: In 1982, after apologizing for his opposition to racial desegregation, who was re-elected for an unprecedented fourth term as Governor of Alabama?

Q37: In 1962, after losing a bid to become California Governor, which Republican told reporters: "You won't have him to kick around anymore"?

Q38: In 1898, while running for Governor of New York, which Republican made 19 speeches in one day?

Q39: In 1982, former Arkansas Governor Bill Clinton was running to recapture the Governorship he had lost in 1980. He was scheduled to show up at a debate with his primary opponent. Instead, Hillary Clinton showed up. He had never met her. He told *The Guardian* in 2016: "I was expecting Bill, and he sent her … and she stomped on me. She was well prepared, and she went after me hard, and I was not prepared to respond. I have no question in that little mountain community she whipped me that day." This man became Governor when Bill Clinton assumed the Presidency in 1992. Who was this man?

A30:   David Duke

A31:   Earl Warren. He won the election, garnering 90% of the vote.

A32:   Bob Bullock

A33:   Bobby Jindal

A34:   Susana Martinez

A35:   Allan Shivers. His name appeared on the ballot twice. In effect, he ran against himself.

A36:   George Wallace. He carried all ten of the state's African-American majority counties.

A37:   Richard M. Nixon. Six years later he was elected President.

A38:   Theodore Roosevelt. He won the election.

A39:   Jim Guy Tucker

Q40: Who was the first Asian-American elected Governor of a state?

Q41: In 2002, which Democratic New Mexico Gubernatorial nominee broke the *Guinness Book of World Records* record for handshakes in one day? He shook the hands of 13,992 people.

Q42: Who is the youngest former Governor in U.S. history?

Q43: Which Louisiana Governor had a policy whereby every constituent that garnered a job working for his administration was expected to donate 5-10 percent of his/her salary to his political machine?

Q44: Which Republican Florida Gubernatorial nominee canceled a planned meeting with *Tampa Bay Times* news reporters because the campaign said he needed to spend more time devising a platform?

Q45: In 2020, while Republican Presidential nominee Donald Trump won just 30.67% of the vote in Vermont, performing worse only in the District of Columbia, which Vermont Republican Governor was re-elected with 68.49% of the vote (greater than any Green Mountain State Republican Gubernatorial nominee since 1950?)

Q46: In 2002, scandal-plagued and unpopular Republican Illinois Governor George Ryan did not seek re-election. Fortuitously for the Democratic Gubernatorial nominee, the Republican Party nominated someone with the same last name as the scandal-riddled unpopular George Ryan. The new nominee was Jim Ryan, the Attorney General of Illinois. Which Democrat running for re-election defeated Republican Jim Ryan?

Q47: In 1968, which St. Louis Cardinals legend served as the co-chairman of the re-election campaign for Democratic Missouri Governor Warren Hearns?

Q48: When this 1990 Republican Texas Gubernatorial nominee was asked why the state's Hispanic voter should support him, he responded: "I met Modesta [his wife] at a Mexican restaurant." Who was this Gubernatorial nominee?

Q49: In the 1990 Arkansas Democratic Gubernatorial primary, which candidate held a press conference at the Capitol Rotunda, excoriating the record of his opponent, Governor Bill Clinton? Clinton's wife Hillary was passing by and interrupted the press conference to talk about the past praise which the candidate's foundation had heaped upon her husband.

A40:   George Ariyoshi. He was elected Governor of Hawaii in 1974.

A41:   Bill Richardson

A42:   Bill Clinton. At 34 years of age, he lost re-election to Republican Frank White in 1980. At the time, the state had two-year terms, and Clinton won back the reins of power in 1983, handily defeating White.

A43:   Huey Long. In the aggregate, this added up to more than $1 million for the machine. Long kept the proceeds in a locked box he named "The Deduct Box" which he kept in the Roosevelt Hotel New Orleans. However, Long would not tell anyone where he kept it. In fact, after Long was shot by lone assassin Carl Weiss, MD, one of Long's best friends, Seymour Weiss, the owner and manager of the hotel, visited Long in the hospital just before he died, and asked Long about the location of the Deduct Box: "Huey, where's the Deduct Box?" Long responded, "I'll tell you later Seymour." Long then died. The Deduct Box has still not been found. A replica of it is emplaced in the hotel lobby, and guests sometimes try to find it.

A44:   Ron DeSantis, in 2018

A45:   Phil Scott

A46:   Rob Blagojevich. Blagojevich was successful in linking Jim Ryan with the scandal-ridden and unpopular George Ryan: Blagojevich exclaimed: "Mr. Ryan is trying to suggest he's the agent of change. Well, it ain't change if you replace one Ryan with another." Knowing he would be the first Democrat elected Governor since 1972, Blagojevich exclaimed: "Thirty years ago Elvis [Pressley] was alive and doing Vegas. It's been 30 years of *Heartbreak Hotel* for the Democrats. But when we win in November, the Republicans will be "All Shook Up."

A47:   Stan Musial

A48:   Clayton Williams

A49:   Tom McRae. McRae was the head of the Winthrop Rockefeller Foundation (a private grant-making organization) for 14 years.

Chapter XXIV

State and Territory Facts

Q1:   In 2013, which state became the first to have an all-female Congressional Delegation and Governor?

Q2:   Which five states do not operate with a Lieutenant Governor?

Q3:   The Massachusetts State House sits on the land once owned by the first Governor of Massachusetts. Who was this Governor?

Q4:   Which State Senate musters the largest population per state senator of any state?

Q5:   How much money do New Hampshire State legislators make annually?

Q6:   How many states host nuclear reactors?

Q7:   In how may states is the Governor and Lieutenant Governor elected separately, and can even be members of different political parties?

Q8:   Which state Legislative chamber is the second largest legislative body behind the U.S. House of Representatives, which has 435 voting members?

Q9:   In 2013, the Republicans controlled both houses of which state legislature for the first time since 1874?

State and Territory Facts

A1:   New Hampshire

A2:   Arizona, Maine, New Hampshire, Oregon, and Wyoming

A3:   John Hancock

A4:   California. Each of the forty State Senators garners well over 900,000 constituents. They have more constituents than a member of the states U.S. House delegation.

A5: $100

A6:   31

A7:   18

A8:   The New Hampshire House of Representatives, with 400 members. Each Representative from New Hampshire has approximately 3,000 constituents.

A9:   Arkansas

State and Territory Facts

Q10: Which state was the first to use the Australian (secret) ballot in elections?

Q11: Which state is the only state where the Legislature is unicameral (composed of one house)?

Q12: Which U.S. territory has the only non-partisan and bi-cameral legislature?

Q13: Which state does not require motorists to wear a safety belt?

Q14: Which state has the longest operational Constitution in the world?

Q15: About how much does the Federal Government own of Nevada?

Q16: Which state instituted the first container-deposit legislation?

Q17: In which two states does the State Legislature decide between the top two finishers in the event no Gubernatorial candidate garners a majority of the vote?

Q18: Which was the first state to establish a Presidential Preference Primary?

Q19: Which four states prohibit the sale of consumer fireworks?

A10: Massachusetts

A11:   Nebraska. It is also non-partisan (Nebraska had a bi-cameral legislature until it was condensed to just one legislative body effective 1937).

A12   The America Samoa Legislature, called the Fono. Fono means legislature.

A13:   New Hampshire

A14: The Alabama Constitution. It contains 357,157 words.

A15:   86%

A16:   Oregon. The 1972 statute mandates certain beverages be returned for a refund.

A17:   Mississippi and Vermont

A18:   Oregon. The state delegation was required to support the winner at their respective conventions. 1912 was the first year when their primary system was instituted. Twelve other states followed Oregon and held partisan primaries that year.

A19:   Delaware, Massachusetts, New Jersey, and New York

Q20: In 1912, which state became the first to enact a minimum wage law?

Q21: In 1908, which state became the first to institute a recall for state officials?

Q22: Which was the first state to ratify the Bill of Rights to the U.S. Constitution?

Q23: Which are the only states that hold statewide election contests in odd years?

Q24: Which is the only state to have a state-owned bank?

Q25: Which are the only two states where motorists are not required to purchase automobile insurance?

Q26: Which four U.S. states are "Commonwealths?"

Q27: Which are the only two states where it is illegal for customers to pump their own gas?

Q28: Which state has the oldest state legislative chamber in continuous use in the U.S.?

Q29: What is the official name of the Democratic Party of Minnesota?

A20: Massachusetts. It applied to women and children only.

A21: Oregon

A22: New Jersey

A23: Kentucky, Louisiana, Mississippi, New Jersey, and Virginia

A24: North Dakota. The institution has been in operation since 1919 and was started by Socialist Party Activist A.C. Townley.

A25: New Hampshire and Wisconsin

A26: Kentucky, Massachusetts, Pennsylvania, and Virginia. The term means that the "government [is] based on the common consent of the people." As a practical matter, the difference between a commonwealth and a state is semantic. However, the term takes on a different meaning when applying to the Commonwealths of Puerto Rico and the Northern Mariana Islands. In this case, the U.S. Department of State defines a Commonwealth as a territory that is "self-governing under a constitution of its adoption and whose right of self-government will not be unilaterally withdrawn by Congress."

A27: Oregon and New Jersey

A28: New Hampshire. The Representative Hall in Concord, New Hampshire, which houses the New Hampshire Legislature has met there since 1829.

A29: The "Democratic-Farmer-Labor Party" (DFL). In 1944, the Democratic Party merged with the redoubtable third party called the Farmer-Labor Party.

Q30: What nine states have no income tax?

Q31: What is the only state where Appeals Court justices wear red robes?

Q32: The atomic bombs dropped by the U.S. on Japan (Hiroshima and Nagasaki) in WWII were loaded into war planes on the island of Tinian, in what is now a part of which U.S. territory?

Q33: What was the first state to allow abortions?

Q34: In what two states is there a tax on soft drinks?

Q35: What is the only U.S. Territory without a Lieutenant Governor?

Q36: Which four states were once independent nations?

Q37: Which was the first state to disallow slavery?

Q38: Which is the only state without a Balanced Budget Amendment enshrined in its Constitution?

Q39: In which state are voters afforded the opportunity to select: "None of these choices"?

State and Territory Facts

A30: Alaska, Florida, Nevada, New Hampshire, South Dakota, Tennessee, Texas, Washington, and Wyoming.

A31: Maryland

A32: The Northern Mariana Islands

A33: Colorado. The practice was only allowed in cases of rape, incest, and in cases where the pregnancy could lead to permanent physical disability of the mother.

A34: Arkansas and West Virginia

A35: Puerto Rico

A36: California, Hawaii, Texas, and Vermont

A37: Vermont, in 1793

A38: Vermont

A39: Nevada

Chapter XXV

Mayors

Mayors

Q1:   In 2006, which New York City Mayor fired an employee for playing solitaire at work?

Q2:   In 1965, after Hurricane Betsy flooded much of his city, which New Orleans Mayor told residents: "Don't believe any false rumors, unless you hear them from me"?

Q3:   In 2008, this former New York City Mayor purchased a burial plot at the Trinity Church Cemetery in Manhattan. He told the Associated Press "This is my home. The thought of having to go to New Jersey was so distressing to me." Who was the former New York City Mayor who uttered these words?

Q4:   Which Democratic Los Angeles Mayor traveled to Vietnam to support U.S. troops while the war was becoming exceedingly unpopular with his liberal base who dubbed him: "Saigon Sam"?

Q5:   Which Philadelphia Mayor and former Police Commissioner once observed: "The streets are safe in Philadelphia. It's only the people who make them unsafe"?

Q6:   In 2005, this Las Vegas Mayor took questions from fourth-graders at the Joe Mackey Elementary School in Las Vegas? One student asked him if he had a hobby. He responded: "Drinking Bombay Sapphire Gin." Some constituents were offended that he would say that to young children. He replied, "I'm the George Washington of mayors. I can't tell a lie. If they didn't want the answer, the kid shouldn't have asked the question." Who was this Las Vegas Mayor?

Q7:   In 1990, FBI agents arrested which Washington D.C. Mayor for possession of crack cocaine? In referring to his former girlfriend, the Mayor exclaimed: "Bitch set me up . . . I shouldn't have come up here . . . goddamn bitch."

Q8:   The Office of the Mayor of Boston is almost omnipotent in that the city has a strong Mayor system and a weak City Council. In 1967, when this future four-term Mayor was about to assume the office of Mayor, his predecessor John Collins told him: "It's Not Mayor, It's Emperor." Who was this new Emperor of Boston?

Q9:   At a 2008 press conference to announce the tenth anniversary of the Vagina Monologues V-Day Celebration, which New Orleans Mayor told the assembled reporters: "I am a vagina-friendly Mayor"?

Mayors

A1:   Michael Bloomberg. He was visiting the city's legislative office in Albany and greeted employees and posed for photographs with them. He happened to encounter Legislative assistant Edward Greenwood IX, a six-year employee of the office. The Mayor noticed he had the game solitaire on his screen. The Mayor made no comment at the time of the photographing. However, he ordered an aide to fire him for playing the game on office time. Greenwood was making just $27,000 a year and was a 39-year-old with three kids. Greenwood averred: "I'm the little guy, and he decided to make a statement and do what he did."

A2:   Victor Schiro

A3:   Ed Koch

A4:   Sam Yorty. He accrued the nickname by opponents of the U.S. war in Vietnam after he visited the South Vietnam capital. Unlike many other Los Angeles Democrats, Yorty was a steadfast supporter of the War.

A5:   Frank Rizzo

A6:   Oscar Goodman

A7:   Marian Berry

A8:   Kevin White

A9:   Ray Nagin

Mayors

Q10: Reading a speech, this Chicago Mayor misread the phrase "We shall reach greater and greater plateaus of achievement." Instead, he said: "We shall reach greater and greater platitudes of achievement." Who was this Mayor?

Q11: Which major city, now a citadel of Liberalism, had all Republican mayors from 1912-1964? Since then, all Mayors have been Democrats.

Q12: Who was the first openly Gay candidate to win the Mayorship of a Capital city?

Q13: Which Boston Mayor and Massachusetts Governor outlived his first wife and 7 of his 9 children? He died in 1958 at age 66.

Q14: Future tabloid talk show host Jerry Springer served for one year as Mayor of which city?

Q15: Which Boston Mayor threw out the first pitch at the first game in Fenway Park in 1912?

Q16: Which Civil Rights Activist was jailed in the 1960's in Atlanta and years later became Mayor of that city? When he became Mayor, he deadpanned that he was: "glad to be a mayor of the city where once the mayor had thrown me in jail."

Q17: In 1887, local temperance activist Susanna M. Salter's name was placed on the ballot in her hometown of Angora, Kansas as a prank. She won, mustering her which position and which distinction?

Q18: In 1999, which Dallas Mayor removed a *Star Trek* parody advertisement for his re-election campaign, calling himself "The captain of the *Dallas Enterprise*," after Paramount Studios, the owner of the name *Star Trek,* sent the Dallas Mayor's campaign a cease-and-desist letter?

Q19: In 2000, Joseph Riley Jr., the long-time Mayor of which South Carolina City, led a five-day, 113-mile protest march to the state's Capital City of Columbia, demanding for the removal of the Confederate flag from the Statehouse dome?

Mayors

A10:   Richard J. Daley

A11:   San Francisco

A12:   David N. Cicilline was elected Mayor of Providence, RI in 2006.

A13:   Joseph Michael Curley

A14:   Cincinnati, OH

A15:   John "Honey" Fitz. His grandson, U.S. Senator Edward M. Kennedy (D-MA), threw out the first pitch at the Boston Red Sox season home opener in 2009.

A16:   Andrew Young

A17:   Salter became the first woman elected mayor of a U.S. municipality.

A18:   Ron Kirk. Not to be confused with Captain James T. Kirk, the Captain of the *Starship USS Enterprise*.

A19:   Charleston. The flag was finally removed from the State House in 2015, during Riley's last year as Mayor.

Chapter XXVI

Political Terms

Political Terms

Q1: In a precedent established in the Supreme Court case of *New York Times Co. v. Sullivan*, the Court ruled that to establish libel against a public official, knowing falsity or reckless disregard for the truth must be proven. What is the official term for this?

Q2: What is a measure that appears on the ballot which in non-binding? It is mostly used to engage popular opinion.

Q3: What is the power of a Court to review lower Court decisions, and accept, modify or even overturn the decision of a lower-level court?

Q4: What was the name of an effort funded by newspaper publisher Richard Mellon Scaife to find damaging information on Bill Clinton?

Q5: What is the name of the system employed in the United States in which all ballots are marked in secret?

Q6: The Federal Government has which type of system, where there are two separate legislative chambers?

Q7: Article 1 Section 9 of the U.S. Constitution disallows which practice at the state and federal levels where an individual is punished without a trial?

Q8: What is the term for appropriations earmarked "secret" (usually military projects)?

Q9: What is the term coined by the CIA referring to the future negative unintended consequences of U.S. foreign policy, including covert operations?

Political Terms

A1: Actual Malice

A2: Advisory Referendum

A3: Appellate Jurisdiction

A4: The Arkansas Project

A5: The Australian ballot

A6: Bicameral

A7: A Bill of Attainder

A8: Black Budget. These types of appropriations are kept hidden for national security purposes?

A9: Blowback

Political Terms

Q:10   What is the term for Democrats who are from the more conservative parts of the country, including the South and the West, where the national Democratic Party is often looked upon as too liberal?

Q11:   What is the term for the credo that the U.S. will not distinguish between terrorists themselves and those who harbor the terrorists, and will use force if necessary to "take out" regimes which represent a potential threat to the U.S?

Q12:   What is the name for the credo that the U.S. would intervene militarily if necessary?

Q13:   What is the name for the credo that states: "The U.S. will intervene abroad to defend its values, including human rights anywhere in the Persian Gulf, to defend U.S. national interests"?

Q14:   What is the term for ending a filibuster? This action takes 60 votes in the U.S. Senate.

Q15:   What is the name for the belief that the images Americans see on their TV sets has a direct effect on how they view the foreign policies of their government?

Q16:   What is a measure passed by both Houses of the U.S. Congress that does not have the power of law and does not need the signature of the president?

Q17:   What was the precursor to the United States Congress?

Q18:   What is a Joint Resolution passed by Congress providing funding for government agencies at existing levels? This is a temporary measure to provide funding prior to the Congress and President working out an agreement for the full funding for the fiscal year.

Q19:   What is the term for a now defunct non-profit corporation founded in 1985 to moderate the Democratic Party and expand its voter-base to include moderate voters? Former Chairman Bill Clinton used many of their themes in his presidential campaign in 1992.

Political Terms

A10:   Blue Dog Democrats. The term was coined by U.S. Representative Peter Geren (D-TX 1989-1997) who said that Conservative Democrats were being choked blue by extreme Democrats and Republicans.

A11:   The Bush Doctrine

A12:   The Carter Doctrine

A13:   The Clinton Doctrine

A14:   Cloture

A15:   The *CNN Effect*

A16:   A Concurrent Resolution

A17:   The Congress of the Confederation (the United States Congress Assembled). It was the governing body of the United States from March 1, 1781 to March 4, 1789.

A18:   A Continuing Resolution

A19:   The Democratic Leadership Council

Political Terms

Q20: What does the acronym "DINO" stand for?

Q21: What is the term for candidates for offices, such as U.S. Congress, the state legislature, and municipal positions, whose office is not at the top of the ballot?

Q22: The U.S. has what type of system, where the state and federal governments have separate but equal powers?

Q23: The U.S. Congress grants eighteen specific powers delegated to the United States Congress from Article 1 Section 8 of the United States Constitution. What are they called?

Q24: What is the term for an accord between the President and a foreign head of government that needs a simple up or down vote by both houses of Congress to win approval?

Q25: What is the term for a law passed "after the fact"? Under the U.S. Constitution, no American can be penalized for violating a law before it becomes the law of the land?

Q26: What is the term for the U.S. system that delineates the powers between the federal and state governments?

Q27: What is the name for Eighty-five articles written by John Jay, Alexander Hamilton, and James Madison and published in *The Independent Journal* and *The New York Packet*? They advocated for the ratification of the U.S. Constitution.

Q28: In the U.S. Senate, members are permitted to speak indefinitely on a subject to avoid a vote. Only with 60 votes can the Senate vote to invoke cloture, thus ending debate on voting. What is the term for this procedure to speak indefinitely on a subject to avoid a vote?

Q29: What is the term for the manipulation of the redistricting process at the state level to benefit the majority party and/or all incumbents?

Political Terms

A20: Democrat-In-Name-Only

A21: Down Ballot candidates

A22: Dual Federalism

A23: Enumerated Powers

A24: An Executive Agreement

A25: Ex post Facto Law

A26: Federalism

A27: The Federalist Papers

A28: The Filibuster

A29: Gerrymandering. The term originated to describe Massachusetts Governor Elbridge Gerry's (1810-1812) successful attempt to maximize the numerical political advantage for his Democratic-Republican Party.

Political Terms

Q30: What is the term for the all-encompassing social programs proposed by President Lyndon B. Johnson? Legislation was enacted in areas such as Health Care, Civil Rights, and Education Reform.

Q31: What was the term for a moderate Republican in the latter half of the nineteenth century who favored civil service reform?

Q32: What is the term for the refusal of a sitting president to spend funds for something that the legislature has appropriated funds for?

Q33: What is the term for a measure requiring approval of both chambers of Congress before going to the president for his/her subsequent approval or disapproval?

Q34: What is the term for the power of the Judicial Branch of government to scrutinize for Constitutional permissibility, actions by the Executive and Legislative branch?

Q35: What is the name of the 1959 law that the Texas legislature approved which allows a politician to run for two political offices simultaneously?

Q36: What is the term for the doctrine that the U.S. will provide arms to allies, but will not do the actual fighting for them?

Q37: What is the term for a Primary election in which members of all political parties are invited to participate?

Q38: What is the term for the power of a Court to hear a case for the first time?

Q39: What does the acronym POTUS stand for?

Political Terms

A30: The Great Society

A31: Half-Breed

A32: Impoundment

A33: Joint Resolution

A34: Judicial Review. If the Justices rule the actions to be Unconstitutional, they become null and void.

A35: The LBJ Rule. This benefited Lyndon B. Johnson in 1960 as he sought both re-election to the U.S. Senate and election to the Presidency. After failing to secure the Democratic presidential nomination, he ran for Vice President that year. He subsequently won both the Vice Presidency and re-election to the U.S. Senate.

A36: The Nixon Doctrine

A37: Open Primary

A38: Original Jurisdiction

A39: President of the United States

Political Terms

Q40: What is the name for the doctrine that the U.S. will provide aid to forces fighting against communism, with the grand design of rolling it back?

Q41: What is the term for the process that allows the U.S. Senate to consider any budget legislation without a filibuster?

Q42: What is the term for a political pejorative used to define the common interests of the Republican and Democratic parties by those who think they are two sides of the same coin and have few differences?

Q43: What is the term for a provision attached to unrelated legislation? Sometimes these are provisions that may be too controversial to pass on their own.

Q44: What does the acronym RINO stand for?

Q45: Voters in the District of Columbia elect two residents to serve in this position. They have no office in the U.S. Senate, and have no Senatorial authority. What is the term for this?

Q46: Republicans in the latter half of the nineteenth century who opposed civil service reform were called what?

Q47: What is the Latin phrase for: "to stand by things decided?" This term refers to the judicial theory that previous court decisions should be precedent and not changed.

Q48: Some parts of the U.S., particularly in New England, practice a form of direct democracy in which all registered voters in a municipality are invited to attend and vote on town laws and budgets. What is this called?

Q49: What was the name for the system used in the South in the first half of the twentieth century in which non-white voters were excluded from participating in political primaries?

A40:   The Reagan Doctrine

A41:   Reconciliation

A42:   Republicrat

A43:   Rider

A44:   Republican-In-Name-Only

A45:   Shadow Representative

A46:   Stalwart. They supported the candidacy of Ulysses S. Grant for the Republican nomination in 1880 when he sought a third term for the presidency.

A47:   *Stare decisis*

A48:   Town Meeting

A49:   White Primary. The U.S. Supreme Court ruled this unconstitutional in 1944 in the case of *Smith v. Allwright.*

Chapter XXVII

Political Insults

Political Insults

Q1: After the 1923 death of the President, the esteemed poet Edward Estlin Cummings commented: "The only man, woman, or child who ever wrote a simple declarative sentence with seven grammatical errors is dead?" Who was Cummings speaking about?

Q2: U.S. Senator Ben Tillman (R-SC) once called which President: "a besotted tyrant"?

Q3: Which U.S. Senator, a former mayor of Evansville, IN, was referred to by President Lyndon B. Johnson as "a two-bit mayor from a two-bit town?" The Senator responded: "Well, maybe I'm a two-bit mayor, but I'll tell you one thing: Evansville never was a two-bit town."

Q4: When this man lost to Bill Clinton in the Presidential primaries, he chided President Bill Clinton for not focusing on balancing the federal budget. In response to this comment, former Clinton campaign advisor Paul Begala stated: "The notion that he is questioning the President's moral authority is like getting lectures from [Conservative Talk Show Host] Rush Limbaugh." Who was this losing candidate?

Q5: Which *New York Tribune* publisher labeled 1848 Democratic Presidential nominee Lewis Cass a: "pot-bellied, mutton-headed, cucumber-soled Cass"?

Q6: In 1958, this former President compared former Vice President John Nance Garner to the current Vice President, Richard M. Nixon, by telling a news reporter that Garner was "The Greatest presiding officer the U.S. Senate has ever had." The former President then mused that Garner was much better than "the squirl-head we have now." He then clarified this comment: "I'm talking about Mr. Nixon, if you're wondering who I'm talking about." Who was this former President?

Q7: U.S. Senator William Saxbe (R-OH) called which colleague, and future U.S. Senate Majority Leader: "a hatchet man who couldn't sell beer on a troop ship"?

Q8: U.S. Senator Styles Bridges (R-NH) once said about which Massachusetts colleague: "He agrees with the last man who speaks with him"?

Q9: In explaining why he appointed James Buchanan to the post of Minister to Russia, which President, said: "It was as far as I could send him to get him out of my sight, and where he could do the least harm. I would have sent him to the North Pole if we kept a Minister there"?

Political Insults

A1: Warren G. Harding

A2: Grover Cleveland

A3: Vance Hartke (D-IN)

A4: Paul Tsongas

A5. Horace Greeley. He disdained 1848 Democratic Presidential nominee Lewis
     Cass. Cass had a history of buying parcels of land cheaply and selling them at
     very high prices.   *The Tribune* labeled Cass as a man: "whose life has been spent
     in grasping greedily after vast tracts of land, buying up large estates round Detroit,
     and selling them out in small town lots, huckster fashion, at immense profits to
     tradesman and immigrants."

A6: Harry S. Truman

A7: Bob Dole (R-KS)

A8: Leverett Saltonstall

A9: Andrew Jackson

Political Insults

Q10: U.S. House Majority Leader Tip O'Neill (D-MA) had no problem publicly belittling this Republican President. He called him: "worse than [Warren G.] Harding and [Herbert] Hoover put together." Yet O'Neill and the President had a friendly personal relationship. They often golfed together. The President took O'Neill's criticisms in stride, knowing that they were not personal, just politics." Who was this President who O'Neill poked fun at?

Q11: President Benjamin Harrison did not support the particular version of Civil Service Reform favored by which future President, then a member of the Civil Service Commissioner? In response, he blasted Harrison, branding him: "a cold-blooded, narrow-minded, prejudiced, obstinate, timid old psalm-singing Indianapolis politician." Harrison had appointed him to his incumbency. Which future President made this outrageous dig?

Q12: Which former President thought Lyndon B. Johnson should have run for re-election in 1968? He said Johnson had: "no guts . . . Instead, he let a mob of anti-war protestors run him out of the White House."

Q13: As Assistant Secretary of the U.S. Navy, Theodore Roosevelt said of the current President: "he has no more backbone than a chocolate eclair."

Q14: Which President prevented the Bank of the United States from getting a new charter? He did not want them to regulate the money supply. Not a man to mince words, he wrote to the Bank Directors: "You are a den of vipers and thieves . . . I intend to route you out and by the Eternal God, I will route you out."

Q15: Which U.S. House Speaker once called his fellow Texas lawmaker Lyndon B. Johnson "A damn independent boy; independent as a hog on ice"?

Q16: Harry S. Truman called which future President "a coward" for not publicly condemning U.S. Senator Joseph McCarthy (R-WI) for suggesting that U.S. Secretary of Defense George Marshall was enveloped in a grand Communist conspiracy?

Q17: When young hippies heckled this Presidential candidate, he responded: "You come up when I get through and I'll autograph your sandals for you. That is, if you got any on . . . You need a good haircut. That's all that's wrong with you . . . There are two four-letter words I bet you folks don't know: 'work' and 'soap." He got an uproarious ovation from his mostly blue-color supporters in the crowd. Which Presidential candidate made these remarks?

Q18: A Connecticut Governor called businessman Donald Trump "a dirtbag," to which Trump responded you are "a fat slob who couldn't get elected dog catcher in Connecticut." Who was the Governor who got in a dustup with Donald Trump?

Q19: Which President excoriated the left wing of the Democratic Party (led by U.S. Senator George McGovern (D-SD)) as "very difficult to please? If they get 95 percent of what they want, they can only remember the other five percent"?

A10:   Gerald R. Ford

A11:   Theodore Roosevelt

A12:   Harry S. Truman

A13:   William McKinley. However, as fate would have it, in 1900 Roosevelt became McKinley's Vice Presidential Running Mate.

A14:   Andrew Jackson

A15:   Sam Rayburn

A16:   Dwight D. Eisenhower

A17:   George Wallace

A18:   Lowell Weicker. During the 1990's, New York businessman Donald Trump wanted to open a casino in Bridgeport, CT.   Weicker told him he could not do that because the state's Native American tribes had priority because of deals which were struck with them. Trump insisted he should be afforded the right to construct the casino, telling a Congressional Committee that the Native American casino owners "don't look like Indians." After those remarks, Weicker exploded, calling Trump "a dirtbag." He continued: "The United States of America says they are Indians. And I don't need someone to come along and tell me, they don't look like Indians and they aren't Indians. To me that's bigotry." Trump responded by branding Weicker as: "a fat slob who couldn't get elected dog catcher in Connecticut." Weicker responded on the program, *Face the State*: "I can lose weight a lot faster than a bigot can lose bigotry." Years after the dust up, Trump was asked by *The Hartford Courant* if he regrets his comment about Weicker being a fat slob. Trump deadpanned: "at least I'm accurate."

A19:   Jimmy Carter. He was responding to a statement by McGovern that: "The present economic and social policies of this administration are out of step with the platform of 1976, the platform of 1972 and the platform of 1968. These are the kind of things that mainstream Democrats have deplored when advocated by Republicans, and I don't see why we should be silent when they are advocated by a Democrat." Moreover, McGovern said that Carter's policies were so close to his vanquished Republican opponent, Gerald R. Ford, that it is sometimes "difficult to remember who won last fall."

Political Insults

Q20: In 1967, George Romney, the early front-runner for the Republican Presidential nomination, discussed his newfound opposition to the U.S. role in Vietnam. He said that his past support for the war was the result of the fact that during a trip to Vietnam, "I just had the greatest brainwashing that anybody can get, not only by the generals but also by the diplomatic corps over there. When informed about Romney's comments about being brainwashed, which Democratic Presidential candidate quipped: "A light rinse would have sufficed"?

Q21: In 1944, Alice Roosevelt Longworth, the daughter of President Theodore Roosevelt, observed that the Republican Presidential nominee: "looks like the little man on the wedding cake." Who was she referring to?

Q22: While campaigning for the Democratic Presidential nomination in 1960, this U.S. Senator told a crowd in La Croix, Wisconsin, "*Time*, *Look* and *Life* [Popular magazines at that time] don't give a damn about dairy prices. They don't know the difference between a corn cob and a ukulele." Who was this Senator?

Q23: Which President said of his successor Warren G. Harding: "Harding is incapable of thought, because he has nothing to think with?" He also said of Harding: "He has a bungalow mind."

Q24: In 1972 Richard M. Nixon was re-elected in a 49-state landslide. The day after the election, which Presidential Chief of Staff ordered a meeting of the President's Cabinet and called for the resignation of all Cabinet members. He told them: "You are all a bunch of burned-out volcanoes." Who was this Chief of Staff who insisted that all of the Cabinet members resign?

Q25: Which former President, a member of the Democratic-Republican Party, was disconsolate that the nation had elected Whig William Henry Harrison in 1840? He said: "The Republic may suffer under the present imbecile chief, but the sober second thought of the people will restore it at our next Presidential election."

Q26: During a speech in Des Moines, IA in 2004, which Democratic Presidential candidate said: "Many years ago doctors would bleed patients with leeches. Today, the insurance companies do that?"

Q27: When asked her opinion of 1984 Democratic Vice Presidential nominee Geraldine Ferraro, she averred: "I can't say it, but it rhymes with 'rich.'" Who made this statement?

Q28: Which President referred to Herbert Hoover as a "fat, timid capon."?

Q29: Which former President branded Woodrow Wilson: "A Byzantine logothete backed by flubdubs and mollycoddles?"

Political Insults

A20: Eugene McCarthy

A21: Thomas E. Dewey

A22: Hubert Humphrey

A23: Woodrow Wilson

A24: H.R. Haldeman

A25: Andrew Jackson

A26: Dennis Kucinich

A27: Barbara Bush. Her husband, Vice President George H.W. Bush was Geraldine Ferraro's opponent.

A28: Franklin D. Roosevelt

A29: Theodore Roosevelt (Translation: A logothete is an administrator; a flubdub means non-sense; mollycoddle means pampered.)

Political Insults

Q30: In 1983, this Democratic Governor was asked by his opponent David Treen: "How come you talk out of both sides of your mouth? In response, the Governor retorted: "so people like you with only half a brain can understand me." Who was this Governor?

Q31: During his successful 1966 campaign for the position of California Governor, he told *The Sacramento Bee*: "Unemployment insurance is a pre-paid vacation for freeloaders." Which future President made this statement about unemployment freeloaders?

Q32: Former Republican Presidential nominee Bob Dole commented about which President when asked about this President's experience on foreign affairs: "Well, he got this new globe for Christmas?"

Q33: After the organization "Americans for Tax Reform" alleged that this Democratic U.S. House member had changed his position on Health Insurance Reform, his office issued a press release branding the organization as "lying sacks of scum." Who was this U.S. Representative who made this allegation?

Q34: Which President said of Dwight D. Eisenhower: "The General doesn't know any more about politics than a pig knows about Sunday?"

Q35: Which President said of U.S. House Minority Leader Gerald R. Ford (R-MI): "You've got a little baby boy. Well, you take his little building blocks and go up and explain to Jerry Ford what we're trying to do."

Q36: Which Democratic U.S. Senator told *Esquire Magazine* in 1996 that President Bill Clinton was "an unusually good liar"?

Q37: Oval Office tapes reveal that Richard M. Nixon referred to which Indian Prime Minister as an "old witch"?

Q38: *New York Times* Columnist Paul Krugman called this former U.S. House Speaker by writing: "He's a stupid man's idea of what a smart person sounds like." Which House Speaker was Paul Krugman referring to?

Q39: In secretly recorded tapes, Richard M. Nixon said of this Governor: "On a personal basis, [he] is terrible. He just isn't pleasant to be around. He's just an uncomfortable man to be around . . . strange." Who was President Nixon referring to?

471

A30: Edwin Edwards

A31: Ronald Reagan

A32: George W. Bush

A33: Gene Taylor (D-MS).

A34: Harry S. Truman

A35: Lyndon B. Johnson

A36: Bob Kerrey of Nebraska. He clarified his comment, telling *UPI* that the remark was "not an angry comment. It was actually intended as an off-hand compliment."

A37: Indira Gandhi

A38: Newt Gingrich (R-GA)

A39: Ronald Reagan (R-CA)

Chapter XXVIII

Political Debate Moments

Q1:   In 1980, this Republican Presidential candidate in a debate averred : "Well, I
        don't think we've gotten around to the issues yet. I was hoping we would get
        around to issues before the campaign is over, whether they're single issues. All I
        hear is talk about momentum. I don't know that momentum is an issue. I hear
        talk about little Mo and big Mo, and I don't know who's who. But whatever the
        issues are, I think it's time we address them, certainly abortion, certainly gun
        control, certainly energy and inflation. That's the responsibility we have, and it's
        not too late for the people of this state to find out what we know about the issues.
        It would be refreshing if somebody asked me about an issue, instead of a poll. It
        also, in my case, would be very helpful." Who was this Republican Presidential
        candidate who was so concerned with issues?

Q2:   At the 1996 Vice Presidential debate, Democrat Al Gore said this to his
        Republican rival, a former NFL Quarterback: "If you won't use any football
        stories, I won't tell any of my warm and humorous stories about chlorofluoro-
        carbon abatement." Who was Al Gore speaking to?

Q3:   In a 2012 Presidential debate in Jacksonville, Florida, this candidate was asked
        by host Wolf Blitzer about a proposal offered by one of his opponents, former
        U.S. House Speaker Newt Gingrich (R-GA), to colonize the moon. The candidate
        mustered uproarious laughter for his response: "Well, I don't think we should go
        to the moon. I think we maybe should send some politicians up there." Who was
        the candidate that made this funny statement?

Q4:   During the 1988 Vice Presidential debate, Republican Dan Quayle suggested
        that he had more experience than John F. Kennedy had in 1960 when he was
        elected President. In what became one of the most remembered lines in
        Presidential debate history, which Democratic Vice Presidential nominee
        deadpanned: "Senator, I served with Jack Kennedy. Jack Kennedy was a friend
        of mine. Senator, you're no Jack Kennedy." Quayle called the remark "uncalled
        for." Who was this Democratic candidate?

Q5:   In a 1984 Democratic Presidential debate, U.S. Senator Ernest "Fritz" Hollings
        (D-SC) asked this contender: "But what have you done in 'this' world?"

Q6:   During a 2016 Democratic Presidential debate, this candidate explained his 1999
        vote to repeal parts of the Glass-Steagall Act this way: "The Glass-Steagall was
        my very first vote. I'd just arrived to the Senate. My dad had died in office. I just
        arrived to Senate. I think we get some takeovers and that was one. It was my
        very first vote, and it was 95, 90 to 5. The record." Who was this candidate?

Q7:   Since 1976, there was only one year where there was no Vice Presidential
        debate. What was that year?

Q8:   During a 2000 Republican Presidential debate, contestant Allan Keyes asked his
        opponent, John McCain, why he said this was his favorite band?

Q9:   During a 1984 Democratic Presidential debate, after former Vice President
        Walter Mondale discussed his economic plan, this opponent shot back: "That's
        the same vague gobbledygook of nothing that we've been hearing throughout
        this campaign." Who was this Mondale opponent?

Political Debate Moments

A1:   Bob Dole. Dole failed to garner momentum in New Hampshire, mustering just 0.4% of the vote, and subsequently withdrew from the race to successfully seek a third term to the U.S. Senate.

A2:   Jack Kemp

A3:   Ron Paul

A4:   Lloyd Bentsen

A5:   John Glenn. Glenn was the first man to orbit the earth from outer space.

A6:   Lincoln Chafee. The Glass-Steagall Act separated commercial from investment banking.

A7:   1980

A8:   Nine Inch Nails. Keyes averred: "Not long ago, Senator McCain, you were on a television program. You were asked what your favorite rock group was, and you said "Nine-Inch Nails." They then embarrassed you by putting up the "Nine-Inch Nails" lyrics, and it was filled with the 'F' word and other kind of vulgarities. Don't you think that as leaders, we ought to be a little bit more serious about the kind of influences that are now destroying the lives of our children, and before we open our mouths, we ought to know what we're talking about instead of aiding and abetting the cultural murder that is taking place of our young people? McCain retorted with amusement: "Can I get a lifeline? Moderator Tim Russert asked him: "Who do you want to call?" McCain answered: "My fifteen-year-old daughter." You know Allen, in politics, we try to use a lot of humor. We get tense. We try to use a lot of humor. I went to the *MTV* music awards with my now fifteen-year-old daughter. I saw some very interesting people, Puff Daddy, Busta Rhymes, Back Street Boys. . . Yes, I was trying to be amusing and it was a poor choice. Keyes then retorted: "let me tell you, I'm a father and I'm not laughing." McCain responded: "I haven't been able to entertain you in the past."

A9:   John Glenn. Mondale kept on trying to interrupt Glenn, and then got up out of his chair and bellowed: "There's just been a six-minute speech and all of it is baloney. The reason we have a $200 billion budget deficit is because you voted for Reaganomincs." Former Florida Governor Ruben Askew then commented about Glenn and Mondale criticizing each other and stating that both Glenn and Mondale "were right about each other." Uproarious laugher ensued.

Q10:   During a Presidential debate, which Republican Presidential nominee bragged about having been given binders full of women job applicants?

Q11:   In a 2016 Presidential debate between Hillary Clinton and Donald Trump, the moderated was *NBC News* Anchor Lester Holt. Trump supporters were irate that Holt asked tough questions of Trump. Accordingly, they went to Twitter and excoriated Holt. The problem was that they typed "Lester" and got a famous baseball player instead. One such Trump supporter suggested Lester might be trying to get an appointment in a Hillary Clinton administration, to which the other Lester responded: "I'll be pretty busy doing my own thing so I think I'll be okay. Perhaps you should send this to Lester Holt." Who was this other Lester everyone seemed to be angry with and tweeting by mistake?

Q12:   In 2004, this Independent Presidential nominee did not obtain the requisite 15% in the polls to be allowed on the Presidential debate stage. He told members of the University of Miami's Faculty Club: "If I could go through the ducts and leap out in a cape - - - that's my dream."   Who was this Independent candidate?

Q13:   During a Vice Presidential debate, which candidate joked: "I can tell you my wife out there, she wants me to go out in the private sector," to which his opponent, Dick Cheney replied: "I'm trying to get you there"?

Q14:   In a 1976 Presidential debate, this President mendaciously asserted: "There is no Soviet domination over Eastern Europe." Which President made this untrue statement?

Q15:   In 2008, which Republican Presidential candidate joked in a Republican debate: "We've had a Congress that spent money like John Edwards at a beauty shop"? John Edwards was a Democratic candidate who spent $1,250 to fly Beverly Hills hair stylist Joseph Torrenueva to Atlanta to give Edwards a haircut.

Q16:   During a 2008 Democratic Presidential debate, a member of the audience asked the candidates to look to the left and tell the audience one thing you like and one thing you dislike about that candidate. One candidate looked to his left and found U.S. Representative Dennis Kucinich (D-OH) and said: "Dennis, the thing I like best about you is your wife." Which candidate made this rather odd remark?

Q17:   During a 1988 Presidential debate, George H.W. Bush lambasted his opponent for his answer about the bulging national budget deficit: "That answer is about as clear as Boston Harbor." Who was Bush demeaning?

Q18:   During a 2003 Democratic Presidential debate, this candidate was asked if he had ever smoked marijuana. His answer was: "Well, you know I have a reputation for giving unpopular answers at Democratic debates. I never used marijuana, sorry." Who made this comment?

Q19.   In a 1988 Democratic Presidential debate, which candidate told rival Al Gore to "keep in mind a good healthy tone" in the campaign?

A10:   Mitt Romney. He was referencing three-ring binders that his staff had put together for him containing resumes of females who had applied for jobs in his Gubernatorial administration in Massachusetts. He referred to the binders as: "Binders full of women"

A11: John Lester. He was a pitcher for the Chicago Cubs professional baseball team.

A12: Ralph Nader

A13: Joe Lieberman

A14: Gerald R. Ford

A15: Mike Huckabee

A16: Joe Biden. Kucinich is married to the former Denise Harper, 31 years his junior.

A17:   Michael Dukakis. Dukakis was the incumbent Governor of Massachusetts. At the time, Boston Harbor was among the dirtiest harbors in the nation.

A18:   Joe Lieberman

A19.   Paul Simon. Gore fired back: "If you can't stand the heat, get out of the kitchen."

Q20: During a debate of 1988 Democratic Presidential candidates, Richard Gephardt suggested which candidate was employing a Southern strategy and would bring the party back to its days of supporting states' rights?

Q21: During the only 1980 Presidential debate, Jimmy Carter said he asked his daughter Amy what the most important issue was to her. What was her reply?

Q22: Which Democratic Presidential candidate (a Mayor of a city with over 200,000 citizens) was allowed in few Democratic Presidential debates in 1992. He showed up at one debate as an audience member and was arrested for heckling the moderator. Who was this Presidential candidate?

Q23: In 1992, Democratic Presidential candidate Paul Tsongas opposed a middle-class tax cut plan supported by some of his opponents. Tsongas, a deficit hawk, supported what can be called "root canal economics." He proposed raising the gas tax and effectuating federal spending cuts. He stated in a Presidential debate: "I'm no Santa Clause." Which opponent retorted: "I appreciate the fact that you are not Santa Clause, but you're beginning to sound like the Grinch who stole Christmas."?

Q24: In 1984, Democratic Presidential candidate Gary Hart ran on the slogan "New ideas." During a debate, this opponent said to him: "When I hear your new ideas, I'm reminded of that ad, 'Where's the beef.'" This drew uproarious laughter from the crowd. The line was taken from a Wendy's commercial, which humorously alleged that its competitors put very little beef in their sandwiches. Who was Hart's opponent who made this very memorable analogy?

Q25: In 1956, in anticipation of the Florida Presidential primary, which two Democratic Presidential candidates debated live on television in Miami? This was the first time two Democratic Presidential candidates debated on television.

Q26: During a debate in 1988, a Democratic Presidential candidate accused rival Al Gore of "sounding like a tough kid on the block." Who made this comment?

Q27: During a spirited debate for the Democratic Presidential nomination, Bill Clinton argued that should his opponent become President, hundreds of nuclear power plants would be constructed in the U.S. Which opponent was he referring to?

Q28: In 1956, Democrat former First Lady Eleanor Roosevelt, serving as proxy for Democratic Presidential nominee Adlia Stevenson, and U.S. Senator Margaret Chase Smith (R-ME) serving as a surrogate for Republican Presidential nominee Dwight D. Eisenhower, debated for their candidates on which Sunday morning public affairs program?

Q29: During a 1995 Republican Presidential debate, which contestant compared his well-healed Republican opponents as the true peers of Football great OJ Simpson, who was on trial for a double murder?

A20: Al Gore. He said: "The fact is that you and I and the rest of us agree on more than we disagree on, so let's not raise differences between Democrats and Dixiecrats. I don't think we ought to try to bring Strom Thurmond back into the Democratic Party."

A21: Nuclear Arms

A22: Larry Agran, the Mayor of Irvine, California

A23: Bob Kerrey

A24: Walter Mondale

A25: Adlai Stevenson and Estes Kefauver. Stevenson won the primary, and the Democratic National Convention selected Kefauver as his Vice Presidential running mate.

A26: Bruce Babbitt

A27: Paul Tsongas. Tsongas shot back: "That is a lie, that is a lie, that is a lie." Clinton then retorted: "Then just say no, it's easy." Tsongas did not rule it out, and Clinton averred: "No one can argue with Paul, he's always perfect." Tsongas responded: "I'm not perfect, but I'm honest."

A28: *Face the Nation* on *CBS*. This was the first time any woman appeared on the television show.

A29: Bob Dornan. He branded Simpson: "a Riviera Country Club millionaire who told Congressman David Dryer (R-CA) that he voted for George [H.W.] Bush." After frontrunner Bob Dole issued a statement reading: "My thoughts and prayers -- and those of all Americans -- will remain with the families of the victims for many years to come," Dornan pounced, calling his statement "cowardly." Dornan continued: "Bob Dole had a lawyer on his extensive, overpaid, gutless, consultant staff write that for him." Interestingly, Dornan raised his family about three blocks from Simpson's home.

Q30: Which Republican Vice Presidential nominee said during a debate with Democrat Walter Mondale: "I figured it up the other day: If we added up the killed and wounded in Democrat wars in the century, it would be about 1.6 million Americans – enough to fill the city of Detroit"?

Q31: During a 2003 Presidential primary debate, moderator George Stephanopoulos asked this candidate if he was too nice to take on Republican President George W. Bush in the General Election. The candidate answered "I'd like to come over and strangle you George." Who was this candidate?

Q32: Which Governor was asked during a debate for re-election if he would serve out his full term and he responded: "You bet." After being re-elected, he embarked on "a secret tour" of the state to ask voters what they thought of him breaking his pledge and running for president. He concluded that most of his constituents either wanted him to run for president or were indifferent to him running. Accordingly, he broke the pledge and ran. Who was this Governor?

Q33: During a 2011 Republican Presidential debate, this former New Mexico Governor joked: "My next-door neighbor's two dogs have created more shovel-ready jobs than this current [Barack Obama] administration." Who made this comment?

Q34: In a 2000 Democratic Presidential debate, which candidate dared opponent Al Gore to "walk down the hall" to tell his boss, President Bill Clinton, to sign an Executive Order disallowing racial profiling"?

Q35: In 1992, the Democratic Presidential candidate, once a major force in the Democratic Party, was excluded from most Presidential debates. When he finally was invited to one, he amused the crowd by deadpanning: "This is the highest-ranking Democratic organization that's let me talk to them for 20 years. I've got a lot of things to say." Who made this comment?

Q36: In defending his attacks on his opponents' health care reform proposal, which candidate averred: "Nothing I have said in this campaign has been mean-spirited. Some people confuse free-spirited debate with negativity"?

Q37: During a 2008 Presidential debate, after being asked why some voters liked her opponent more than Hillary Clinton, Clinton replied: "Well that hurts my feelings but I'll try to go on. He's very likable. I don't think I'm that bad." This rival interjected: "Your likable enough Hillary, don't worry about it." Who said this?

Q38: During a 2019 Democratic Presidential debate, which candidate averred: "Hell, yes, we're going to take your AR-15 and your AK-47"?

Q39: During the battle for the 1948 Oregon Republican Presidential primary, over 60 million Americans listened to these two candidates debate the outlawing of the Communist Party USA. Who were these two candidates?

A30:   Bob Dole

A31:   Joe Lieberman

A32:   Bill Clinton. His mother told him: "It's only a wise man who changes his mind. A fool never does."

A33:   Gary Johnson

A34:   Bill Bradley. Gore responded: "I don't think Bill Clinton needs a lecture from Bill Bradley about how to stand up and fight for African Americans."

A35:   Eugene McCarthy. He was a former U.S. Senator from Minnesota, who garnered 42.4% of the vote in the New Hampshire Presidential primary in 1968, contributing to the decision of President Lyndon B. Johnson not to seek re-election. He subsequently abandoned the party, running for President as an Independent in 1976, then supported Republican nominee Ronald Reagan in 1980.

A36:   Al Gore. He was debating Bill Bradley for the 2000 Democratic Presidential nomination.

A37:   Barack Obama

A38:   Beto O'Rourke

A39:   Thomas E. Dewey, who opposed the outlawing of the party, and Harold Stassen, who supported banning the Party USA.

Chapter XXIX

Political Bloopers

Q1: Prior to delivering his National Radio Address, which President averred to news reporters: "My fellow Americans, I've signed legislation that will outlaw Russia forever. We begin bombing in five minutes"?

Q2: In his 1992 bid for re-election, President George H.W. Bush blasted his Democratic opponent, Arkansas Governor Bill Clinton, as being "the Governor of a state with a profitable chicken industry on the Mississippi River between Texas and Oklahoma." However, Bush was geographically incorrect in his comment. What states should Bush have stated in his comment?

Q3: In 2011, this Republican Presidential aspirant made an address to a crowd in Concord, New Hampshire. In the address, she said: "You're the state where the shot was heard around the world at Lexington and Concord, and you put a marker in the ground and paid with the blood of your ancestors." She was referring to the first shot fired during the Revolutionary War, which did not happen in Concord New Hampshire, but in Concord, Massachusetts. Who made this geographic mistake?

Q4: This Republican Presidential nominee told a San Diego audience: "We're honored to be back in San Francisco." Members of the audience yelled "San Diego" prompting the nominee to shoot back: "Oh San Diego, Sure." Who made this geographic mistake?

Q5: During the 1994 U.S. Senate race in Massachusetts, venture capitalists John Lakian accidently referred to this Republican opponent as "Mr. Mormon," then he referred to him as "Mr. Mormey." Who was Lakian referring to?

Q6: In 1987, this Democratic Presidential candidate mistakenly referred to President James Knox Polk as James K. Knox. Who made this verbal mistake?

Q7: During a joint appearance with his Republican opponent John H. Chichester, this Virginia Lieutenant Gubernatorial nominee averred: "I'm a human. I am not a conservative. I am not a moderate. I am a liberal." He meant to say: "I am not a liberal." Who was this Lieutenant Gubernatorial nominee?

Q8: During the 2000 New Hampshire Bisquick Pancake Presidential Primary Flip-off, this Republican Presidential candidate, trying to catch a pancake with his spatula, fell backwards through a curtain. Mocking a popular Visa commercial from the time, he quipped: "Cost of spatula and skillet, $32. Candidate falling off platform: Priceless." Who was this candidate?

Q9: During a 2003 trip to Madrid, Spain, which Governor referred to King Juan Carlos as: "The President of the Republic of Spain"? In actuality, the nation has not been a Republic since the Spanish Civil War, which ended in 1939 with General Francisco Franco defeating his political opponents.

A1:   Ronald Reagan. He later found out that his microphone was on and that his statement was broadcast worldwide.

A2:   Bush was wrong in stating Texas and Oklahoma. To be accurate, he should have said Louisiana and Missouri. This *faux paus* was especially embarrassing for Bush because he was a resident of Texas. Bill McDonnell, Clinton's Oklahoma campaign chairman, had a field day with Bush's gaffe, averring: "The man who promised he would be America's Education President doesn't know his geography. How can he claim to know the needs of the people of Oklahoma, Texas, and Arkansas, and the rest of America, when he doesn't even know where we live?" Clinton then joked: "Christopher Columbus discovered America, but after three years in the White House, Bush hasn't found it yet."

A3:   Michele Bachmann

A4:   Bob Dole

A5:   Mitt Romney. Some observers came to the conclusion that Lakian had made the *faux pas* deliberately, and the press excoriated him for the statement. Wayne Woodlief of *The Boston Herald* called Lakian "A lying laughingstock." Though Lakian outspent Romney, he lost the election of the financial titans in an electoral landslide. Later in life, Lakian went to jail for security fraud and defrauding investors.

A6:   Al Gore. This mistake was especially embarrassing, because Polk, like Gore, was a Tennessean.

A7:   Douglas Wilder. Wilder was trying to disassociate himself from the National Democratic Party, which was viewed as liberal in conservative Virginia. Former Republican Governor Mills Goodwin charged that Wilder was "trying to hoodwink" voters by keeping his liberalism a secret. In actuality, Wilder was trying to make the case that he was a non-ideological pragmatist. The assembled crowd appeared stunned. Wilder realized the guffaw he made and in an embarrassed tone said: "Talk about putting your foot in it."

A8:   Gary Bauer

A9:   Jeb Bush of Florida

Q10: In an interview with *NBC*'s Katie Couric, this Democratic Vice Presidential nominee stated: "When the stock market crashed, Franklin Roosevelt got on the television and didn't just talk about the princes of greed. He said, 'Look, here's what happened." Actually, Herbert Hoover, not Franklin D. Roosevelt, was President when the Stock Market crashed in 1929. In addition, television was an experimental medium at the time and very few Americans had access to it. Who was the Vice Presidential nominee to make this error?

Q11: During a 2007 campaign appearance in Murrells, South Carolina, this Republican Presidential candidate was asked by an audience member: "When do we send them an airmail message to Tehran?" The candidate began singing: "That old Beach Boys song, Bomb Iran, Bomb Bomb Bomb." The actual name of the song was *Barbara Ann*. Who was this Presidential candidate?

Q12: During a 2012 Republican Presidential debate, this candidate was asked which departments in the Federal Government he would abolish. 'It's three agencies of the government that when I get there that are gone, Commerce, Education, and the uh, um, what's the third one there, let's see . . . The third agency of government I would do away with, Education, the uh, Commerce, and let's see. I can't, the third one, sorry. Oops.' The agency he could not come up with was the Department of Energy. Ironically, he later became U.S. Energy Secretary. Which Presidential candidate made these statements?

Q13: During a 2016 appearance on *MSNBC*'s *Morning Joe*, which candidate was asked by panelist Mike Barnacle: "What would you do, if you were elected, about Aleppo?" Befuddled, the candidate asked: "What is Aleppo?" prompting Barnacle to aver: "You're kidding me?" Aleppo is an important city in the war-torn country of Syria. He later apologized, saying he just blanked. Who was this candidate?

Q14: In 1989, Vice President Dan Quayle Told a Nashville crowd: "As America celebrates the twentieth anniversary of Neal Armstrong, Buzz Lukens and walking on the moon. . . ." (Lukens was a U.S. Representative from Ohio who was convicted of paying an underage girl for sex). Who did Quayle mean to refer to?

Q15: Which President, while reading a campaign speech, accidently read in the margin of his speech ("with emphasis"): "I say to you this is nonsense with emphasis!" Who read aloud the comment in the margin of his presentation?

Q16: Which First Lady was given the honor of christening two ambulance planes to be used by the Army and Navy. The First Lady had a bottle of Champaign, and began to hit it on the plane's nose. However, the bottle would not break. No one scored the glass before the event. Accordingly, the First Lady continued to try to break the bottle but to no avail. Who was this misfortunate First Lady?

Q17: This Washington D.C. Mayor asserted: "Outside of the killings, [Washington] D.C. has one of the lowest crime rates in the nation." Who was this mayor who made this rather bizarre statement?

Q18: Which President, reading from a cue card at a town hall in Exeter, NH, exclaimed: "Message, I care"? This was during an economic downturn, and some Republicans were turning to his Republican Primary opponent, Pat Buchanan.

A10:   Joe Biden

A11: John McCain

A12:   Rick Perry

A13:   Gary Johnson

A14:   Buzz Aldrin. This Buzz is the astronaut who went to the Moon.

A15:   Gerald R. Ford

A16:   Bess Truman

A17: Marion Barry

A18:   George H.W. Bush